Mechanics

Mechanics

R. C. Smith
Faculty of Mathematics
Open University, Bletchley
Buckinghamshire

and

P. Smith
Department of Mathematics
University of Keele
Staffordshire

S.I. Unit Edition

JOHN WILEY & SONS LTD
CHICHESTER   NEW YORK   BRISBANE   TORONTO

First published © 1968 John Wiley & Sons Ltd.
S.I. Unit Edition Copyright © 1971 John Wiley
& Sons Ltd. All Rights Reserved. No part of this
publication may be reproduced, stored in a retrieval
system, or transmitted, in any form or by any means,
electronic, mechanical photocopying, recording or
otherwise, without the prior written permission of
the Copyright owner.

Library of Congress Catalog Card No. 74–171979

ISBN 0 471 80350 2

Reprinted April 1972
Reprinted February 1973
Reprinted January 1975
Reprinted November 1977

Printed in Great Britain by J. W. Arrowsmith Ltd., Bristol

Introductory Mathematics for Scientists and Engineers

Foreword to the Series

The increasing use of high speed digital computers and the growing desire for numerical answers in many disciplines have led to a steady expansion in the numbers of mathematics courses in the first year or two of college and university studies. Many of these courses are intended for students of physics, chemistry, engineering, biology and economics who will regard mathematics as a tool, but a tool with which they must develop some proficiency. This series is designed for such students. However, that does not prevent prospective mathematicians from reading these books with profit.

The authors have, in general, avoided the strict axiomatic approach which is favoured by some pure mathematicians, but there has been no dilution of the standard of mathematical argument. Learning to follow and construct a logical sequence of ideas is one of the important attributes of a course in mathematics.

While the authors' purpose has been to stress mathematical ideas which are central to applications and necessary for subsequent studies, they have attempted, when appropriate, to convey some notion of the connection between a mathematical model and the real world. Exercises have been included which take account of the ready availability of electronic digital computers.

The careful explanation of difficult points and the provision of large numbers of worked examples and exercises should ensure the popularity of the books in this series with students and teachers alike.

D. S. JONES
Department of Mathematics
University of Dundee

Preface

This book, based on courses in dynamics and vectors given in the University of Keele, is designed to give students a thorough grounding in particle dynamics and elementary rigid body dynamics. The contents are presently being taught to first-year undergraduates who are taking mathematics as one of two main degree subjects, and we find that the material can be covered in about 36 hours of lectures. Many worked examples have been introduced into the text and we have endeavoured, where possible, to use plausible models of problems in physics and engineering in the examples and exercises.

The introduction contains a brief survey of the development of mechanics and some general comments on the art of successful modelling of dynamical problems and the importance of approximations in applied mathematics. We have found that students entering higher education now have such varied backgrounds that frequently topics required for a complete treatment of dynamics have been omitted from their previous work. With this in mind, we have included a chapter on vectors and a chapter on elementary techniques for solving ordinary differential equations. Both topics are of particular importance in a modern approach to dynamics. For those students who have already completed courses in these subjects, chapters 1 and 4 can be used for reference. Choice of material must be exercised in a book of this length and we have restricted our attention to such topics as simple rocket motion, oscillations and orbits which can be studied in some detail without drawing on too many mathematical techniques. A standard course in elementary differentiation and integration should be a sufficient prelude for the reader.

There is a current trend in Britain to the universal adoption of a metric system of units. In the Anglo–American sphere the foot–pound–second system is still in common use with the added confusion in terminology in that, for example, the American ton and gallon are different from their British equivalents. On the continent of Europe the metric system based on the centimetre–gram–second or metre–kilogram–second predominates and no doubt in time one or other of these will come into general use in Britain. We have decided in the present circumstances to use both British and metric systems for the convenience of readers who may be more familiar with one particular set of units.

Answers to the exercises are given at the end of the book, and to some of these we have added comments which indicate the method of solution.

Finally we should like to acknowledge our indebtedness to several persons involved in the production of this text; to Professor D. S. Jones for his helpful criticism and comments during the writing; to Miss Valerie Cook for her expert typing of the manuscript; to Miss Cynthia Kelsall for her assistance with the diagrams; and to our wives for their help in the checking of the manuscript.

R. C. SMITH

1968   P. SMITH

PREFACE TO S.I. UNIT EDITION

The main difference between the two editions of this book is in the units used throughout. It is now written, with minor exceptions, in terms of Standard International Units which are becoming the prominent system in the scientific world. We have also taken the opportunity of correcting some of the errors and making some minor modifications to the notation.

Contents

An introduction to the study of mechanics

Motivation

The modern theoretical study of mechanics has a long history dating from the early part of the seventeenth century. The first major contribution to particle dynamics was made by Galileo (1564–1642) with his elementary theory of the motion of a projectile. The fundamental importance of Galileo's approach lay in his attempt to relate theory and experimental evidence; at the time this was a new concept of scientific method. Prior to this breakthrough scientific theories of mechanics were put forward solely on this basis of reason and the authoritative statement. Galileo's writings had a profound effect on subsequent developments. The work of Galileo was continued and developed further by Huygens (1629–95).

From this early incomplete theory of particle dynamics Newton (1642–1727), in his great work *Principia* (1687), established particle dynamics as a scientific and mathematical discipline. Newton introduced the notions of force and mass and set forth his laws of motion (now known as Newton's laws of motion) for particle motion substantially in the form that appears in modern textbooks of dynamics. Significantly, he was able to use his laws to show that they were consistent with the numerical data on planetary motion obtained earlier by Kepler and Brahë, usually expressed in Kepler's laws of planetary motion (see chapter 9). For this purpose he needed to propound a law of gravitation and secondly, perhaps more significant for the study of dynamics in particular and in the wider context of mathematics, he made the first tentative steps towards the discovery of mathematical calculus, a powerful analytic tool in applied mathematics. For these obvious reasons the subject has come to be known as Newtonian mechanics.

Newton's principles were extended to rigid-body dynamics by Euler (1736), d'Alembert (1743) and by Lagrange (1788) in his famous *Mécanique Analytique*.

This short summary of the early history of the subject serves as a prototype for the modern conception of mechanics. The aim is to be able to predict the behaviour of the phenomena on the basis of certain postulates. But the postulates can only be tested by experimental evidence and clearly only a limited number of experiments are available to us. In the light of experience many of our fundamental assumptions must be modified. Thus whilst Newtonian mechanics is appropriate to the laboratory experiment or the motion of the planets in the solar system, significant departures from Newton's theories appear in very large and very small scale phenomena. For this reason relativistic and quantum mechanics have taken over in these two spheres. Applied mathematics must be a continuous interplay between experiment and experience on the one hand and fundamental hypothesis on the other. Hence dynamics has not developed as a completely deductive discipline based on certain consistent axioms. The study of dynamics requires a firm grasp of the intuitive meaning of such physical quantities as force, mass, energy etc., rather than seeing them as components of a strictly mathematical argument. And herein lies one of the difficulties of applied mathematics: the need to continuously assess and interpret the results of the mathematics involved in solving a problem.

Space and time

The fundamentals of mechanics involve assumptions which are often left unsaid. Newtonian mechanics assumes that space is Euclidean and this seems a natural view of space. It assumes that there exists an absolute reference system relative to which all other points in space can be described. Time is supposed continuous and measurable according to an absolute time scale so that observers at different positions in space can synchronize their clocks with this time scale. An event has an absolute position and takes place at an absolute time.

The simple intuitive notions of space and time have been highly successful, for example, in predicting the orbital paths of the planets, with the exception of a few minor deviations which cannot be explained by the Newtonian theory of dynamics. Only by rejecting the principles of absolute space and time through Einstein's relativistic theory can these discrepancies be accounted for. However, the principles of Newtonian mechanics have that element of simplicity and logical clarity which make them the best introduction to mechanics. Whilst relativistic theories can, in principle, give finer detail it is given at the expense of greater analytical difficulty.

Units

The international standard of length is the *metre* defined as a certain number of wavelengths of a radiation from krypton. It used to be defined by a standard metre rod made of platinum and iridium and kept at a specified temperature in a suburb of Paris. The unit of time is the second which has two definitions. The astronomical definition is 1/31,556,925·975 of the tropical year 1900 (the tropical year is the time interval between successive south-north transits by the sun across the earth's equatorial plane). The atomic definition (which will probably eventually become the universal standard) is a given number of periods of oscillations of the Caesium atom.

Newton's laws of motion

The laws of motion arise partially as the answers to certain questions. Both historically and philosophically the right questions to ask taxed many scholars for many years. With hindsight we can express our ideas with greater awareness of the consequences of the postulates. Our considerations here are kept deliberately general: greater detail will be found in later chapters. First we ask: what happens to a body which is completely isolated in space from all other material objects? We answer this question by postulating that the body continues in a state of rest or of uniform motion in a straight line. The object will only deviate from this state if it is subject to some external influence or force. This is essentially Newton's first law and contains a qualitative definition of force.

We next ask: what quantitative effect does a force have on an object? Since velocity is a relative concept (that is, an isolated observer cannot detect his own velocity), we must suppose that force is independent of velocity. However, in Newtonian mechanics *acceleration* can be measured. Newton's second law of motion states that the force acting on a body is proportional to the acceleration induced in the body, the constant of proportionality being the mass of the body, a measure of the quantity of material of which it is composed. This law is a simple *linear* relation between force and acceleration, and it is not inconsistent with the first law.

These two laws do not form a complete basis for dynamics. Consider a simple coil spring which has been compressed. The internal compressive force will endeavour to bring the spring back to its natural length and its external effect will be experienced at the two ends of the spring. Newton's third law postulates how the compressive reaction will be distributed at the two ends. We assume that action and reaction are equal and opposite: in our illustration the spring exerts equal and opposite forces at both ends. For the same reason we suppose that the earth exerts the same gravitational pull on the moon as the moon does on the earth.

These are the basic postulates of Newtonian mechanics which are assumed to hold universally. However, they must be backed up by hypotheses concerning the constitutive nature of the force which appears in Newton's second law. We cannot solve the equation

$$\text{force} = \text{mass} \times \text{acceleration}$$

until we specify the nature of the force. Returning to the illustration above we must specify how the force varies with, for example, the extension or contraction of the spring. In a compressed linear spring the constitutive law is taken to be

$$\text{force} \propto \text{contraction},$$

but it is obvious that not all springs behave in this way for large contractions. A modified law may have to be devised for large contractions perhaps involving further parameters.

The nature of gravitational force must be specified and Newton's law of universal gravitation states that the gravitational attraction between any two bodies is proportional to their masses and inversely proportional to the square of the distance between them. The test of this law can be found in the large amount of data collected on the positions of the planets in the solar system. The only significant discrepancies detected so far can be accounted for by relativistic theories.

Much of the elegance of Newtonian mechanics lies in its dependence on simple premises. More complicated dynamical theories may be capable of giving finer detail and wider application but this is often at the expense of more elaborate mathematical analysis. Many problems are capable of solution within the terms of reference of the Newtonian system and they can serve as models for further physical situations.

Modelling

This book is in large part devoted to particle dynamics but this is not to say that we restrict ourselves to 'particles'. Mathematically a particle can be considered as a point in space which has finite mass, or physically as an object of negligible dimension but with finite mass. Whilst the former definition is an idealization, the latter definition may be a useful approximation to a real situation depending on whether we can justify the adjective 'negligible'. The earth's diameter is approximately 6,400 km and the radius of the earth's orbit about the sun is about 1.5×10^8 km, and in certain problems it is useful to think of the earth as a particle moving about the sun since its dimensions are so small compared with the dimension of its orbit. However, if we are interested in computing eclipses between the earth, moon and sun, the diameters of the earth and moon are of particular importance.

As we shall see later, the centre of mass of a rigid body behaves like a particle whose mass equals the mass of the body. Thus the application of particle dynamics is not restricted simply to particles but does have application to bodies. Whilst we can determine the position of the centre of mass of a rigid body using the principles of particle dynamics, we cannot discuss the orientation of the body about its centre of mass. We can track a rocket leaving the earth but we cannot discuss how it is tumbling about its centre of mass.

The art of modelling is often a difficult compromise. In constructing a model for a real situation, one is attempting to achieve simplicity whilst still retaining what one hopes are the significant features of the problem. In practice this often entails *ad hoc* estimates of the relative weight one must attach to various effects which may be present. To some extent this is overcome by examining 'control' problems where various effects are isolated in a single problem. For example, a car may be considered as a particle if we are interested in its acceleration and velocity, a box on four springs if we are concerned with its damping characteristics, or a box on four springs which are attached to four wheels if we are interested in its more general dynamical behaviour.

The real test of a good model lies in tolerable agreement between the theoretical and experimental results. However, it is not always possible to test agreement for reasons of expense. We can find the maximum load which a bridge can tolerate by simply adding weights until the bridge collapses. Clearly non-destructive testing is cheaper, and a theoretical assessment of the bridge's characteristics together with a sufficient margin of safety between the theoretical maximum load and the permitted load is a more reasonable approach to the problem.

Mathematical analysis and approximation

All discussion of fundamental postulates and modelling loses much of its point if it leads to heavy or intractable mathematical analysis. An important feature of particle dynamics from a teaching point of view is that many problems can be constructed which do have simple analytic answers. However, much criticism has been levelled at the artificality of the traditional sort of examination question which has achieved a conventionality of its own. The sphere rolling down the inclined face of a wedge which can slide on a rough horizontal plane has taxed the ingenuity of teacher and student alike for many decades. Indeed some textbooks of dynamics approach the subject as a self-contained discipline with no apologies to the reader. The ideal problem would state: model the following situation and solve the resulting equations. This would be unfair on the beginner since what may seem to be reasonable assumptions may lead to a system of equations which cannot be readily solved. We have attempted to include at the end of each chapter a rather mixed collection of problems which cover the theory and application without resorting too much to the artificial type of exercise cited above.

The art of approximation depends greatly on experience. The applied mathematician tries to keep one eye on the practical implications of an approximation and the other on the mathematics which it entails. The most elegant theory is the one which supplies useful information with the minimum of mathematical analysis.

Differential equations play a key role in dynamics and because of this we have included a chapter on ordinary differential equations. Most problems in dynamics lead to one or more ordinary differential equations, and it seems appropriate to include the necessary theory in an introductory book on dynamics. Differential equations can be usefully classified into two categories, those which are linear and those which are non-linear. There are a number of general methods of solving certain types of linear ordinary differential equations. On the other hand, non-linear ordinary differential equations can only usually be solved, if at all, by the use of miscellaneous _ad hoc_ techniques. For this sound practical reason applied mathematics has developed a heavy emphasis towards the linear or approximately linear phenomena.

Unfortunately we are surrounded by non-linearities in nature and we have to try to accommodate them with the mathematical aids at our disposal. The alternative is to adopt a completely numerical approach from the beginning by using techniques for solving differential equations numerically with the aid of calculating machines and computers. However, generality and details of principle may be sacrificed. A number of numerical techniques have been included to indicate how more elaborate problems can be approached. In this context one problem concerning a projectile is treated in considerable detail in chapter 4.

1

Vectors

1.1 Definitions

In the study of mechanics it is useful to distinguish between quantities which have magnitude only and those which have magnitude, are associated with a direction in space and combine in a certain way. The former are called *scalars*, for example mass, time, length and temperature, and the latter are called *vectors*, for example velocity and acceleration. A vector is simply a directed quantity with a certain property. Geometrically, if a magnitude and direction is associated with a point in space, we have a directed line segment such as $\overrightarrow{AB}$ in figure 1. The order of the letters indicates that the directed line segment is in the direction 'A to B'. The magnitude of the directed line segment is the length AB.

FIGURE 1   Geometrical notion of a vector

Geometrically a vector specifies only the direction and magnitude of a directed line segment but not its position in space. Thus $\overrightarrow{CD}$ is a representative of the same vector as $\overrightarrow{AB}$. In fact, any directed line segment parallel to $\overrightarrow{AB}$ and with the same magnitude as $\overrightarrow{AB}$ is a representative of the vector. We write this vector as $\overline{AB}$ or $\overline{CD}$ since it stands for a whole collection of directed line segments rather than just an individual one.

In some of our work with vectors in mechanics we will find that we are treating directed line segments as vectors. Most of the time the difference does not lead us to any wrong conclusions since we are simply

1

short-cutting some rigour, but it is as well to be aware of the distinction between the two.

1.2 Addition of vectors

Consider the triangle ABC in figure 2. In the triangle $\overline{AB}$, $\overline{AC}$, $\overline{BC}$ represent vectors. We define the *sum* of $\overline{AB}$ and $\overline{BC}$ to be $\overline{AC}$ and we write

$$\overline{AB} + \overline{BC} = \overline{AC}.$$

(It is important to observe the order in which the 'letters' are written down.) One consequence of this law is the following:

$$\overline{AB} + \overline{BA} = \overline{AA} \tag{1}$$

where $\overline{AA}$ is defined as the zero or null vector. Thus (1) may be written as

$$\overline{BA} = -\overline{AB}.$$

This tells us that if we write the letters of a vector in the reverse order, we must introduce a negative sign in any additive processes we are considering. Care must therefore be exercised when writing down any vector equation to ensure that all the vectors are written down in the correct sense.

This property, that vectors add according to the triangle law, is what distinguishes a vector from a directed quantity as such. There are some directed quantities, a rotation for example, which do not combine like vectors and so we cannot represent them by vectors in the normal sense.

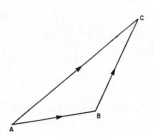

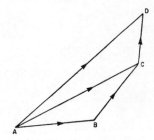

FIGURE 2   Triangle law of addition for vectors   FIGURE 3   Extended triangle law

The triangle law can be readily extended to the addition of three or more vectors. For example in figure 3

$$\overline{AD} = \overline{AC} + \overline{CD}$$
$$= \overline{AB} + \overline{BC} + \overline{CD}.$$

1.3 An alternative notation

The geometrical notation is not particularly adaptable to the require-ments of dynamics. The alternative notation in which bold-face type, **b**, represents a vector and the ordinary italic, *b*, a scalar is more convenient. On the blackboard the form $\bar{b}$, $\underline{b}$ or $\underset{\sim}{b}$ can be used to distinguish vectors from scalars. Always remember that a representative of a vector **b** can be interpreted mentally as a straight line joining two points Q and R. The magnitude of **b** is denoted by |**b**| (called the modulus of **b**) or simply *b*. The vector −**b** is a vector in the opposite direction to, but with the same magnitude as, **b**. Geometrically it will be $\overline{RQ}$.

In the application of the triangle law to the sum **a** + **b** we draw **a** and **b** as the two sides of a triangle in sense indicated by the arrows in figure 4. The sum is represented by the third side **c**.

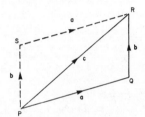

FIGURE 4   Alternative notation

Vectors obey the following rules which can be deduced from the tri-angle law:

(i) $\mathbf{a} + \mathbf{b} = \mathbf{b} + \mathbf{a}$;

(ii) $\mathbf{a} + (\mathbf{b} + \mathbf{c}) = (\mathbf{a} + \mathbf{b}) + \mathbf{c}$;

(iii) $m(\mathbf{a} + \mathbf{b}) = m\mathbf{a} + m\mathbf{b}$.

The first may be verified by inspection of figure 4. The left-hand side of (i) is represented in the figure by the path PQR whilst the right-hand side is represented by the dashed path PSR. Since PQRS is a parallelogram, both of these by the triangle law are equal to **c**. The proofs of (ii) and (iii) are left as exercises for the reader. In (iii) *m***a** is vector of magnitude *m*|**a**| in the direction of **a** if *m* is positive, and in the opposite direction to **a** if *m* is negative.

The zero or null vector we defined geometrically in section 1.2 we now write **0**. Thus

$$\mathbf{a} - \mathbf{a} = \mathbf{0}.$$

1.4 Scalar and vector products

Whilst reasonable and consistent meaning can be attached to the product of a scalar and a vector, the 'product' of two vectors has no obvious intuitive interpretation. There are, however, two product forms which are respectively scalar and vector and which have physical applications.

The *scalar product* of two vectors **a** and **b** is a scalar defined as the product of a, b and the cosine of the angle θ between the vectors (see figure 5). We denote it by **a** · **b** (called **a** dot **b**). Thus

$$\mathbf{a} \cdot \mathbf{b} = ab \cos \theta, \qquad 0 \leqslant \theta \leqslant \pi.$$

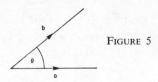

FIGURE 5

Example 1 *Show that* **a** · **b** = **b** · **a**.

By definition
$$\mathbf{a} \cdot \mathbf{b} = ab \cos \theta$$
$$= ba \cos \theta = \mathbf{b} \cdot \mathbf{a}.$$

Example 2 *Show that* **a** · (**b** + **c**) = **a** · **b** + **a** · **c**.

We note that, by definition
$$\mathbf{a} \cdot \mathbf{b} = a(b \cos \theta)$$
$$= a \times \text{(magnitude of the projection of } \mathbf{b} \text{ on } \mathbf{a}).$$

Using figure 6
$$\mathbf{a} \cdot \mathbf{b} + \mathbf{a} \cdot \mathbf{c} = a \times \text{OP} + a \times \text{RS}$$
$$= a \times \text{OP} + a \times \text{PQ}$$
$$= a \times \text{OQ}$$
$$= a \times \text{(projection of } \mathbf{b} + \mathbf{c} \text{ on } \mathbf{a})$$
$$= \mathbf{a} \cdot (\mathbf{b} + \mathbf{c}).$$

We note that if m is a number,
$$m(\mathbf{a} \cdot \mathbf{b}) = (m\mathbf{a}) \cdot \mathbf{b} = \mathbf{a} \cdot (m\mathbf{b})$$
by the definition of scalar product.

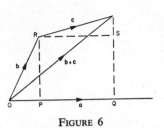

FIGURE 6

If $\mathbf{a} \cdot \mathbf{b} = 0$ and neither $\mathbf{a}$ nor $\mathbf{b}$ is a null vector, then $\cos \theta$ must vanish, implying that $\theta = \frac{1}{2}\pi$ which means the vectors are perpendicular.

The *vector* (or *cross*) *product* of $\mathbf{a}$ and $\mathbf{b}$ is a *vector* $\mathbf{c}$ whose magnitude is $ab \sin \theta$ where θ is the angle between $\mathbf{a}$ and $\mathbf{b}$ such that $0 \leqslant \theta \leqslant \pi$. The direction of $\mathbf{c}$ is perpendicular to both $\mathbf{a}$ and $\mathbf{b}$ and such that $\mathbf{a}, \mathbf{b}$ and $\mathbf{c}$ form a right-hand system of vectors. The right-hand screw rule applied to $\mathbf{a}, \mathbf{b}, \mathbf{c}$ states that a right-handed screw rotation along $\mathbf{c}$ turns from $\mathbf{a}$ to $\mathbf{b}$ through the angle θ (figure 7). This is a conventional definition: in vectors

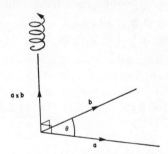

FIGURE 7 Vector product and right-hand screw convention

and mechanics we adopt the right-hand rather than the left-hand convention. We write the product as

$$\mathbf{c} = \mathbf{a} \times \mathbf{b}, \quad \text{(said as } \mathbf{a} \text{ vec } \mathbf{b}, \text{ or } \mathbf{a} \text{ cross } \mathbf{b})$$

where

$$|\mathbf{c}| = |\mathbf{a} \times \mathbf{b}| = ab \sin \theta.$$

Example 3   Show that $\mathbf{a} \times \mathbf{b} = -\mathbf{b} \times \mathbf{a}$. Unlike the scalar product, the vector product is not commutative.

The vector $\mathbf{a} \times \mathbf{b}$ has magnitude $ab \sin \theta$ and a direction determined by the right-hand screw rule. The vector $\mathbf{b} \times \mathbf{a}$ also has magnitude $ab \sin \theta$ but its direction is opposite to $\mathbf{a} \times \mathbf{b}$ by a second use of the rule (figure 8). If two vectors are equal in magnitude but opposite in direction, their sum vanishes and it therefore follows that

$$\mathbf{a} \times \mathbf{b} = - \mathbf{b} \times \mathbf{a}.$$

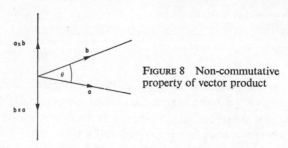

FIGURE 8　Non-commutative property of vector product

This example indicates that care must be taken when writing down vector products.

We quote the following two results without proof:

(i) $\mathbf{a} \times (\mathbf{b} + \mathbf{c}) = \mathbf{a} \times \mathbf{b} + \mathbf{a} \times \mathbf{c}$,

(ii) $m(\mathbf{a} \times \mathbf{b}) = (m\mathbf{a}) \times \mathbf{b} = \mathbf{a} \times (m\mathbf{b})$.

If $\mathbf{a} \times \mathbf{b} = 0$ and neither $\mathbf{a}$ nor $\mathbf{b}$ is a null vector then $\sin \theta$ must vanish, implying that $\theta = 0$ or π. The two vectors are therefore parallel, pointing in the same direction if $\theta = 0$ and in opposite directions if $\theta = \pi$.

The vector product has a geometrical interpretation in that its magnitude is the area of the parallelogram constructed on the representatives of $\mathbf{a}$ and $\mathbf{b}$ drawn from the same point.

1.5 Unit vectors. Rectangular axis

A *unit vector* is simply a vector of unit magnitude. For any vector $\mathbf{b}$, $\mathbf{b}/b$ is a unit vector in the same direction as $\mathbf{b}$. Unit vectors provide a useful means of specifying directions in space.

An important set or triad of unit vectors is associated with the Cartesian or rectangular frame reference. A frame of reference is necessary in order to describe the location of a point in space in relation to other points. The simplest frame is the rectangular Cartesian one and it consists of three mutually perpendicular straight lines or axes Ox, Oy, Oz intersecting in the point O, called the origin (figure 9). We again choose to use a right-handed system in the sense that a right-handed screw rotation along the z-axis turns from Ox to Oy through a right angle: if Oy and Oz in figure 9 are in the plane of the paper Ox will point at the reader.

Any point P can be related to axes by a triad of numbers a, b, c which are the perpendicular distances of P from each of the planes Oyz, Oxz, Oxy. From figure 9 these are equal respectively to OQ, OR, OS. We now adopt the convention that distances measured in the directions Ox, Cy, Oz are positive whilst distances measured from O in the opposite directions are negative. The numbers (a, b, c) are the coordinates of P.

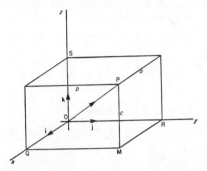

FIGURE 9   Rectangular Cartesian coordinate system: unit vectors

We may associate these unit vectors with the directions of the axes. These are customarily written $\mathbf{i}$, $\mathbf{j}$, $\mathbf{k}$ and are in the directions Ox, Oy, Oz respectively. Using the triangle law of addition in figure 9,

$$\overline{OP} = \overline{OQ} + \overline{QM} + \overline{MP}$$
$$= a\mathbf{i} + b\mathbf{j} + c\mathbf{k},$$

Since P is any point this implies that any vector can be expressed in terms of these Cartesian unit vectors and, as we shall see, this representation is particularly important in computations involving vectors. When a point P and an origin O in space determine a directed line segment $\overrightarrow{OP}$ and hence a vector $\overline{OP}$, we call that vector the *position vector* of P with respect to O and denote it by $\mathbf{r}$. In figure 9

$$|\mathbf{r}| = r = OP = (OQ^2 + QP^2)^{\frac{1}{2}}$$
$$= (OP^2 + QM^2 + MP^2)^{\frac{1}{2}}$$
$$= (a^2 + b^2 + c^2)^{\frac{1}{2}}.$$

The numbers (a, b, c) as well as being the coordinates of P are also referred to as the components of $\mathbf{r}$ in the appropriate context and are the projections of $\mathbf{r}$ on the coordinate axes.

Example 4   *Write down the position vector of the point with coordinates* $(1, -1, 2)$.

The position vector of this point is given by
$$\mathbf{r} = \mathbf{i} - \mathbf{j} + 2\mathbf{k}.$$

Example 5   *Find the vector* $\overline{AB}$ *where* A *and* B *have coordinates* $(-1, 3, 5)$ *and* $(2, -1, 3)$.

By the triangle law
$$\overline{OB} = \overline{OA} + \overline{AB},$$
$$\overline{AB} = \overline{OB} - \overline{OA}.$$

The position vectors of A and B are given by
$$\overline{OA} = -\mathbf{i} + 3\mathbf{j} + 5\mathbf{k},$$
$$\overline{OB} = 2\mathbf{i} - \mathbf{j} + 3\mathbf{k},$$
and therefore
$$\overline{AB} = (2\mathbf{i} - \mathbf{j} + 3\mathbf{k}) - (-\mathbf{i} + 3\mathbf{j} + 5\mathbf{k})$$
$$= 3\mathbf{i} - 4\mathbf{j} - 2\mathbf{k}.$$

Note that the vector equation
$$\mathbf{a} = \mathbf{b}$$
where $\mathbf{a} = a_1\mathbf{i} + a_2\mathbf{j} + a_3\mathbf{k}$ and $\mathbf{b} = b_1\mathbf{i} + b_2\mathbf{j} + b_3\mathbf{k}$, means that
$$a_1\mathbf{i} + a_2\mathbf{j} + a_3\mathbf{k} = b_1\mathbf{i} + b_2\mathbf{j} + b_3\mathbf{k},$$
which implies the three scalar equations
$$a_1 = b_1, \qquad a_2' = b_2, \qquad a_3 = b_3.$$
Vector notation is a shorthand method of expressing scalar equations.

Since the Cartesian system is right-handed, the unit vectors $\mathbf{i}, \mathbf{j}, \mathbf{k}$ satisfy the following relations:

(i) $\mathbf{i} \cdot \mathbf{j} = \mathbf{j} \cdot \mathbf{k} = \mathbf{k} \cdot \mathbf{i} = 0$;

(ii) $\mathbf{i} \cdot \mathbf{i} = \mathbf{j} \cdot \mathbf{j} = \mathbf{k} \cdot \mathbf{k} = 1$;

(iii) $\mathbf{i} \times \mathbf{i} = \mathbf{j} \times \mathbf{j} = \mathbf{k} \times \mathbf{k} = 0$;

(iv) $\mathbf{i} \times \mathbf{j} = \mathbf{k}, \mathbf{j} \times \mathbf{k} = \mathbf{i}, \mathbf{k} \times \mathbf{i} = \mathbf{j}$, (note the cyclic order in $\mathbf{i}, \mathbf{j}, \mathbf{k}$).

The scalar product of two vectors $\mathbf{a}$ and $\mathbf{b}$ in terms of their components is given by
$$\mathbf{a} \cdot \mathbf{b} = (a_1\mathbf{i} + a_2\mathbf{j} + a_3\mathbf{k}) \cdot (b_1\mathbf{i} + b_2\mathbf{j} + b_3\mathbf{k})$$
$$= a_1 b_1 \mathbf{i} \cdot \mathbf{i} + a_1 b_2 \mathbf{i} \cdot \mathbf{j} + a_1 b_3 \mathbf{i} \cdot \mathbf{k} + \dots$$
$$= a_1 b_1 + a_2 b_2 + a_3 b_3,$$

using Example 2 and (i) and (ii) above. In particular if $\mathbf{a} = \mathbf{b}$, we note that $|\mathbf{a}| = (\mathbf{a} \cdot \mathbf{a})^{\frac{1}{2}}$.

The vector product of two vectors is given by

$$
\begin{aligned}
\mathbf{a} \times \mathbf{b} &= (a_1\mathbf{i} + a_2\mathbf{j} + a_3\mathbf{k}) \times (b_1\mathbf{i} + b_2\mathbf{j} + b_3\mathbf{k}) \\
&= a_1b_1\mathbf{i} \times \mathbf{i} + a_1b_2\mathbf{i} \times \mathbf{j} + a_1b_3\mathbf{i} \times \mathbf{k} + a_2b_1\mathbf{j} \times \mathbf{i} + a_2b_2\mathbf{j} \times \mathbf{j} \\
&\quad + a_2b_3\mathbf{j} \times \mathbf{k} + a_3b_1\mathbf{k} \times \mathbf{i} + a_3b_2\mathbf{k} \times \mathbf{j} + a_3b_3\mathbf{k} \times \mathbf{k} \\
&= a_1b_2\mathbf{k} - a_1b_3\mathbf{j} - a_2b_1\mathbf{k} + a_2b_3\mathbf{i} + a_3b_1\mathbf{j} - a_3b_2\mathbf{i} \\
&= (a_2b_3 - a_3b_2)\mathbf{i} + (a_3b_1 - a_1b_3)\mathbf{j} + (a_1b_2 - a_2b_1)\mathbf{k},
\end{aligned}
$$

by (iii) and (iv) above. For those readers familiar with determinants the vector product may be written symbolically as

$$
\mathbf{a} \times \mathbf{b} = \begin{vmatrix} \mathbf{i} & \mathbf{j} & \mathbf{k} \\ a_1 & a_2 & a_3 \\ b_1 & b_2 & b_3 \end{vmatrix}
$$

and evaluated as such.

Example 6 *Find a formula for the angle between two vectors* $\mathbf{a}$ *and* $\mathbf{b}$ *in terms of their components.*

By definition

$$
\mathbf{a} \cdot \mathbf{b} = ab \cos \theta,
$$

where θ is the angle between the vectors. Thus

$$
\cos \theta = \frac{\mathbf{a} \cdot \mathbf{b}}{ab} = \frac{a_1b_1 + a_2b_2 + a_3b_3}{(a_1^2 + a_2^2 + a_3^2)^{\frac{1}{2}}(b_1^2 + b_2^2 + b_3^2)^{\frac{1}{2}}}.
$$

Example 7 *If* $\mathbf{a} = \mathbf{i} + 2\mathbf{j} - \mathbf{k}$ *and* $\mathbf{b} = 2\mathbf{i} + \mathbf{j} + 3\mathbf{k}$ *determine* (i) $\mathbf{a} \cdot \mathbf{b}$, (ii) $\mathbf{a} \times \mathbf{b}$, (iii) $(\mathbf{a} \times \mathbf{b}) \times \mathbf{a}$.

(i) $\mathbf{a} \cdot \mathbf{b} = 2 + 2 - 3 = 1$.
(ii) $\mathbf{a} \times \mathbf{b} = [6 - (-1)]\mathbf{i} + (-2 - 3)\mathbf{j} + (1 - 4)\mathbf{k} = 7\mathbf{i} - 5\mathbf{j} - 3\mathbf{k}$.
(iii) Using (ii)

$$
\begin{aligned}
(\mathbf{a} \times \mathbf{b}) \times \mathbf{a} &= (7\mathbf{i} - 5\mathbf{j} - 3\mathbf{k}) \times (\mathbf{i} + 2\mathbf{j} - \mathbf{k}) \\
&= [5 - (-6)]\mathbf{i} + [-3 - (-7)]\mathbf{j} + [14 - (-5)]\mathbf{k} \\
&= 11\mathbf{i} + 4\mathbf{j} + 19\mathbf{k}.
\end{aligned}
$$

1.6 Triple products

Example 7(iii) above is an illustration of a *triple product* between three vectors. A triple product between three vectors involving scalar and vector products can only be constructed in certain ways, which must be consistent with the original definitions. For example, $(\mathbf{b} \cdot \mathbf{c}) \times \mathbf{a}$ has no meaning since the term in parentheses is a scalar and its vector product with $\mathbf{a}$ is undefined. The product $\mathbf{a} \times \mathbf{b} \times \mathbf{c}$ is ambiguous since there is no indication of the order in which the products should be taken.

A product between three vectors involving a scalar and a vector product is called a *scalar triple product*. For example, $\mathbf{a} \cdot \mathbf{b} \times \mathbf{c}$ is a scalar triple product and the answer is a scalar. No brackets are needed since the product is unambiguous: the vector product must be evaluated first, followed by the scalar product. Geometrically, the absolute value of $\mathbf{a} \cdot \mathbf{b} \times \mathbf{c}$ is the volume of the parallelepiped constructed on the representatives of $\mathbf{a}, \mathbf{b}, \mathbf{c}$ drawn from the same point. This can be seen from

$$\mathbf{a} \cdot \mathbf{b} \times \mathbf{c} = abc \sin \theta \cos \phi$$

and figure 10, using the definitions of scalar and vector product. If $\mathbf{a}, \mathbf{b}$ and $\mathbf{c}$ are all non-zero vectors, $\mathbf{a} \cdot \mathbf{b} \times \mathbf{c} = 0$ implies that the volume of the parallelepiped vanishes and that $\mathbf{a}, \mathbf{b}$ and $\mathbf{c}$ are coplanar, that is they lie in the same plane when drawn from the same point.

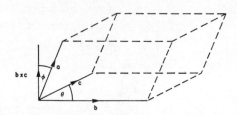

FIGURE 10   Parallelepiped formed by the vectors $\mathbf{a}, \mathbf{b}$ and $\mathbf{c}$

With

$$\mathbf{a} = a_1\mathbf{i} + a_2\mathbf{j} + a_3\mathbf{k}, \quad \mathbf{b} = b_1\mathbf{i} + b_2\mathbf{j} + b_3\mathbf{k}, \quad \mathbf{c} = c_1\mathbf{i} + c_2\mathbf{j} + c_3\mathbf{k}$$

the scalar triple product in terms of Cartesian components becomes

$$\mathbf{a} \cdot \mathbf{b} \times \mathbf{c} = a_1(b_2c_3 - b_3c_2) + a_2(b_3c_1 - b_1c_3) + a_3(b_1c_2 - b_2c_1)$$

$$= \begin{vmatrix} a_1 & a_2 & a_3 \\ b_1 & b_2 & b_3 \\ c_1 & c_2 & c_3 \end{vmatrix}$$

in determinant form. The reader can verify directly, or by interchanging rows in the determinant, that

$$\mathbf{a} \cdot \mathbf{b} \times \mathbf{c} = \mathbf{c} \cdot \mathbf{a} \times \mathbf{b} = \mathbf{b} \cdot \mathbf{c} \times \mathbf{a}.$$

Note that the cyclic order is preserved.

The *vector triple product* involves two vector products between three vectors. Thus, **a** × (**b** × **c**) is an example of a vector triple product. The brackets are now important since in general,

$$\mathbf{a} \times (\mathbf{b} \times \mathbf{c}) \neq (\mathbf{a} \times \mathbf{b}) \times \mathbf{c}.$$

This can be verified by a counter-example or by the following geometrical argument. Referring back to figure 10, we recall that **b** × **c** is perpendicular to the plane of **b** and **c**. Further **a** × (**b** × **c**) will be perpendicular to **a** and **b** × **c**, that is it must lie in the plane of **b** and **c**. By a similar chain of reasoning (**a** × **b**) × **c** lies in the plane of **a** and **b**. Except in the case when the resultant is in the direction **b**, the inequality is demonstrated.

The vector triple product satisfies the following identity in terms of scalar products

$$\mathbf{a} \times (\mathbf{b} \times \mathbf{c}) = (\mathbf{a} \cdot \mathbf{c})\mathbf{b} - (\mathbf{a} \cdot \mathbf{b})\mathbf{c}.$$

This can be verified by expressing both sides in terms of their Cartesian components. We leave this as an exercise for the reader.

1.7 Moment of a vector

The moment **M** about the origin O of the representative of the vector **F** located at P (usually abbreviated by 'F at P') which has position vector **r** is defined as

$$\mathbf{M} = \mathbf{r} \times \mathbf{F}$$

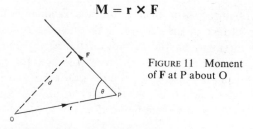

FIGURE 11   Moment of F at P about O

From the definition of the vector product

$$|\mathbf{M}| = |\mathbf{r}||\mathbf{F}| \sin(\pi - \theta) \qquad \text{(figure 11)}$$

$$= |\mathbf{F}| OP \sin \theta$$

$$= |\mathbf{F}| d$$

where $(\pi - \theta)$ is the angle between the actual direction of the two vectors and d is the perpendicular distance from O onto the line through **F** at P.

If the vectors $\mathbf{F}_1, \mathbf{F}_2,...$ act at the points with position vectors $\mathbf{r}_1, \mathbf{r}_2,...$, the total moment is the sum of the individual moments, that is

$$\mathbf{M} = \mathbf{r}_1 \times \mathbf{F}_1 + \mathbf{r}_2 \times \mathbf{F}_2.... .$$

1.8 Spherical polar coordinates

Many other coordinate systems are available and useful for particular classes of problems. The coordinates r, θ, ϕ shown in figure 12 are spherical polar coordinates. The point P can be considered as the intersection of a sphere ($r = $ constant), a cone ($\theta = $ constant) and a plane ($\phi = $ constant). For this reason spherical polar coordinates usually find their application

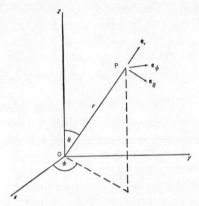

FIGURE 12   Spherical polar coordinates

in problems involving cones or spheres. For those familiar with geographical location on the surface of the earth, ϕ is the measure of longitude (from the Greenwich meridian on the surface of the earth) and θ is the co-latitude (the latitude being measured from the equator on the earth), where we have taken the origin at the centre of the earth and z-axis through the north pole. The relation between Cartesian and spherical polar co-ordinates can be worked out from figure 12:

$$x = r \sin\theta \cos\phi, \qquad y = r \sin\theta \sin\phi, \qquad z = r \cos\theta.$$

We can associate unit vectors $\mathbf{e}_r$, $\mathbf{e}_\theta$, $\mathbf{e}_\phi$ with this coordinate system such that $\mathbf{e}_r$ is in the direction in which θ and ϕ are constant, with r increasing, etc. By analogy with the earth's surface again, $\mathbf{e}_r$ is pointing vertically upward, $\mathbf{e}_\theta$ points to the south and $\mathbf{e}_\phi$ to the east. Unlike the Cartesian triad $\mathbf{i}$, $\mathbf{j}$, $\mathbf{k}$, the unit vectors $\mathbf{e}_r$, $\mathbf{e}_\theta$, $\mathbf{e}_\phi$ do not point in fixed directions in space. The unit vectors are right-handed and orthogonal so that

$$\mathbf{e}_r = \mathbf{e}_\theta \times \mathbf{e}_\phi, \qquad \mathbf{e}_\theta = \mathbf{e}_\phi \times \mathbf{e}_r, \qquad \mathbf{e}_\phi = \mathbf{e}_r \times \mathbf{e}_\theta.$$

1.9 Plane vectors

Many problems occurring in later chapters will be essentially two-dimensional. In these cases we can locate any point in the plane of the two dimensions by reference to two rectangular axes Ox, Oy. If P is a point in the plane with coordinates (x,y) its position can be determined by the plane position vector

$$\mathbf{r} = x\mathbf{i} + y\mathbf{j}$$

(see figure 13). If vector products are included then the third dimension specified is required since the vector product of any two plane vectors will be in the direction $\mathbf{k}$ perpendicular to the Oxy plane.

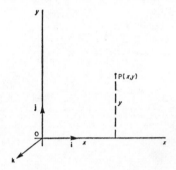

FIGURE 13   Plane vectors

A second useful representation of a point P is by *polar coordinates* (r,θ) where $r = |\mathbf{r}|$ and θ is the angle between the position vector and the positive direction of the axis (figure 14). Clearly

$$x = r \cos \theta, \qquad y = r \sin \theta,$$
$$r = (x^2 + y^2)^{\frac{1}{2}}, \quad \tan \theta = y/x.$$

With each of the coordinates r and θ we can associate unit vectors $\mathbf{e}_r$ and $\mathbf{e}_\theta$ as shown in figure 14: $\mathbf{e}_r$ is called the *unit radius vector* and $\mathbf{e}_\theta$ the *unit transverse vector*. We observe that $\mathbf{r} = r\mathbf{e}_r$. For comparison with the three-dimensional spherical polar coordinates $\mathbf{e}_\theta$ is into the page and the x-y axes here become the z-y axes.

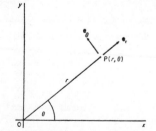

FIGURE 14   Plane polar coordinates

1.10 Velocity and acceleration

We wish now to consider derivatives of vectors and this can be most usefully illustrated through velocity and acceleration. Consider a particle P moving along a straight line such that its displacement x from a fixed point O of the line is given at time t by $x(t)$ (by this symbol we mean that x is a function of t or depends on t). At time t_1 the particle will have a displacement $x(t_1)$ (the point P_1 in figure 15). In the time interval $t - t_1$, the particle will move a distance $x(t) - x(t_1)$. The *average velocity* $\bar{v}$ over this interval is defined by

$$\bar{v} = \frac{x(t) - x(t_1)}{t - t_1}. \tag{2}$$

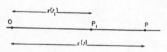

FIGURE 15

The *instantaneous velocity* v of the particle at time t is defined as the value of the right-hand side of (2) as t_1 approaches t. This is the mathematical notion of limit. Thus

$$v = \lim_{t_1 \to t} \frac{x(t) - x(t_1)}{t - t_1},$$

which is, by definition, the derivative of x with respect to t expressed as

$$v = \frac{dx}{dt} \quad \text{or} \quad \dot{x}. \tag{3}$$

Speed is the magnitude of the velocity or $|\dot{x}|$.

Example 8   *If the displacement, in metres, of a particle is given by*

$$x = 12(t^2 + 2t)$$

where t is measured in seconds, find its velocity after three seconds.

At any time t

$$v = \frac{dx}{dt} = 12(2t + 2) \text{ metres per second (m/s).} \tag{4}$$

At $t = 3$ s, $v = 12(6 + 2) = 96$ m/s.

Whilst velocity is rate of change of displacement, acceleration f is, in turn, rate of change of velocity. Thus

$$f = \lim_{t_1 \to t} \frac{v(t) - v(t_1)}{t - t_1} = \frac{dv}{dt} = \frac{d^2x}{dt^2} \quad \text{or} \quad \ddot{x}$$

using (3): acceleration is the second time derivative of displacement.

Example 9 Show that the acceleration in example 8 is constant at all times.

From (4)

$$\frac{dv}{dt} = 12(2) = 24 \text{ metres per second per second (m/s}^2\text{)}.$$

which is independent of time and constant.

An important alternative formula for acceleration exists if we consider speed depending on displacement, and use the rule for the derivative of a function of a function in calculus:

$$f = \frac{dv}{dt} = \frac{dv}{dx} \cdot \frac{dx}{dt} = v\frac{dv}{dx},$$

a form which will be used frequently in subsequent work.

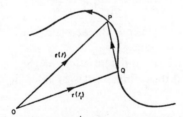

FIGURE 16   Position vector **r** of a particle describing a curve in space

When a particle moves along a space curve, as indicated in figure 16, its position vector **r** will be dependent on time t. Let the particle be at Q at time t_1 and at P at time t. We define the *average velocity* of the particle over the interval $t - t_1$ as

$$\frac{\overline{QP}}{t - t_1} = \frac{\overline{OP} - \overline{OQ}}{t - t_1} = \frac{\mathbf{r}(t) - \mathbf{r}(t_1)}{t - t_1}$$

by the triangle law. The instantaneous velocity **v** at time t is then the limit of this ratio as t_1 approaches t, or

$$\mathbf{v} = \lim_{t_1 \to t} \frac{\mathbf{r}(t) - \mathbf{r}(t_1)}{t - t_1}. \tag{5}$$

Express $\mathbf{r}(t)$ and $\mathbf{r}(t_1)$ in terms of their components so that

$$\mathbf{r}(t) = x(t)\mathbf{i} + y(t)\mathbf{j} + z(t)\mathbf{k} \quad \text{and} \quad \mathbf{r}(t_1) = x(t_1)\mathbf{i} + y(t_1)\mathbf{j} + z(t_1)\mathbf{k}.$$

Equation (5) becomes

$$\mathbf{v} = \mathbf{i} \lim_{t_1 \to t} \frac{x(t) - x(t_1)}{t - t_1} + \mathbf{j} \lim_{t_1 \to t} \frac{y(t) - y(t_1)}{t - t_1} + \mathbf{k} \lim_{t_1 \to t} \frac{z(t) - z(t_1)}{t - t_1}$$

$$= \mathbf{i}\frac{dx}{dt} + \mathbf{j}\frac{dy}{dt} + \mathbf{k}\frac{dz}{dt}$$

$$= \frac{d}{dt}(x\mathbf{i} + y\mathbf{j} + z\mathbf{k}) = \frac{d\mathbf{r}}{dt} \quad \text{or} \quad \dot{\mathbf{r}} \tag{6}$$

because **i**, **j**, **k** are fixed vectors independent of t. The velocity vector is the time derivative of the position vector, and as $\overline{QP}$ contracts **v** will become tangential to the curve at P. The magnitude of the velocity given by $|\mathbf{v}|$ is called the speed. This is consistent with our earlier definition of speed and agrees with it if we imagine the particle moving in a straight line parallel to the x-axis.

The *acceleration* **f** is the time derivative of the velocity:

$$\mathbf{f} = \frac{d\mathbf{v}}{dt} = \frac{d^2\mathbf{r}}{dt^2} = \frac{d^2x}{dt^2}\mathbf{i} + \frac{d^2y}{dt^2}\mathbf{j} + \frac{d^2z}{dt^2}\mathbf{k} \quad \text{or} \quad \ddot{x}\mathbf{i} + \ddot{y}\mathbf{j} + \ddot{z}\mathbf{k}$$

using (6). Note that, in general, the acceleration is *not* tangential to the path described by the particle.

The rules governing the differentiation of the sums and products of vectors are similar to the familiar rules of calculus. If **a**, **b** and c are dependent on t, then

$$\frac{d}{dt}(\mathbf{a} + \mathbf{b}) = \frac{d\mathbf{a}}{dt} + \frac{d\mathbf{b}}{dt},$$

$$\frac{d}{dt}(\mathbf{a} \cdot \mathbf{b}) = \frac{d\mathbf{a}}{dt} \cdot \mathbf{b} + \mathbf{a} \cdot \frac{d\mathbf{b}}{dt},$$

$$\frac{d}{dt}(c\mathbf{a}) = \frac{dc}{dt}\mathbf{a} + c\frac{d\mathbf{a}}{dt},$$

$$\frac{d}{dt}(\mathbf{a} \times \mathbf{b}) = \frac{d\mathbf{a}}{dt} \times \mathbf{b} + \mathbf{a} \times \frac{d\mathbf{b}}{dt}.$$

These can be most easily verified by expressing **a** and **b** in terms of their components. In the last formula the order of the vector products is important.

Example 10   Show that the velocity of a particle is independent of the origin to which its position vector is referred.

Let O and O′ be two fixed origins with **a** the position vector of O′ relative to O. Let **r** and **r′** be the position vectors of P relative to O and O′ respectively (figure 17).

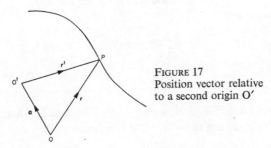

FIGURE 17
Position vector relative
to a second origin O′

Let **v** be the velocity of P so that

$$\mathbf{v} = \frac{d\mathbf{r}}{dt}.$$

By the triangle law **r** = **a** + **r′** and consequently

$$\mathbf{v} = \frac{d}{dt}(\mathbf{a} + \mathbf{r}') = \frac{d\mathbf{a}}{dt} + \frac{d\mathbf{r}'}{dt}.$$

But **a** is a constant vector (that is, constant in magnitude and direction) and therefore $d\mathbf{a}/dt = 0$ and

$$\mathbf{v} = \frac{d\mathbf{r}'}{dt},$$

which is the velocity of P relative to O′.

Example 11   Show that the path of a particle whose position vector at time t is given by

$$\mathbf{r} = a \cos \omega t \mathbf{i} + a \sin \omega t \mathbf{j} \quad (a, \omega \text{ are constants})$$

is a circle. Find the velocity and acceleration of the particle and show that $\mathbf{v} \cdot \mathbf{f} = 0$.

The components of the position vector are

$$x = a \cos \omega t, \qquad y = a \sin \omega t$$

and squaring and adding

$$x^2 + y^2 = a^2(\cos^2 \omega t + \sin^2 \omega t) = a^2.$$

This is the equation of a circle with centre at the origin and radius a.

The velocity $\mathbf{v}$ is given by

$$\mathbf{v} = \frac{d\mathbf{r}}{dt} = \frac{d}{dt}(a \cos \omega t \mathbf{i} + a \sin \omega t \mathbf{j})$$

$$= - a\omega \sin \omega t \mathbf{i} + a\omega \cos \omega t \mathbf{j}.$$

The acceleration

$$\mathbf{f} = \frac{d\mathbf{v}}{dt} = \frac{d}{dt}(- a\omega \sin \omega t \mathbf{i} + a\omega \cos \omega t \mathbf{j})$$

$$= - a\omega^2 \cos \omega t \mathbf{i} - a\omega^2 \sin \omega t \mathbf{j}. \qquad (7)$$

Now

$$\mathbf{v} \cdot \mathbf{f} = (- a\omega \sin \omega t \mathbf{i} + a\omega \cos \omega t \mathbf{j}) \cdot (- a\omega^2 \cos \omega t \mathbf{i} - a\omega^2 \sin \omega t \mathbf{j})$$
$$= a^2\omega^3 \sin \omega t \cos \omega t - a^2\omega^3 \cos \omega t \sin \omega t = 0.$$

Since the velocity vector is a tangent to the circle, this implies that the acceleration is radial. Its direction can be deduced from (7) which can be written in the form

$$\mathbf{f} = -\omega^2\mathbf{r}.$$

Thus $\mathbf{f}$ is opposite in direction to the position vector and points towards the origin.

Example 12   A vector has constant magnitude but its direction varies with time. Show that its derivative is always perpendicular to itself.

Let $\mathbf{a}(t)$ denote the vector. We are given that $\mathbf{a} \cdot \mathbf{a} = |\mathbf{a}|^2 = $ constant. Differentiating this equation with respect to t, we get

$$\frac{d}{dt}(\mathbf{a} \cdot \mathbf{a}) = 0$$

or

$$\frac{d\mathbf{a}}{dt} \cdot \mathbf{a} + \mathbf{a} \cdot \frac{d\mathbf{a}}{dt} = 0,$$

that is,

$$\mathbf{a} \cdot \frac{d\mathbf{a}}{dt} = 0,$$

the required result since the scalar product vanishes.

Physically the vector in this example can be interpreted as the position vector of a point which moves on the surface of a sphere. The velocity or rate of change of **a** must be perpendicular to **a**.

In terms of plane polars we saw in section 1.9 that

$$\mathbf{r} = r\mathbf{e}_r.$$

We wish now to find the components of velocity and acceleration in the directions of the unit vectors $\mathbf{e}_r$ and $\mathbf{e}_\theta$. The velocity

$$\mathbf{v} = \frac{d\mathbf{r}}{dt} = \frac{d}{dr}(r\mathbf{e}_r) = \frac{dr}{dt}\mathbf{e}_r + r\frac{d\mathbf{e}_r}{dt}, \tag{8}$$

where it must be noted that $\mathbf{e}_r$ is not a constant vector. Referring back to figure 14, it is clear that

$$\mathbf{e}_r = \cos\theta\mathbf{i} + \sin\theta\mathbf{j}, \qquad \mathbf{e}_\theta = -\sin\theta\mathbf{i} + \cos\theta\mathbf{j}.$$

Thus

$$\frac{d\mathbf{e}_r}{dt} = (-\sin\theta\mathbf{i} + \cos\theta\mathbf{j})\frac{d\theta}{dt} = \dot\theta\mathbf{e}_\theta,$$

$$\frac{d\mathbf{e}_\theta}{dt} = (-\cos\theta\mathbf{i} - \sin\theta\mathbf{j})\frac{d\theta}{dt} = -\dot\theta\mathbf{e}_r.$$

(Note the significance of Example 12 in this context.) Equation (8) becomes

$$\mathbf{v} = \dot r\mathbf{e}_r + r\dot\theta\mathbf{e}_\theta,$$

where $v_r = \dot r$ is the radial component and $v_\theta = r\dot\theta$ is the transverse component of the velocity.

The acceleration **f** is given by

$$\mathbf{f} = \frac{d\mathbf{v}}{dt} = \frac{d}{dt}(\dot r\mathbf{e}_r + r\dot\theta\mathbf{e}_\theta)$$

$$= \ddot r\mathbf{e}_r + \dot r\frac{d\mathbf{e}_r}{dt} + \dot r\dot\theta\mathbf{e}_\theta + r\ddot\theta\mathbf{e}_\theta + r\dot\theta\frac{d\mathbf{e}_\theta}{dt}$$

$$= \ddot r\mathbf{e}_r + \dot r\dot\theta\mathbf{e}_\theta + \dot r\dot\theta\mathbf{e}_\theta + r\ddot\theta\mathbf{e}_\theta - r\dot\theta^2\mathbf{e}_r$$

$$= (\ddot r - r\dot\theta^2)\mathbf{e}_r + (2\dot r\dot\theta + r\ddot\theta)\mathbf{e}_\theta.$$

Here the radial component of the acceleration $f_r = \ddot r - r\dot\theta^2$ and the transverse component

$$f_\theta = 2\dot r\dot\theta + r\ddot\theta = \frac{1}{r}\frac{d}{dt}(r^2\dot\theta).$$

In particular, if a particle is describing a circle of radius a and centre at the origin, $r = a$ and the velocity and acceleration become

$$\mathbf{v} = a\dot{\theta}\mathbf{e}_\theta, \qquad \mathbf{f} = -a\dot{\theta}^2\mathbf{e}_r + a\ddot{\theta}\mathbf{e}_\theta.$$

The speed $v = |\mathbf{v}| = a|\dot{\theta}|$ and the radial component of acceleration can be written $f_r = -v^2/a$, an important result. If we denote by ω the *angular rate* $\dot{\theta}$ at which the particle moves round the circle, $f_r = -a\omega^2$. The angular rate $\dot{\theta}$ is measured in radians per second (there are π radians in $180°$ and 1 radian $= 57\cdot296°$).

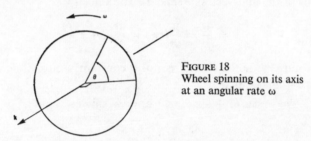

FIGURE 18
Wheel spinning on its axis
at an angular rate ω

We can also introduce the concept of the angular velocity of a body. Consider a wheel spinning on its axle (figure 18). The angle $\theta = \theta(t)$ is a measure of its angular displacement at any time t. The position vector of a point on the wheel is $r\mathbf{e}_r$ where r is a constant. The velocity of this point must be $r\dot{\theta}\mathbf{e}_\theta$. The *angular velocity* ω is defined as $\dot{\theta}\mathbf{k}$ where $\mathbf{k}$ is a unit vector in the direction of the axle and its magnitude is the magnitude of the angular rate $|\dot{\theta}|$. This description refers only to rotation about a *fixed* axis. We observe that the velocity of a point of the wheel is

$$r\dot{\theta}\mathbf{e}_\theta = \omega \times \mathbf{r},$$

a formula which can be generalized to variable angular velocity.

1.11 Integration of vectors

If a vector $\mathbf{a}$ depends on t, then the interpretation of the integral of $\mathbf{a}$ with respect to t presents no special difficulty if we express $\mathbf{a}$ in terms of its components. Thus we may define

$$\mathbf{I} = \int_{t_1}^{t_2} \mathbf{a}(t)\, \mathrm{d}t$$

$$= \int_{t_1}^{t_2} [a_1(t)\mathbf{i} + a_2(t)\mathbf{j} + a_3(t)\mathbf{k}]\, \mathrm{d}t$$

$$= \mathbf{i}\int_{t_1}^{t_2} a_1(t)\, \mathrm{d}t + \mathbf{j}\int_{t_1}^{t_2} a_2(t)\, \mathrm{d}t + \mathbf{k}\int_{t_1}^{t_2} a_3(t)\, \mathrm{d}t,$$

the scalar integrals having their usual meaning.

Example 13 *Evaluate* $\displaystyle\int_1^2 \mathbf{a}(t)\,dt$ *where* $\mathbf{a}(t) = t\mathbf{i} + \sin \pi t\mathbf{j} + \dfrac{1}{t}\mathbf{k}$.

$$\int_1^2 \mathbf{a}(t)\,dt = \int_1^2 \left(t\mathbf{i} + \sin \pi t\mathbf{j} + \frac{1}{t}\mathbf{k} \right) dt$$

$$= \left(\tfrac{1}{2}t^2\mathbf{i} - \frac{\cos \pi t}{\pi}\mathbf{j} + \ln t\mathbf{k} \right)_1^2$$

$$= \tfrac{1}{2}(4 - 1)\mathbf{i} - \frac{1}{\pi}(\cos 2\pi - \cos \pi)\mathbf{j} + (\ln 2 - \ln 1)\mathbf{k}$$

$$= \frac{3}{2}\mathbf{i} - \frac{2}{\pi}\mathbf{j} + \ln 2\,\mathbf{k}.$$

More elaborate integrals can be constructed in which the integrand contains scalar or vector products—for example

$$\int_{t_1}^{t_2} \mathbf{r} \cdot \mathbf{r}\,dt, \qquad \int_{t_1}^{t_2} \mathbf{r} \times \frac{d\mathbf{r}}{dt}\,dt, \qquad \int_{t_1}^{t_2} a(t)\mathbf{r} \times \frac{d^2\mathbf{r}}{dt^2}\,dt,$$

where we write $a(t)$ to emphasize that it is not necessarily a constant, $\mathbf{r}$ we assume to be dependent on t. It is important to recognize whether an integral is a scalar or a vector. Above, the first integral is a scalar and the other two are vectors. In all cases we evaluate the product in the integrand and integrate the resulting scalar or vector accordingly.

Example 14 *Evaluate* $\displaystyle\int_0^\pi \mathbf{r} \cdot \ddot{\mathbf{r}}\,dt$ *where* $\mathbf{r} = \cos \omega t\mathbf{i} + \sin \omega t\mathbf{j}$.

$$\int_0^\pi \mathbf{r} \cdot \ddot{\mathbf{r}}\,dt = \int_0^\pi (\cos \omega t\mathbf{i} + \sin \omega t\mathbf{j}) \cdot (- \omega^2 \cos \omega t\mathbf{i} - \omega^2 \sin \omega t\mathbf{j})\,dt$$

$$= - \omega^2 \int_0^\pi (\cos^2 \omega t + \sin^2 \omega t)\,dt$$

$$= - \omega^2 \int_0^\pi dt = -\pi\omega^2.$$

1.12 Line integrals

We shall require to integrate variables along a given path in space. For example, we might wish to find the total effect of the wind on a cyclist as he pedals along a meandering road from P_1 to P_2 in figure 19. If $\mathbf{r}$ is the position vector of a point on the path C and $\mathbf{r} + \delta\mathbf{r}$ is a neighbouring point, $\delta\mathbf{r}$ is a chord of the path. Now scalars and vectors may be functions of position as well as time. Thus $\phi(x,y,z)$ is a scalar dependent on position

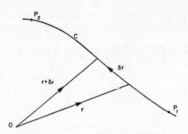

FIGURE 19   Path of integration for a line integral

and is called a scalar field and $\mathbf{F}(x,y,z)$ is a vector dependent on position and is called a vector field, the vector being interpreted as

$$\mathbf{F}(x,y,z) = F_1(x,y,z)\mathbf{i} + F_2(x,y,z)\mathbf{j} + F_3(x,y,z)\mathbf{k}$$

where F_1, F_2, F_3 are scalar functions. The temperature of the atmosphere is a scalar function of position at any instant of time. The integrals

$$\int_C \phi \, d\mathbf{r}, \qquad \int_C \mathbf{F} \cdot d\mathbf{r}, \qquad \int_C \mathbf{F} \times d\mathbf{r},$$

are examples of line integrals. In these integrals x, y, z take their values on the path C. The simplest way of specifying the curve C is to express the position vector in terms of a parameter t, so that

$$\mathbf{r}(t) = x(t)\mathbf{i} + y(t)\mathbf{j} + z(t)\mathbf{k}.$$

Thus the second integral can be written

$$\int_{t_1}^{t_2} \mathbf{f}(t) \cdot \frac{d\mathbf{r}}{dt} \, dt,$$

where $\mathbf{f}(t) = \mathbf{F}[x(t), y(t), z(t)]$ and $\mathbf{r}(t_1)$ and $\mathbf{r}(t_2)$ are the position vectors of P_1 and P_2. The integral can now be evaluated. The following example will supply the details.

Example 15   Evaluate $\displaystyle\int_0^P \mathbf{F} \cdot d\mathbf{r}$ *where* $\mathbf{F} = xy\mathbf{i} + yz^2\mathbf{j} + y^2z\mathbf{k}$, O *is the origin and* P *is* (1, 1, 1) *along*
   (a) *the path* $x = t^2$, $y = t^3$, $z = t^4$,
   (b) *the straight lines* (0, 0, 0) *to* (0, 0, 1), *and* (0, 0, 1) *to* (1, 1, 1).

The two paths are shown in figure 20.

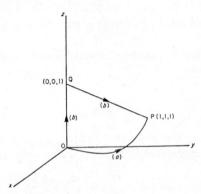

FIGURE 20

(*a*) Along this path

$$F = \mathbf{f}(t) = t^2 \cdot t^3 \mathbf{i} + t^3 \cdot t^8 \mathbf{j} + t^6 \cdot t^4 \mathbf{k}$$

$$= t^5 \mathbf{i} + t^{11} \mathbf{j} + t^{10} \mathbf{k},$$

and

$$\frac{d\mathbf{r}}{dt} = \frac{d}{dt}(t^2 \mathbf{i} + t^3 \mathbf{j} + t^4 \mathbf{k})$$

$$= 2t\mathbf{i} + 3t^2 \mathbf{j} + 4t^3 \mathbf{k}.$$

Thus

$$\mathbf{f}(t) \cdot \frac{d\mathbf{r}}{dt} = 2t^6 + 3t^{13} + 4t^{13} = 2t^6 + 7t^{13}.$$

At O, $t = 0$ and at P, $t = 1$ so that

$$\int_O^P \mathbf{F} \cdot d\mathbf{r} = \int_0^1 (2t^6 + 7t^{13}) \, dt = \frac{2}{7} + \frac{1}{2} = \frac{11}{14}.$$

(*b*) We can write

$$\int_O^P \mathbf{F} \cdot d\mathbf{r} = \int_O^Q \mathbf{F} \cdot d\mathbf{r} + \int_Q^P \mathbf{F} \cdot d\mathbf{r}.$$

Along OQ, $x = y = 0$ with the result that $\mathbf{F} = 0$ and the first integral on the right-hand side makes no contribution.

Along QP, $x = y$ and $z = 1$. Now, in general,

$$\int \mathbf{F} \cdot d\mathbf{r} = \int (xy \, dx + yz^2 \, dy + y^2 z \, dz)$$

$$= \int (x^2 \, dx + x \, dx) \qquad \text{(putting } y = x \text{ and } z = 1)$$

$$= \int (x^2 + x) \, dx$$

along QP. Thus

$$\int_O^P \mathbf{F} \cdot d\mathbf{r} = \int_0^1 (x^2 + x)\, dx = \tfrac{1}{3} + \tfrac{1}{2} = \tfrac{5}{6}.$$

We note that the value of the line integral between O and P depends on the path joining the points.

1.13 Grad and curl

Suppose that $\phi(x,y,z)$ is a scalar dependent on position defined in some region of space. The gradient (grad) of ϕ is a *vector* defined by

$$\text{grad } \phi = \frac{\partial \phi}{\partial x}\mathbf{i} + \frac{\partial \phi}{\partial y}\mathbf{j} + \frac{\partial \phi}{\partial z}\mathbf{k}$$

in terms of its Cartesian components. Grad ϕ will, in turn, be a *vector* dependent on position.

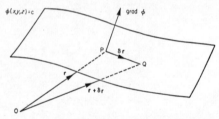

FIGURE 21   The gradient at a point of the surface $\phi = $ constant

Given the scalar field $\phi(x,y,z)$, then *equation* $\phi(x,y,z) = c$, a constant, will represent a surface in space. Consider a point P on the surface with position vector $\mathbf{r}$ and a neighbouring point Q on the surface with position vector $\mathbf{r} + \delta\mathbf{r}$. Since P and Q both lie on the surface (figure 21),

$$0 = \phi(x + \delta x, y + \delta y, z + \delta z) - \phi(x, y, z)$$

$$= \frac{\partial \phi}{\partial x}\delta x + \frac{\partial \phi}{\partial y}\delta y + \frac{\partial \phi}{\partial z}\delta z$$

to the first order in δx, δy, δz. This equation can be written

$$\text{grad } \phi \cdot \delta\mathbf{r} = 0.$$

In the limit as $|\delta\mathbf{r}| \to 0$, $\delta\mathbf{r}$ will become a tangent to the surface at P. We conclude that geometrically grad ϕ is normal to the surface at P.

Example 16 *Find a unit vector normal to* $xy^2z^3 = 1$ *at* $(1, 1, 1)$.

We see that
$$\text{grad } (xy^2z^3) = y^2z^3\mathbf{i} + 2xyz^3\mathbf{j} + 3xy^2z^2\mathbf{k}.$$
At $(1, 1, 1)$, grad $(xy^2z^3) = \mathbf{i} + 2\mathbf{j} + 3\mathbf{k}$. A unit normal to the surface is given by

$$\mathbf{n} = \frac{\mathbf{i} + 2\mathbf{j} + 3\mathbf{k}}{(1 + 4 + 9)^{\frac{1}{2}}} = (\mathbf{i} + 2\mathbf{j} + 3\mathbf{k})/\sqrt{14}.$$

The *curl* of a vector

$$\mathbf{V}(x, y, z) = V_1(x, y, z)\mathbf{i} + V_2(x, y, z)\mathbf{j} + V_3(x, y, z)\mathbf{k}$$

is defined by

$$\text{curl } \mathbf{V} = \left(\frac{\partial V_3}{\partial y} - \frac{\partial V_2}{\partial z}\right)\mathbf{i} + \left(\frac{\partial V_1}{\partial z} - \frac{\partial V_3}{\partial x}\right)\mathbf{j} + \left(\frac{\partial V_2}{\partial x} - \frac{\partial V_1}{\partial y}\right)\mathbf{k}$$

or

$$\begin{vmatrix} \mathbf{i} & \mathbf{j} & \mathbf{k} \\ \dfrac{\partial}{\partial x} & \dfrac{\partial}{\partial y} & \dfrac{\partial}{\partial z} \\ V_1 & V_2 & V_3 \end{vmatrix}$$

the latter being a symbolic determinant representation.

Example 17 *If* $\mathbf{V} = xyz\mathbf{i} + \cos y\mathbf{j} + x\,e^{-y}\mathbf{k}$, *find* curl $\mathbf{V}$.

$$\text{curl } \mathbf{V} = \left[\frac{\partial}{\partial y}(x\,e^{-y}) - \frac{\partial}{\partial z}(\cos y)\right]\mathbf{i} + \left[\frac{\partial}{\partial z}(xyz) - \frac{\partial}{\partial x}(x\,e^{-y})\right]\mathbf{j} +$$
$$\left[\frac{\partial}{\partial x}(\cos y) - \frac{\partial}{\partial y}(xyz)\right]\mathbf{k}$$
$$= -x\,e^{-y}\mathbf{i} + (xy - e^{-y})\mathbf{j} - xz\mathbf{k}.$$

The importance of the curl derives in part from the following result. If $\mathbf{V} = \text{grad } \phi$, that is, if $\mathbf{V}$ is the gradient of a scalar,

$$\text{curl } \mathbf{V} = \text{curl grad } \phi$$
$$= \left(\frac{\partial^2\phi}{\partial y\partial z} - \frac{\partial^2\phi}{\partial z\partial y}\right)\mathbf{i} + \left(\frac{\partial^2\phi}{\partial z\partial x} - \frac{\partial^2\phi}{\partial x\partial z}\right)\mathbf{j} + \left(\frac{\partial^2\phi}{\partial x\partial y} - \frac{\partial^2\phi}{\partial y\partial x}\right)\mathbf{k}$$
$$= 0,$$

assuming ϕ is sufficiently smooth. In this case we say that $\mathbf{V}$ has associated with it a *scalar potential* ϕ. The converse, that curl $\mathbf{V} = 0$ implies the existence of ϕ such that $\mathbf{V} = \text{grad } \phi$, is also true but we shall omit the proof.

Example 18 If $\mathbf{V} = e^{-x}(-yz\mathbf{i} + z\mathbf{j} + y\mathbf{k})$, *show that* curl $\mathbf{V} = 0$ *and find the scalar potential.*

$$\text{curl } \mathbf{V} = \left[\frac{\partial}{\partial y}(y\,e^{-x}) - \frac{\partial}{\partial z}(z\,e^{-x}) \right]\mathbf{i} + \left[\frac{\partial}{\partial z}(-yz\,e^{-x}) - \frac{\partial}{\partial x}(y\,e^{-x}) \right]\mathbf{j} +$$

$$\left[\frac{\partial}{\partial x}(z\,e^{-x}) - \frac{\partial}{\partial y}(-yz\,e^{-x}) \right]\mathbf{k}$$

$$= (e^{-x} - e^{-x})\mathbf{i} + (-y\,e^{-x} + y\,e^{-x})\mathbf{j} + (-z\,e^{-x} + z\,e^{-x})\mathbf{k}$$

$$= 0.$$

Thus $\mathbf{V}$ has a scalar potential ϕ such that

$$\frac{\partial \phi}{\partial x} = -e^{-x}yz, \qquad \frac{\partial \phi}{\partial y} = z\,e^{-x}, \qquad \frac{\partial \phi}{\partial z} = y\,e^{-x}.$$

Integrating each of these with respect to x, y, z respectively:

$$\phi = -\int e^{-x}yz\,dx + f_1(y,z) = e^{-x}yz + f_1(y,z),$$

$$\phi = \int z\,e^{-x}dy + f_2(z,x) = e^{-x}yz + f_2(z,x),$$

$$\phi = \int y\,e^{-x}dz + f_3(x,y) = e^{-x}yz + f_3(x,y),$$

where f_1, f_2, f_3 are arbitrary functions. We now match f_1, f_2, f_3 in the three equations. Obviously we choose $f_1 = f_2 = f_3 = C$, a constant, which gives the answer as $\phi = yz\,e^{-x} + C$. Note that the scalar potential always contains an arbitrary additive constant.

Returning to the line integral

$$I = \int_{P_1}^{P_2} \mathbf{F} \cdot d\mathbf{r}$$

considered in section 1.12, we observe that if the integral is independent of the path joining P_1 and P_2, then the line integral around a closed contour is zero since if P_1AP_2 and P_1BP_2 are two different paths between P_1 and P_2,

$$I = \int_{P_1AP_2BP_1} \mathbf{F} \cdot d\mathbf{r} = \int_{P_1AP_2} \mathbf{F} \cdot d\mathbf{r} + \int_{P_2BP_1} \mathbf{F} \cdot d\mathbf{r}$$

$$= \int_{P_1AP_2} \mathbf{F} \cdot d\mathbf{r} - \int_{P_1BP_2} \mathbf{F} \cdot d\mathbf{r} = 0.$$

As a corollary to this there is a theorem in vector calculus, which we shall not prove here, which states the following:

If $\mathbf{F}$ *is well-behaved in a simply connected region R, then* $\int_C \mathbf{F} \cdot d\mathbf{r} = 0$ *implies* curl $\mathbf{F} = \mathbf{0}$ *and conversely, where C is any closed contour in the region.* A *simply connected* region means that all contours within the region can be deformed into each other. This would be true for a contour, or an elastic band for example, inside a pipe but not true of the region exterior to the pipe since an elastic band looped around the pipe could not be deformed into one not looped around the pipe. The two conditions, that $\mathbf{F}$ is well-behaved and that the region is simply connected, can be important for it is possible, if these are not satisfied, to have curl $\mathbf{F} = \mathbf{0}$ but $\int_C \mathbf{F} \cdot d\mathbf{r} \neq 0$ for some closed contours C, as is seen in Example 3 of chapter 5.

Vector fields which have the property that the line integral is independent of the path are said to be *conservative* and since this property is nearly always implied by curl $\mathbf{F} = \mathbf{0}$, we have a much simpler test to apply than the almost impossible task of showing that the value of a line integral does not change whatever path we choose.

A vector field $\mathbf{V}$ is tangential at each point to a curve or *vector line* in space. For a conservative vector field these vector lines are everywhere normal to a family of surfaces where members are of the form ϕ = constant.

Exercises

1. Show that if G divides the line P_1P_2 in the ratio λ_2 to λ_1 then the position vector of G is given by

$$\mathbf{r}_G = \frac{\lambda_1 \mathbf{r}_1 + \lambda_2 \mathbf{r}_2}{\lambda_1 + \lambda_2},$$

where $\mathbf{r}_1$ and $\mathbf{r}_2$ are the position vectors of P_1 and P_2 respectively.

2. A ship sails 10 km due north, 4 km N 60° E and then 7 km due east. Find the position vector of the final position of the ship relative to its initial position. What is the distance of the ship from its initial position?

3. If $a = i + 2j + k$, $b = -i + k$ and $c = 3i + j - k$, evaluate

(i) $a \cdot b$ (iii) $a \cdot (b \times c)$

(ii) $a \times b$ (iv) $a \times (b \times c)$.

4. Find a unit vector perpendicular to $i + j + k$ and $i + 3j - k$.

5. An equation $ax + by + cz = d$ represents a plane in Cartesian coordinates. Show that $(r - A) \cdot B = 0$, where $r = xi + yj + zk$ and A and B are constant vectors, is the vector equation of a plane. Interpret the vectors A and B.

6. Show that both the equations

$$r = ct + d \quad \text{and} \quad (r - d) \times c = 0$$

represent straight lines through the point with position vector d in the direction of the vector c.

7. Show that the position vector r of an aircraft circling above an airfield at height h in a circle of radius a with constant speed V can be expressed as

$$r = a[i \cos (Vt/a) + j \sin (Vt/a)] + hk,$$

in terms of the time t.

8. The position vector of a particle is given by

$$r = a \cos \omega t i + a \sin \omega t j + bt k,$$

where a, ω and b are constants. Sketch the path taken by the particle. Find the velocity and acceleration vectors.

9. The position vector of a particle is given by

$$r = a \cos \omega t \sin \Omega t i + a \sin \omega t \sin \Omega t j + a \cos \Omega t \, k,$$

where a, ω and Ω are constants. Show that the particle moves on a sphere of radius a. Find the velocity of the particle and show that its magnitude is given by $a(\Omega^2 + \omega^2 \sin^2 \Omega t)^{\frac{1}{2}}$. Deduce that the minimum speed must occur at the highest and lowest points of the sphere and that the maximum speed occurs where the path of the particle cuts the horizontal plane through the centre of the sphere.

10. A particle describes a path with position vector

$$\mathbf{r} = a \cos \omega t \mathbf{i} + b \sin \omega t \mathbf{j}.$$

Show that

(i) the path is the ellipse

$$\frac{x^2}{a^2} + \frac{y^2}{b^2} = 1,$$

(ii) the acceleration is directed towards the origin,

(iii) $\displaystyle\int_t^{t+t_1} \mathbf{r} \times d\mathbf{r} = \omega a b t_1 \mathbf{k},$

and interpret this result.

11. The vectors **a** and **b**, and the scalar *c* are functions of the single variable *t*. By expressing **a** and **b** in terms of their components prove that

(i) $\dfrac{d}{dt}(\mathbf{a} \cdot \mathbf{b}) = \dfrac{d\mathbf{a}}{dt} \cdot \mathbf{b} + \mathbf{a} \cdot \dfrac{d\mathbf{b}}{dt},$

(ii) $\dfrac{d}{dt}(c\mathbf{a}) = \dfrac{dc}{dt}\mathbf{a} + c\dfrac{d\mathbf{a}}{dt},$

(iii) $\dfrac{d}{dt}(\mathbf{a} \times \mathbf{b}) = \dfrac{d\mathbf{a}}{dt} \times \mathbf{b} + \mathbf{a} \times \dfrac{d\mathbf{b}}{dt}.$

12. If $\mathbf{a} = t^2\mathbf{i} + (2t + 1)\mathbf{j} + t\mathbf{k}$ and $\mathbf{b} = (t - 1)\mathbf{i} - t\mathbf{j} + \mathbf{k}$ find

(i) $\dfrac{d}{dt}(\mathbf{a} + \mathbf{b}),$ (ii) $\dfrac{d}{dt}(\mathbf{a} \cdot \mathbf{b}),$ (iii) $\dfrac{d}{dt}(\mathbf{a} \times \mathbf{b}).$

13. The polar coordinates of a particle are given by $r = e^t, \theta = t$. Find the radial and transverse components of velocity and acceleration.

14. If $\mathbf{r} = t^2\mathbf{i} - t\mathbf{j} + t^3\mathbf{k}$, O is the origin and P is the point $(1, -1, 1)$, evaluate the following line integrals :

(i) $\displaystyle\int_O^P \mathbf{r} \cdot d\mathbf{r}$ (iii) $\displaystyle\int_O^P \dot{\mathbf{r}} \cdot d\mathbf{r}$

(ii) $\displaystyle\int_O^P \mathbf{r} \times d\mathbf{r}$ (iv) $\displaystyle\int_O^P \dot{\mathbf{r}} \times d\mathbf{r}.$

15. If $\mathbf{F} = x\mathbf{i} + yz\mathbf{j} + xyz\mathbf{k}$, evaluate:

$$\text{(i)} \quad \int_C \mathbf{F} \cdot d\mathbf{r}, \qquad\qquad \text{(ii)} \quad \int_C \mathbf{F} \times d\mathbf{r},$$

where C is the curve $x = t$, $y = t^2$, $z = t$ joining the origin to (1,1,1).

16. If $\phi = e^{xyz}$, find grad ϕ.

17. Which of the following vector fields has a scalar potential?

        (i) $yz\mathbf{i} + zx\mathbf{j} + xy\mathbf{k}$ (iii) $f(r)\mathbf{r}$

        (ii) $y\mathbf{i} + z\mathbf{j} + x\mathbf{k}$ (iv) $x\mathbf{r}$.

18. A point moves with constant speed V along the cardioid $r = a(1 + \cos\theta)$. Show that the magnitude of the angular velocity is $(V/2a)\sec\frac{1}{2}\theta$ and that the radial component of the acceleration is constant.

2

Kinematics

2.1 Introduction

Kinematics is concerned with the description of the motion of a body or system of bodies without consideration of the laws of motion or the precise nature of the forces which are acting. It is connected with the geometry of mechanics and for this reason it is independent of the laws of motion of classical mechanics. It may, for example, be concerned with the geometry of a gear mechanism, a cam on a rotating shaft or the effects of a given acceleration on a mechanical system. The following sections will indicate some of the problems which are within the scope of kinematics.

2.2 Relative velocity

We shall introduce the subject by considering two particles A and B moving along the same straight line with displacements $x_A(t)$ and $x_B(t)$ from some fixed origin O of the line. The velocities of A and B are $V_A = dx_A/dt$ and $V_B = dx_B/dt$. The displacement of B relative to A is $x_B - x_A$ and the velocity of B relative to A is the time derivative of this displacement or $V_B - V_A$: it is the velocity that B appears to have when observed from A.

Example 1   Suppose that the straight line in figure 22 represents a road and that B is a car which leaves O at 10.00 a.m. travelling at a constant speed of 50 km/h (kilometres

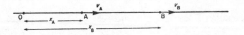

FIGURE 22   Relative velocity for motion in a straight line

per hour). A second car A leaves O at 10.15 a.m. and travels at a constant speed of 60 km/h in the same direction as B. Find where and when A overtakes B.

31

With x_A and x_B as the two displacements, we know that $dx_B/dt = 50, dx_A/dt = 60$. These two *differential equations* have elementary *solutions*

$$x_B = 50t + C, \qquad x_A = 60t + D$$

which can be verified by substitution. Here C and D are two constants to be determined by the *initial conditions*. Measuring the time from 10.00 a.m. and noting that time is measured in hours and distance in kilometres, the initial conditions are

$$\text{at } t = 0 \qquad x_B = 0$$
$$\text{at } t = \tfrac{1}{4} \qquad x_A = 0.$$

Thus $C = 0$ and $0 = 60 \times \tfrac{1}{4} + D$ or $D = -15$. The required solutions are

$$x_B = 50t, \qquad x_A = 60t - 15.$$

Car A overtakes B when their relative displacement is zero, that is when $x_B - x_A = 0$, or

$$50t - (60t - 15) = 0,$$

or $t = 1\tfrac{1}{2}$ hours. At 11.30 a.m. and at 75 km from O, A overtakes B.

The ideas of one-dimensional relative motion can be readily generalized to motion in three dimensions. Let $r_A(t)$ and $r_B(t)$ be the position vectors at time t of two particles A and B with respect to a fixed frame of reference with origin O. By the triangle law (see figure 23),

$$\overline{AB} = r_B - r_A = R, \text{ say.}$$

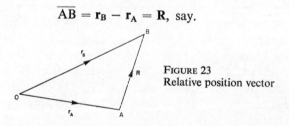

FIGURE 23
Relative position vector

The vector R is the position vector of B relative to A. The velocity V of B *relative* to A is defined as the time derivative of R:

$$V = \frac{dR}{dt} = \frac{dr_B}{dt} - \frac{dr_A}{dt}.$$

The relative velocity V is the velocity which B appears to have when observed from A. In a similar manner the acceleration f of B relative to A is defined by

$$f = \frac{d^2R}{dt^2} = \frac{d^2r_B}{dt^2} - \frac{d^2r_A}{dt^2}.$$

Looked at another way, relative motion (in this context) is concerned with measuring displacement, velocity and acceleration relative to a frame with origin A (figure 24) whose axes Ax', Ay', Az' remain always parallel to Ox, Oy, Oz of the fixed frame as A accelerates. In other words frame A can be *translated* into the fixed frame *without rotation*. Rotating axes will be discussed in chapter 8.

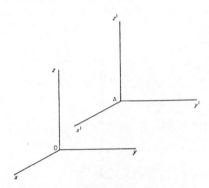

FIGURE 24   Translating frame of reference

Example 2   To a cyclist travelling due north along a straight road at 16 km/h the wind appears to come from the east. If he increases his speed to 30 km/h it appears to blow from the north-east. Find the speed and direction of the wind.

Select a two-dimensional Cartesian frame on the earth's surface with **i** pointing east and **j** north. Let the velocity of the wind be $\mathbf{v_w} = v_1\mathbf{i} + v_2\mathbf{j}$. If $\mathbf{v_c}$ is the velocity of the cyclist, the velocity of the wind relative to the cyclist is $\mathbf{v_w} - \mathbf{v_c}$. In the first case $\mathbf{v_c} = 16\mathbf{j}$ and

$$\mathbf{v_w} - \mathbf{v_c} = v_1\mathbf{i} + v_2\mathbf{j} - 16\mathbf{j} = v_1\mathbf{i} + (v_2 - 16)\mathbf{j}.$$

The wind appears to come from the east so that the **j**-component of $\mathbf{v_w} - \mathbf{v_c}$ must vanish. Hence $v_2 = 16$. In the second case $\mathbf{v_c} = 30\mathbf{j}$ and

$$\begin{aligned}\mathbf{v_w} - \mathbf{v_c} &= v_1\mathbf{i} + v_2\mathbf{j} - 30\mathbf{j} = v_1\mathbf{i} + (v_2 - 30)\mathbf{j} \\ &= v_1\mathbf{i} - 14\mathbf{j}.\end{aligned}$$

Since the wind appears to blow from the north-east the **i**- and **j**-components must be equal. Hence $v_1 = -14$.

The wind speed is therefore $|\mathbf{v_w}| = \sqrt{(6^2 + 14^2)} = \sqrt{452} = 21.2$ km/h approximately, and comes from a direction θ where $\tan \theta = -8/7$, that is from 49° south of east approximately.

Example 3   A ship is steaming due north at 20 km/h and a second ship, 10 km north-west of it initially, is steaming due east at 10 km/h. Find the shortest distance between the ships subsequently.

Take the origin O at the initial position of the first ship, A, with the *x*- and *y*-axes east and north. The initial positions and velocities of A and the second ship B are shown in figure 25. The velocity of A is 20**j** and that of B is 10**i**.

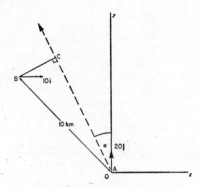

FIGURE 25

The velocity of A relative to B is (20**j** − 10**i**) and the direction of this vector is shown by the dotted line drawn from the origin in figure 25. This is the path which A appears to take when viewed from B. Clearly A and B are at their closest distance when A reaches position C, the foot of the perpendicular from B to the relative path. Thus the required distance

$$BC = 10 \sin(\pi/4 - \alpha) = 10(\sin \tfrac{1}{4}\pi \cos \alpha - \cos \tfrac{1}{4}\pi \sin \alpha)$$

$$= \frac{10}{\sqrt{2}}(\cos \alpha - \sin \alpha),$$

where $\tan \alpha = \tfrac{1}{2}$. Therefore $BC = \dfrac{10}{\sqrt{2}}\left(\dfrac{2}{\sqrt{5}} - \dfrac{1}{\sqrt{5}}\right) = \sqrt{10} = 3\cdot16$ km.

We can also find the time which elapses before A reaches C. The speed of A relative to B is $\sqrt{(10^2 + 20^2)} = 10\sqrt{5}$ km/h and the distance

$$AC = \sqrt{(10^2 - 10)} = 3\sqrt{10} \text{ km.}$$

Thus the ships reach their closest distance after $\dfrac{3\sqrt{10}}{10\sqrt{5}} = \dfrac{3\sqrt{2}}{10} = 0\cdot42$ hours.

Note that the problem can be solved graphically by measuring BC in figure 25, using a suitable scale.

Example 4 The runway of an airfield faces west. A helicopter, flying north at a height of 2 km and at a speed of 360 km/h on a path which passes over a point one mile west of the runway end, is spotted $2\sqrt{2}$ km horizontally south-west of the runway end. At this time an aircraft takes off from the airfield and climbs at an angle of 45° with a constant speed of 480 km/h. Show that the helicopter and aircraft are in danger of collision.

Take a Cartesian frame with its origin at the runway end, **i** pointing west, **j** south and **k** vertically as shown in figure 26.

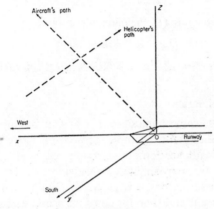

FIGURE 26

As we shall see the two machines considered as particles do not actually meet but we shall show that they pass at a distance which is within the dimensions of both. If two aircraft pass within several tens of metres of each other there is a risk of collision.

We shall employ an alternative method to that used in example 3. If v_H and v_A are the velocities of the helicopter and aircraft, we have

$$\mathbf{v_H} = \frac{d\mathbf{r_H}}{dt} = -360\mathbf{j}, \qquad \mathbf{v_A} = \frac{d\mathbf{r_A}}{dt} = 240\sqrt{2}(\mathbf{i} + \mathbf{k}).$$

Integrating these simple differential equations, we find that

$$\mathbf{r_H} = -360t\mathbf{j} + \boldsymbol{\alpha}, \qquad \mathbf{r_A} = 240\sqrt{2}t(\mathbf{i} + \mathbf{k}) + \boldsymbol{\beta},$$

where $\boldsymbol{\alpha}$ and $\boldsymbol{\beta}$ are constant vectors. Initially ($t = 0$), the helicopter is at $2\mathbf{i} + 2\mathbf{j} + 2\mathbf{k}$ and the aircraft is at the origin. Thus

$$\boldsymbol{\alpha} = 2\mathbf{i} + 2\mathbf{j} + 2\mathbf{k}, \qquad \boldsymbol{\beta} = \mathbf{0},$$

and

$$\mathbf{r_H} = 2\mathbf{i} + 2(1 - 180t)\mathbf{j} + 2\mathbf{k}, \qquad \mathbf{r_A} = 240\sqrt{2}t(\mathbf{i} + \mathbf{k}).$$

At time t the distance D between them is given by

$$D^2 = |\mathbf{r}_A - \mathbf{r}_H|^2 = 8(120\sqrt{2}t - 1)^2 + 4(1 - 180t)^2$$
$$= 4(90,000t^2 - 120(4\sqrt{2} + 3)t + 3). \tag{1}$$

We now determine when D is a minimum by putting $dD/dt = 0$. This occurs when

$$0 = 180,000t - 120(4\sqrt{2} + 3),$$

or when

$$t = \frac{4\sqrt{2} + 3}{1500} = 0.00577 \text{ hours.}$$

Substituting for t back into (1), the minimum distance

$$D_m = 0.08 \text{ km or } 80 \text{ m.}$$

approximately. This distance is an insufficient margin of safety.

2.3 Constant acceleration

Many problems in mechanics involve or can be approximated to by constant acceleration; for example projectiles move vertically under gravity with constant acceleration (section 3.8) and a car accelerating along a road can be approximately considered as a particle accelerating uniformly. For these reasons it is useful to obtain the formulae relating velocity, displacement and time for constant acceleration along a straight line.

Consider a particle P moving in a straight line with constant acceleration f. If x is its displacement from a fixed origin O on the line,

$$\frac{d^2x}{dt^2} = f. \tag{2}$$

If v is the velocity, the first integral of (2) gives

$$v = \frac{dx}{dt} = \int f\,dt + A = ft + A,$$

where A is the constant of integration. With the initial velocity at $t = 0$ given as u, $A = u$ and

$$v = u + ft. \tag{3}$$

We can integrate this equation a second time since (3) is equivalent to

$$\frac{dx}{dt} = u + ft,$$

and obtain

$$x = \int (u + ft)\, dt + B = ut + \tfrac{1}{2}ft^2 + B,$$

where B is a further constant of integration. Suppose we measure distance from the position the particle occupied initially, that is take $x = 0$ when $t = 0$. Then $B = 0$ and

$$x = ut + \tfrac{1}{2}ft^2. \tag{4}$$

A third formula connecting velocity and displacement can be found by using the following identity:

$$\frac{d^2x}{dt^2} = \frac{dv}{dt} = \frac{dx}{dt} \cdot \frac{dv}{dx} = v\frac{dv}{dx}.$$

We can therefore rewrite equation (2) as

$$v\frac{dv}{dx} = f$$

and integrate it, giving

$$\int v\, dv = \int f\, dx + C,$$

or

$$\tfrac{1}{2}v^2 = fx + C,$$

where C is a constant. With the initial conditions specified above, $v = u$ at $x = 0$, so that

$$v^2 = u^2 + 2fx. \tag{5}$$

Equations (3), (4) and (5) are very important formulae and the reader will find it helpful to remember them. We emphasize, however, that they are valid only for constant acceleration in a straight line.

Example 5   A car can maintain a constant acceleration of 25 m/s². Find the time taken for the car to reach 90 km/h from rest and the distance it travels in this time.

In the notation above we are given that $u = 0$ and

$$v = \frac{90 \times 1,000}{3,600} = 25 \text{ m/s}.$$

Also $f = 2\cdot5 \text{ m/s}^2$ and we require x and t. From (3)

$$t = \frac{v - u}{f} = \frac{25}{2\cdot5} = 10 \text{ s}.$$

From (5)

$$x = \frac{v^2 - u^2}{2f} = \frac{25 \times 25}{2 \times 2\cdot5} = 125 \text{ m.}$$

Thus the car reached 90 km/h in 10 s and 125 m.

Example 6   A train has a maximum speed of 72 km/h which it can achieve at an acceleration of 0·25 m/s². With its brakes fully applied the train has a deceleration (negative acceleration) of 0·5 m/s². What is the shortest time that the train can travel between stations 8 km apart if it stops at both stations?

The journey can be broken into three stages: the acceleration, the uniform speed and the deceleration. We first determine the distance covered by the train during its periods of acceleration and deceleration and, by subtraction, how far it travels at uniform speed. The total time can be found by summing the times over the three stages.

(i) acceleration. In the usual notation $f = 0\cdot25$ m/s², $u = 0$ and

$$v = 72 \text{ km/h} = \frac{72 \times 1{,}000}{60 \times 60} = 20 \text{ m/s.}$$

We require x and t. From (5)

$$x = \frac{v^2 - u^2}{2f} = \frac{20 \times 20}{2 \times 0\cdot25} = 800 \text{ m,}$$

and from (3)

$$t = \frac{v - u}{f} = \frac{20}{0\cdot25} = 80 \text{ s.}$$

(ii) deceleration. We now require the distance before the second station where the brakes must be applied to bring the train to rest at the station. The acceleration is now $f = -0\cdot5$ m/s². The initial speed $u = 20$ m/s and $v = 0$. By (5)

$$x = \frac{v^2 - u^2}{2f} = \frac{-20 \times 20}{-2 \times 0\cdot5} = 400 \text{ m,}$$

and by (3)

$$t = \frac{v - u}{f} = \frac{-20}{-0\cdot5} = 40 \text{ s.}$$

The brakes must be applied 400 m before the second station.

(iii) uniform speed. The train must travel at a constant speed of 72 km/h for 8,000 − 800 − 400 = 6,800 m. This takes a time of 6,800/20 = 340 s.
Thus the minimum time for the journey is 340 + 80 + 40 = 460 s.

2.4 Miscellaneous problems including variable acceleration

Figure 27 shows the acceleration of a car, moving in a straight line and starting from rest, measured against time by an accelerometer (this is an instrument for measuring acceleration).

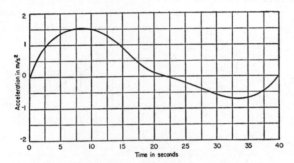

FIGURE 27   A graph of acceleration against time

From this data we can find numerically the velocity and displacement. Consider the time integral of the acceleration between $t = 0$ and $t = t_1$

$$I = \int_{t=0}^{t=t_1} \frac{d^2x}{dt^2} \, dt.$$

This integral will be the area under the curve shown in figure 27. We must remember that the area must be subtracted for that part of the curve for which the acceleration is negative. We can write

$$I = \int_{t=0}^{t=t_1} \frac{dv}{dt} \, dt = \int_{t=0}^{t=t_1} dv = v_1,$$

where v_1 is the velocity at time t_1 (we are given that the car starts from rest). We now put $t_1 = 5, 10, 15,..., 40$ and compute the area by counting up the squares between the curve and the zero line (more grid lines should be inserted in the figure to obtain a good estimate, or the curve can be redrawn on graph paper) but note that the scales are not the same. In other words the 'area' of a square shown in figure 27 is 1·25 units. The result is

t_1	0	5	10	15	20	25	30	35	40
v_1	0	4·2	11·6	17·8	20·1	19·9	18·0	14·7	12·7

and the final velocity of the car is 12·7 m/s. Now plot velocity against time and draw a curve through these points (figure 28). Consider the time integral of velocity over the whole interval:

$$\int_{t=0}^{t=40} \frac{dx}{dt}\, dt = \int_{t=0}^{t=40} dx = X, \quad \text{the total distance covered.}$$

The left-hand side is the area under the curve in figure 28. This can be computed again by inserting additional grid lines in figure 28. Our estimate is that the car covers 552 m in 40 s.

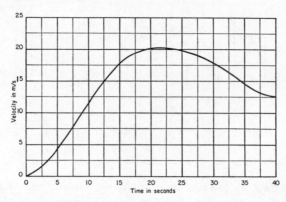

FIGURE 28   Sketch of the velocity-time graph as computed from figure 27

Example 7   Figure 29 shows the cross-section of a simple model for a piston P driving a crankshaft AB. If AB = 2 cm and the connecting rod BP = 4 cm and the crankshaft rotates at a constant rate of 3,000 revolutions per minute (r.p.m.), describe the motion of the piston.

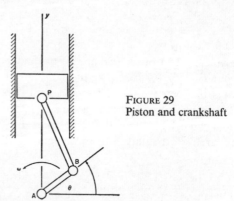

FIGURE 29
Piston and crankshaft

Let θ be the angle AB makes with the horizontal at time t and let $y = $ AP. Applying the cosine rule of trigonometry to triangle ABP, we find that

$$PB^2 = AP^2 + AB^2 - 2AP \cdot AB \cos P\hat{A}B,$$

or

$$16 = y^2 + 4 - 4y \sin \theta,$$

or

$$y^2 - 4y \sin \theta - 12 = 0.$$

Solving this quadratic equation for y:

$$y = \tfrac{1}{2}[4 \sin \theta \pm (16 \sin^2 \theta + 48)^{\frac{1}{2}}].$$

The values of y when $\theta = \tfrac{1}{2}\pi$ indicate that we take the upper of the two signs. Thus

$$y = 2 \sin \theta + 2(\sin^2 \theta + 3)^{\frac{1}{2}}.$$

Let ω (in rad/sec) be the angular velocity of the crankshaft AB. Changing units

$$3{,}000 \text{ rev/min} = \frac{3{,}000}{60} \text{ rev/s}$$

$$= \frac{3{,}000}{60} \times 2\pi \text{ rad/s}$$

$$= 100\pi \text{ rad/s} = \omega.$$

But $\omega = d\theta/dt$ and consequently $\theta = \omega t +$ constant, since ω is constant. Suppose we take $\theta = 0$ when $t = 0$ (the crankshaft horizontal initially). The constant is then zero and $\theta = \omega t$. The displacement of the piston is given by

$$y = 2 \sin \omega t + 2(\sin^2 \omega t + 3)^{\frac{1}{2}}.$$

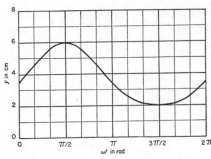

FIGURE 30 Variation of the displacement y of the piston with time

The motion of the piston is periodic with period $2\pi/\omega$, that is the displacement of the piston at time t is the same as that at time $t + 2n\pi/\omega$ where n is any integer. A graph of displacement against ωt in the interval $0 \leqslant \omega t \leqslant 2\pi$ is shown in figure 30.

*Example 8   Figure 31 shows the rear wheel, chain and sprockets of a cycle. The
rear wheel has diameter 60 cm and its sprocket has diameter 10 cm. This sprocket is
driven through the chain by the pedals attached to a larger sprocket of diameter 20 cm.
If the cyclist pedals at the rate of one revolution in two seconds, find the speed of
the cycle.*

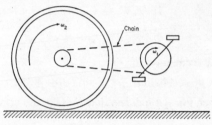

FIGURE 31   Rear wheel and chain of a cycle

Let ω_1 be the angular velocity of the driving sprocket and ω_2 that of the wheel.
Now

$$0.5 \text{ rev/s} = \pi \text{ rad/s},$$

so that $\omega_1 = \pi \text{ rad/s}$. The radius of this sprocket is 10 cm, and consequently the
speed v of the chain is given by

$$v = 10\pi \text{ cm/s}.$$

The speed of a point on the circumference of the smaller sprocket must also be
10π cm/s since it is driven by the chain. Thus

$$\omega_2 = \frac{\text{speed}}{\text{radius}} = \frac{10\pi}{5} = 2\pi \text{ rad/s}.$$

The wheel makes one complete revolution in one second and therefore rolls a
distance equal to its circumference 60π cm in one s. The speed of the cycle is consequently

$$60\pi \text{ cm/s} = \frac{60\pi \times 3{,}600}{10^5} \text{ km/h}$$

$$= 6.79 \text{ km/h}$$

Exercises

1. A ship steaming north at 12 km/h passes a fixed buoy at 12.00 hours. A second
ship steaming east at 16 km/h passes the same buoy at 12.50 hours. At what time are
the two ships closest together and what is then their distance apart?

2. A ship leaves a port A and sails due west at a speed of 32 km/hr. One hour later an aeroplane takes off from an airfield 160 km due south of A to intercept the ship. If the aeroplane's speed is 360 km/hr, find the direction in which it should be flown. Where will the ship be when the aeroplane flies over it?

3. An aeroplane is to fly from a point A to an airfield B 300 km due north of A. If a wind of 30 km/h blows from the north-west, find the direction the plane should be pointing and the time taken to reach B if the speed of the plane relative to still air is 150 km/h.

4. A ship A equipped with radar having a range of 75 km leaves port and steams due north at 10 km/h. At the same time a second ship 150 km north-east of A is steaming due west. Show that this ship will come within the range of A's radar if its speed is between 2·7 km/h and 37·3 km/h approximately.

5. An aircraft is flying due north at 340 km/h relative to the ground and finds that the wind appears to be blowing from north $\theta°$ east where $\tan \theta = \frac{1}{4}$. It then turns and flies east at the same speed and finds that the wind is coming from east $\theta°$ south. Obtain the speed and direction of the wind.

6. In steady rain, raindrops fall at about 16 km/h. On the basis of this figure draw up a table of values of angles of raindrop streaks on train windows which would enable a passenger in the train to estimate his speed in units of 10 km/h.

7. An aeroplane has a speed v and a flying range (out and back) of R in calm weather. Prove that in a north wind of speed n $(n < v)$ its range is

$$\frac{R(v^2 - n^2)}{v(v^2 - n^2 \sin^2 \phi)^{\frac{1}{2}}}$$

in a direction whose true bearing from north is ϕ. What is the maximum value of this range and in what directions may it be attained?

8. An aircraft has a cruising speed of 400 km/h and a safe maximum range of 3,200 km in still air when fully loaded with 100 passengers. For each empty seat the range can be increased by 10 km. How many passengers can the aircraft safely carry for a flight of 3,200 km, flying into a headwind of 50 km/h?

9. In Example 4 find how long the aircraft should wait on the runway before taking off in order that the minimum distance between it and the helicopter should be at least 2 km.

10. A fly crawls with constant speed v along the radial spoke of a wheel which is rotating with constant angular speed ω. If the fly starts from the centre of the wheel find the actual velocity of the fly and the path on which it moves relative to a fixed frame of reference.

11. A rocket is fired vertically from a point on the earth's equator with a speed of 8,000 km/h. Taking account of the earth's rotation, find the actual firing speed relative to a *fixed* equatorial plane.
   The rocket continues its course in a straight line with constant speed. Define suitable unit vectors in the fixed equatorial plane and find the position vectors of the rocket and the launching site relative to the centre of the earth and the rocket relative to the launching site. What is the distance between the launching site and the rocket after four hours have elapsed? [Radius of the earth's equator = 6,400 km.]

12. A car accelerates uniformly from rest to 100 km/hr in 15 sec. Find (a) the acceleration, (b) the distance travelled in this time, (c) its speed after 10 sec.

13. A point is moving in a straight line with constant acceleration. It is seen to move 15 m in the first second and 65 m in the sixth second. How far does it travel in the fourth second?

14. Two trains start 6 minutes apart and attain their maximum speeds of 120 km/hr in 2 km. Assuming constant acceleration show that the first has travelled 10 km before the second starts and that they run 12 km apart at maximum speed.

15. Telegraph poles at the side of a railway track are spaced at intervals of 50 m. A passenger in a train observes that successive poles pass at time intervals of 3 sec and 2·8 sec. Calculate the acceleration of the train (assuming it to be uniform).

16. Two particles A and B are moving with uniform positive accelerations f and $3f$ along parallel straight paths in the same direction. At a certain instant they are level and their speeds are then $2v$ and v respectively. Show that the particles will again draw level after a time v/f has elapsed, and find their velocities.
   If B now moves with constant velocity, show that the particles will draw level for a third time when they have both covered a total distance $21v^2/2f$.

17. A car is fitted with three gear ratios such that, within the speed ranges indicated below, the car can maintain the maximum uniform accelerations given on the right-hand side:

first gear:	0–40 km/h	3 m/s^2
second gear:	30–80 km/h	4 m/s^2
third gear:	60–120 km/h	3 m/s^2

At what speeds should the driver change in order to reach 120 km/h in the shortest possible time? What is this time?

18. The maximum acceleration of a train is α, the maximum retardation is β and its maximum speed is V. Show that it cannot run a distance a from rest to rest in a time less than

$$\left[\frac{2a(\alpha + \beta)}{\alpha\beta}\right]^{\frac{1}{2}} \quad \text{if} \quad a \leqslant \frac{V^2(\alpha + \beta)}{2\alpha\beta},$$

or less than

$$\frac{V}{2}\left(\frac{1}{\alpha} + \frac{1}{\beta}\right) + \frac{a}{V} \quad \text{if} \quad a > \frac{V^2(\alpha + \beta)}{2\alpha\beta}.$$

19. Approximately, the stopping distance of a car travelling at v km/h is given by the expression $\frac{5}{24}\left(v + \frac{v^2}{32}\right)$ m, the first term representing the 'reaction' distance of· the driver and the second the distance through which the brakes are actually applied. Two cars are 35 m apart when the first car, travelling at 45 km/h, makes an emergency stop. The driver of the second car has no prior warning of this hazard. Show that a collision must occur if the speed of the second car exceeds 81 km/h.

20. A closed racing track consists of two semi-circular roads of radii $\frac{1}{2}$ km joined by two straight roads each of length 4 km. What is the shortest time in which a racing car can travel once round the track if its maximum speed on the straight is 250 km/h and on the curved sections is 180 km/h, and its maximum acceleration and retardation are both 4 m/s²?

21. A wheel rolls without slipping along a straight line so that its centre moves with constant velocity V. Find the actual velocity of any point of the wheel and show that its direction is perpendicular to the straight line joining the point to the point of contact of the wheel and line.

22. The crankshaft of an engine of a car is connected through a four-speed gearbox to the rear axle. If the overall gear-ratios between engine and axle are

first gear,	20:1
second gear,	15:1
third gear,	10:1
top gear,	5:1

and the axle drives a wheel 60 cm in diameter, find the speed of the car in the four gears when the engine is turning at 3,000 r.p.m.

23. Show that the hour and minute hands of a clock cross every 12/11 hours.

24. Figure 32 shows a sliding valve V being driven by a circular cam of radius a which rotates with constant angular speed ω about an axis through a point O distance b from its centre. Find the displacement of the valve from O at any time t.

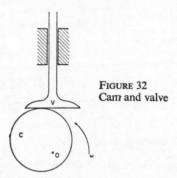

FIGURE 32
Cam and valve

25. Figure 33 shows a plan view of a car turning in a circle in which the mid-point of the rear axle describes a circle, centre on the extension of the rear axle, of radius 7 m. The distance between the wheels is 1·6 m and the distance between the front and rear axles is 2·5 m. Determine the radius of the tracks of the two front wheels. What locks (angles to the car) should the front wheels have in order to minimize slipping between the front tyres and the road?

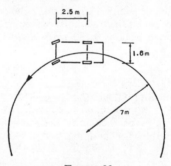

FIGURE 33

The mid-point of the rear axle moves at a constant 24 km/h. Find the angular speed of each wheel of the car if they are each 60 cm in diameter.

26. The table below shows the measured data for the acceleration in m/s^2 at intervals of 10 sec of a car which starts from rest. Compute graphically the final velocity of the car and distance it travels in 80 sec. What is the greatest velocity attained and when does this occur?

acceleration	0	0·5	1·2	1·8	0·5	−0·1	−0·4	−0·8	−0·6	m/s^2
time	0	10	20	30	40	50	60	70	80	s

3

Principles of mechanics

3.1 Inertial frames of reference

Newtonian mechanics presupposes that we can specify a 'fixed' or inertial frame of reference which is unaccelerated and non-rotating. For most phenomena within the solar system it is usual to take a frame which is fixed relative to the background of stars. This inertial frame can be imagined to have its origin at the sun with its axes determined by the directions of certain stars (this ignores small perturbations of the sun due to the motion of the planets about it). Such a hypothesis seems reasonable for local solar phenomena and most time intervals in which we are interested because of the remoteness of the stars (and consequently their small gravitational pull on the sun) and their relatively slow change of orientation.

Whilst such a *sidereal* frame of reference is appropriate for studying the orbits of the planets or the path of an interplanetary rocket, it is not convenient for describing events which occur in the laboratory or in the immediate vicinity of the earth's surface. A frame of reference fixed in the earth would be more useful. However, since the earth rotates on its polar axis and revolves about the sun, a *terrestrial* frame will translate and rotate relative to the sidereal frame.

Let us calculate some typical relative accelerations of the two frames. Imagine a terrestrial frame of reference with origin fixed at the centre of the earth, one axis towards the north pole and two axes moving with the equatorial plane of the earth. Approximately, the earth describes a circular orbit about the sun of radius $a = 1.5 \times 10^{11}$ m in a time of 3.16×10^7 s (one year). The orbital speed v of the earth is therefore given by

$$v = \frac{2\pi \times 1.5 \times 10^{11}}{3.16 \times 10^7} = 3.0 \times 10^4 \text{ m/s.}$$

The acceleration of the earth towards the sun (see section 1.10) is given by

$$\frac{v^2}{a} = 0\cdot6 \text{ cm/s}^2.$$

In addition the earth spins about its polar axis once every 24 h or $8\cdot64 \times 10^4$ s (not strictly true in a sidereal frame due to the orbit of the earth about the sun but sufficiently accurate for our purposes here), which means that each point of the earth describes a circle about the axis. Consider a point P on the earth's surface with latitude $\phi°$ (latitude is the angle between the radius to P and the equatorial plane; see figure 34). The angular speed of the earth is

$$\omega = \frac{2\pi}{8\cdot64 \times 10^4} = 7\cdot27 \times 10^{-5} \text{ rad/s}.$$

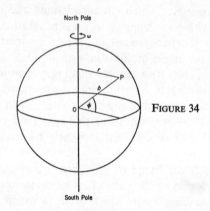

FIGURE 34

The acceleration of P due to the spin of the earth will vary with the latitude of P. If r is the distance of P from the polar axis, the acceleration of P towards the axis is

$$r\omega^2 = b \cos \phi \cdot \omega^2$$
$$= 3\cdot36 \cos \phi \text{ cm/s}^2.$$

where b, the radius of the earth, is taken to be $6\cdot37 \times 10^6$ m. The acceleration induced by the spin varies between zero at the poles and $3\cdot36$ cm/s^2 at the equator. [This discussion ignores the oblateness of the earth and slight variations of the earth's spin.]

We may compare the two figures $0\cdot60$ cm/s^2 and $3\cdot36$ cm/s^2 with the *acceleration due to gravity* near the earth's surface. This is the acceleration with which a body falls freely towards the earth due to the earth's gravitational pull. It is approximately 981 cm/s² (its value is of course not constant since the earth is not perfectly spherical). Both accelerations are small compared with this typical acceleration due to gravity. For this reason we can take the earth as an inertial frame for local phenomena on the earth.

It must be emphasized, however, that it is not always safe to assume that small accelerations effective over long intervals of time can be ignored. A small sustained acceleration can produce significant effects.

3.2 Laws of motion

In the late seventeenth century Newton, following work by Galileo and others, proposed three laws of motion for particles. Mechanics is largely based on these. His first law states that every body continues in its state of rest or uniform motion in a straight line unless acted upon by an external force. Whilst this law is implied by Newton's second law which follows, it adds a qualitative meaning to the notion of force. We introduce the principles of mechanics through the fiction of the particle.

The fundamental empirical law of mechanics for an isolated particle subject to a force $\mathbf{F}$ is that there exists an inertial frame of reference in which

$$\mathbf{F} = m\mathbf{f}, \tag{1}$$

where $\mathbf{f}$ is the acceleration of the particle and m is its mass, a positive scalar magnitude independent of position and time which can be associated with the particle. We shall say more about comparative masses later. Equation (1) is *Newton's second law of motion:* force = mass × acceleration.

Note that (1) is a *vector* equation which implies that the acceleration is always in the direction of the force (this does not mean that the particle is necessarily moving in the direction of the force: for example, the earth revolves about the sun but its acceleration is directed towards the sun in the direction of the gravitational force). If no force acts, $\mathbf{F} = \mathbf{0}$ and $\mathbf{f} = \dot{\mathbf{v}} = \mathbf{0}$. Then $\mathbf{v} = \mathbf{c}$, a constant vector, and the particle moves with constant velocity. Integrating $\mathbf{v} = \dot{\mathbf{r}} = \mathbf{c}$ again:

$$\mathbf{r} = \mathbf{c}t + \mathbf{d},$$

where $\mathbf{d}$ is a further constant vector. The particle moves along a straight line (Exercise 6, chapter 1) with constant velocity confirming Newton's first law.

A particle may be subject simultaneously to several external forces $\mathbf{F}_1, \mathbf{F}_2, ..., \mathbf{F}_n$ (figure 35) each producing accelerations $\mathbf{f}_1, \mathbf{f}_2, ..., \mathbf{f}_n$ so that

$$\mathbf{F}_1 = m\mathbf{f}_1, \mathbf{F}_2 = m\mathbf{f}_2, ..., \mathbf{F}_n = m\mathbf{f}_n.$$

Adding these equations

$$\mathbf{F} = \mathbf{F}_1 + \mathbf{F}_2 + ... + \mathbf{F}_n = m(\mathbf{f}_1 + \mathbf{f}_2 + ... + \mathbf{f}_n) = m\mathbf{f},$$

where $\mathbf{F}$ is the total external force and $\mathbf{f}$ is the resultant acceleration. The relation above emphasises the *linear* character of Newton's law since $\mathbf{F}$ and $\mathbf{f}$ are simple vector sums of the separate forces and accelerations.

The vector $\mathbf{p} = m\mathbf{v}$ is called the *linear momentum* of the particle and if we assume the mass remains constant

$$\mathbf{F} = \frac{d\mathbf{p}}{dt},$$

that is, the force is rate of change of linear momentum. If the force vanishes the linear momentum is *conserved*.

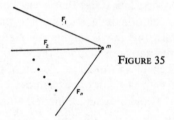

FIGURE 35

Newton's second law of motion is not sufficient in itself to describe the motion of two or more particles since particles may exercise mutual forces on one another. We must add a third postulate which defines the magnitude and direction of these forces. *Newton's third law of motion* asserts that if two particles exert forces on one another, these forces are equal in magnitude and opposite in direction and act along the line joining the two particles.

For example, if the earth and the moon are considered as two particles in isolation, the moon experiences a gravitational attractive force in the direction of the earth, and the earth an equal force in the direction of the moon.

With this simple postulate we can now examine the motion of each particle separately since we know the directions of the forces exerted on the particle by any other particles. Suppose we have two particles A and B with masses m_A and m_B subject only to a mutual force of attraction (see figure 36). By Newton's third law if the force on A due to B is $\mathbf{F}$ then the force on B due to A must be $-\mathbf{F}$. Furthermore both forces must act along the line joining A and B, this property being expressed by the vector equation

$$\mathbf{F} \times (\mathbf{r}_A - \mathbf{r}_B) = 0.$$

Considering each particle in isolation from the other, the equations of motion of A and B are respectively

$$\mathbf{F} = m_A\ddot{\mathbf{r}}_A, \qquad -\mathbf{F} = m_B\ddot{\mathbf{r}}_B,$$

where $\mathbf{r}_A$ and $\mathbf{r}_B$ are their position vectors. Once the nature of $\mathbf{F}$ is known these equations can be solved, in principle, to find the separate motions of A and B.

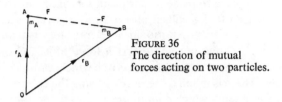

FIGURE 36
The direction of mutual
forces acting on two particles.

The mutual forces between particles can be used to compare masses of particles. Consider a spring with a particle attached to each end and compressed (the system is assumed to be far removed from the influence of other forces). The spring will exert the same force on each particle by Newton's third law. On release we measure the accelerations a_1 and a_2 of the two particles (we assume that motion takes place only in the line of the spring). If F is the magnitude of the force exerted by the spring on each particle, then

$$m_2 a_2 = F = m_1 a_1,$$

where m_1 and m_2 are the masses of the two particles. Thus

$$m_2 = \frac{a_1}{a_2}m_1,$$

and m_2 can be measured in terms of a standard mass m_1. The international standard is the prototype kilogramme (kg), a platinum-iridium cylinder, and masses are compared against this standard. The gram is 10^{-3} kg.

We have now introduced the third fundamental dimension—mass—to add to length and time. The rationalized system of metric units known as the Système International d'Unités (S.I.) is coming into general international use. Britain is currently replacing imperial measures by S.I. units. The S.I. units are derived from six base units, three of which concern us in this book: they are the metre (m), the kilogramme (kg) and the second (s) as the basic length, mass and time. They form the basis of a *coherent* system of units in that the product or quotient of two or more unit quantities in the system is the unit of the resultant quantity. Thus the unit of force is the newton (N) which represents a force of one metre-kilogramme/(second)^2.

It is appropriate to note here the difference between the colloquial and scientific uses of the words 'weight' and 'weigh'. It is convenient in practice to compare masses by weighing. A body on the earth's surface experiences a force of attraction due to the gravitational influence of the earth. This force of attraction is called the *weight* of the body. This force will vary slightly from place to place on the earth's surface, due to the shape of the earth. A mass of 1 kg will, if allowed to fall freely, accelerate at about 9·81 m/s^2. Standard gravitational acceleration is actually taken as $g = 9·80665$ m/s^2. Thus the earth exerts a force of 9·81 N on the mass. The weight of the mass is therefore 9·81 N which can also be described as 1 kg force. There is much to be said for using the coherent unit and avoiding the use of units which contain g.

Colloquially, when it is said that a man weighs 80 kg it means that his weight, as explained above, is the same as the weight of a mass of 80 kg.

The S.I. units are *preferred*, but it is often more convenient to use decimal multiples and sub-multiples of these. In calculations, however, S.I. units themselves should be used to avoid errors. Decimal multiples of 10 raised to a power which is a multiple of 3 are recommended. Some decimal multiples which do not obey the rules of 10^3 and 10^{-3} are however accepted. Thus the centimetre (cm) and the litre = 1 dm^3 are accepted S.I. units. Some multiples and prefixes are given in the table below:

Factor	Prefix	Symbol
10^6	mega	M
10^3	kilo	k
10	deca	da
10^{-1}	deci	d
10^{-2}	centi	c
10^{-3}	milli	m
10^{-6}	micro	μ

It should be noted that S.I. units contain one slight inconsistency in that the unit of mass is the *kilo*gramme. From the table 1,000 N is 1 kN.

The S.I. unit for plane angle, the *radian* (rad), is called a supplementary unit.

Many imperial units are still in extensive use, their values in terms of S.I. units are listed below:

$$1 \text{ ft} \quad = 0·3048 \text{ m}$$
$$1 \text{ mile} \quad = 1·609344 \text{ km}$$

$$1 \text{ ft}^2 \qquad = 0.0929030 \text{ m}^2$$
$$1 \text{ ft}^3 \qquad = 0.0283168 \text{ m}^3$$
$$1 \text{ mile/h} \quad = 0.44704 \text{ m/s}$$
$$1 \text{ pound (lb)} = 0.45359237 \text{ kg}$$
$$1 \text{ poundal} \quad = 0.138255 \text{ N}$$
$$1 \text{ UK gallon} = 4.54609 \text{ dm}^3$$

Example 1 Find the constant thrust required to accelerate uniformly an aircraft, which has mass 10^5 kg, from rest to a speed of 180 km/h in 20s assuming no air resistance.

If the initial thrust is the value found in the first part and this is increased at the constant rate of 6×10^3 N/s, find the time taken to achieve the same speed and the distance covered in that time.

Thrust is an alternative term for force.

In the notation of section 2.3, the aircraft must have an acceleration

$$f = \frac{v - u}{t}$$

where

$$v = 50 \text{ m/s}, \quad u = 0, \quad t = 20\text{s}.$$

Thus

$$f = 2.5 \text{ m/s}^2.$$

By Newton's second law, the required thrust

$$= mf = 2.5 \times 10^5 \text{N}.$$

For the second part the initial thrust is 2.5×10^5 N and the thrust at any time t

$$= (2.5 \times 10^5 + 6 \times 10^3 \, t)\text{N}$$

where t is in seconds.

Therefore by Newton's second law

$$10^5 \frac{dv}{dt} = 2.5 \times 10^5 + 6 \times 10^3 t$$

that is

$$\frac{dv}{dt} = 2.5 + 0.06 \, t.$$

Integrating

$$v = 2.5t + 0.03t^2 + C$$

where $C = 0$ because $v = 0$ when $t = 0$.

When $v = 50$ m/s, t is given by

$$50 = 2.5t + 0.03t^2$$

that is

$$0.03t^2 + 2.5t - 50 = 0.$$

We require the positive root of this equation, which is $t = \dfrac{50}{3}$s.

To find the distance covered we must integrate

$$v = \frac{dx}{dt} = 2.5t + 0.03t^2.$$

This gives

$$x = \frac{2.5t^2}{2} + 0.01t^3$$

since again the constant of integration is zero from the initial condition. Substituting $t = \dfrac{50}{3} s$ we get that the distance covered is approximately 392 m.

*Example 2   The meteorologist measures pressure in millibars (1 millibar $= 10^2$ N/m²).
In laboratory experiments pressures are usually expressed in millimetres (mm) of
mercury whose density (mass per unit volume) is $1\cdot359 \times 10^4$ kg/m³. Normal atmospheric
pressure is taken to be 760 mm of mercury. Find the corresponding pressure in terms of
millibars.*

Pressure is force per unit area.

Suppose that the cross-sectional area of an inverted tube containing mercury is A m². Then:

The mass of 1 m³ of mercury $\qquad = 1\cdot359 \times 10^4$ kg.
The weight of 1 m³ of mercury $\qquad = 1\cdot359 \times 10^4 \times 9\cdot81$ N.
The weight of $0.760\,A$ m³ of mercury $= 1\cdot359 \times 10^4 \times 9\cdot81 \times 0\cdot760\,A$ N.
The force exerted over 1 m² $\qquad = 1\cdot359 \times 10^4 \times 9\cdot81 \times 0\cdot760$ N/m².
Pressure $\qquad\qquad\qquad\quad = 1\cdot359 \times 10^2 \times 9\cdot81 \times 0\cdot760$ millibars.
$\qquad\qquad\qquad\qquad\quad = 1013$ millibars.

3.3 Centre of mass

Given two particles P_1 and P_2 with masses m_1 and m_2, their *mass-centre*
G is defined to be the point between $P_1 P_2$ such that

$$\overline{P_1 G} = \frac{m_2}{m_1 + m_2} \overline{P_1 P_2}$$

(see figure 37). Obviously

$$\overline{G P_2} = \frac{m_1}{m_1 + m_2} \overline{P_1 P_2}.$$

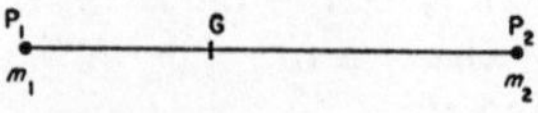

FIGURE 37   The mass-centre G divides $P_1 P_2$ in the ratio $m_2 : m_1$

The definition can easily be translated into vector notation. Let the particles have position vectors $\mathbf{r}_1$ and $\mathbf{r}_2$ (see figure 38). The point G with position vector

$$\bar{\mathbf{r}} = \frac{m_1 \mathbf{r}_1 + m_2 \mathbf{r}_2}{m_1 + m_2} \tag{2}$$

is then the mass-centre. It is easy to verify that $P_1 P_2$ is divided by G in the ratio given above.

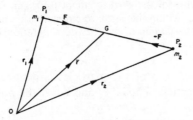

FIGURE 38   The position vector $\bar{r}$ of the mass-centre of two particles

The importance of the mass-centre is revealed by considering again a two-particle system with mutual forces as in figure 38. We have

$$\mathbf{F} = m_1\ddot{\mathbf{r}}_1, \qquad -\mathbf{F} = m_2\ddot{\mathbf{r}}_2,$$

and, adding the equations,

$$m_1\ddot{\mathbf{r}}_1 + m_2\ddot{\mathbf{r}}_2 = \mathbf{0}. \tag{3}$$

Differentiating equation (2) twice with respect to time, we get

$$(m_1 + m_2)\ddot{\mathbf{r}} = m_1\ddot{\mathbf{r}}_1 + m_2\ddot{\mathbf{r}}_2,$$
$$= \mathbf{0},$$

by (3). Thus, since $m_1 + m_2 \neq 0$, $\ddot{\mathbf{r}} = \mathbf{0}$ and the acceleration of the mass-centre vanishes. Its velocity $\dot{\mathbf{r}}$ must be a constant vector which implies that *the mass-centre moves in a straight line with constant velocity*. If the mass-centre is initially at rest it remains so, irrespective of the separate motions of the particles.

Example 3   Using a two-particle model for the earth-moon system, show that the earth and moon revolve about a point approximately 4,800 km from the centre of the earth. Assume that the mass of the earth is 81 times that of the moon and that the distance between them is $3\cdot9 \times 10^5$ km.

If m_1 is the mass of the earth and m_2 the mass of the moon and d is the distance between them, the distance of G from the centre of the earth is

$$\frac{m_2 d}{m_1 + m_2} = d\bigg/\left(\frac{m_1}{m_2} + 1\right)$$

$$= \frac{3\cdot9 \times 10^5}{81 + 1}\,\text{km}$$

$$= 4{,}800\,\text{km}.$$

Mechanics

Since the mean radius of the earth is about 6,400 km, the mass-centre of the earth-moon system lies within the earth. The perturbation in the earth's orbit can be detected as a small oscillation of about 27 days' duration, the lunar month.

The *linear momentum* $\mathbf{p}$ of two particles is defined as the sum of the momenta of each particle. Thus if $\mathbf{r}_1$ and $\mathbf{r}_2$ are the position vectors of the two particles

$$\begin{aligned} \mathbf{p} &= m_1\dot{\mathbf{r}}_1 + m_2\dot{\mathbf{r}}_2 \\ &= (m_1 + m_2)\dot{\mathbf{r}}, \end{aligned}$$

through equation (2). The linear momentum of the two particles is therefore the same as that of a single (fictitious) particle whose mass is the total mass moving with the speed of the mass-centre.

Further, if $\mathbf{F}_1$ and $\mathbf{F}_2$ are the forces which act on the two particles, then the separate equations of motion are

$$\mathbf{F}_1 = m_1\ddot{\mathbf{r}}_1, \qquad \mathbf{F}_2 = m_2\ddot{\mathbf{r}}_2.$$

The addition of these two equations gives

$$\mathbf{F}_1 + \mathbf{F}_2 = m_1\ddot{\mathbf{r}}_1 + m_2\ddot{\mathbf{r}}_2 = (m_1 + m_2)\ddot{\mathbf{r}},$$

with the result that the mass-centre moves as though all the forces act there on a particle whose mass is the total mass. Since any mutual forces between the particles are equal and opposite, $\mathbf{F}_1 + \mathbf{F}_2$ represents the total *external* force on the system.

3.4 Multi-particle systems

It is a straightforward matter to extend the results so far derived for two-particle systems to systems consisting of n particles. Suppose the n particles have masses m_i, position vectors $\mathbf{r}_i$ and are subject to forces (mutual and external) $\mathbf{F}_i$ with $i = 1, 2,..., n$. The *mass-centre* G of the system is defined to be the point with position vector

$$\bar{\mathbf{r}} = \sum_{i=1}^{n} m_i\mathbf{r}_i \Big/ \sum_{i=1}^{n} m_i,$$

where the usual summation notation is used.

The *linear momentum* $\mathbf{p}$ of the system is defined by

$$\mathbf{p} = \sum_{i=1}^{n} m_i\mathbf{v}_i,$$

where $\mathbf{v}_i = \dot{\mathbf{r}}_i$.

For each particle of the system the second law of motion gives

$$\mathbf{F}_i = m_i \ddot{\mathbf{r}}_i, \qquad i = 1, 2, ..., n, \tag{4}$$

where $\ddot{\mathbf{r}}_i$ is the acceleration of the i-th particle. Summing all these equations, we obtain

$$\sum_{i=1}^{n} \mathbf{F}_i = \sum_{i=1}^{n} m_i \ddot{\mathbf{r}}_i = \frac{\mathrm{d}}{\mathrm{d}t}\left[\sum_{i=1}^{n} m_i \mathbf{v}_i \right]$$

$$= \dot{\mathbf{p}}$$

$$= \frac{\mathrm{d}^2}{\mathrm{d}t^2}\left(\sum_{i=1}^{n} m_i \mathbf{r}_i \right)$$

$$= \frac{\mathrm{d}^2}{\mathrm{d}t^2}\left[\left(\sum_{i=1}^{n} m_i \right) \bar{\mathbf{r}} \right] \quad \text{(by the definition of } \bar{\mathbf{r}})$$

$$= \left(\sum_{i=1}^{n} m_i \right) \ddot{\bar{\mathbf{r}}}.$$

We draw two conclusions. The total force $\sum_{i=1}^{n} \mathbf{F}_i$ is the *rate of change of the total linear momentum* and *the mass-centre of the system moves as a particle, whose mass is the total mass, subjected to the total force*. If the total force vanishes (for example, if the forces consist entirely of mutual actions and reactions between the particles) then $\sum_{i=1}^{n} \mathbf{F}_i = \mathbf{0}$ which implies that $\ddot{\bar{\mathbf{r}}} = \mathbf{0}$. In this case the mass-centre moves in a straight line with constant velocity or remains at rest.

Of course, knowledge of the motion of the mass-centre does not help in the description of the separate motions of the particles. Given the forces $\mathbf{F}_i$ in equation (4), the differential equations must be solved separately to achieve this.

3.5 Moment of momentum

Consider a single particle of mass m, position vector $\mathbf{r}$ subject to a force $\mathbf{F}$. The linear momentum $\mathbf{p} = m\mathbf{v}$ where $\mathbf{v} = \dot{\mathbf{r}}$. The moment $\mathbf{h}_o$ of the linear momentum about the origin O is given by

$$\mathbf{h}_o = \mathbf{r} \times \mathbf{p} = m\mathbf{r} \times \mathbf{v}.$$

The vector $\mathbf{h}_o$ is called the *moment of momentum* or *angular momentum about* O. Taking the time derivative of $\mathbf{h}_o$, we have

$$\frac{\mathrm{d}\mathbf{h}_o}{\mathrm{d}t} = \frac{\mathrm{d}}{\mathrm{d}t}(m\mathbf{r} \times \mathbf{v}) = m\mathbf{v} \times \mathbf{v} + m\mathbf{r} \times \dot{\mathbf{v}}$$

$$= \mathbf{r} \times \mathbf{F},$$

since $\mathbf{v} \times \mathbf{v} = 0$ and $\mathbf{F} = m\dot{\mathbf{v}}$. The right-hand side is the moment of the force $\mathbf{F}$ about O. Thus *the moment of the force about* O *is the rate of change of the moment of momentum about* O.

Whilst the linear momentum is the vector whose magnitude and direction is independent of the fixed origin chosen, the moment of momentum vector varies with the choice of origin. In figure 39, let O′ be a second *fixed* origin

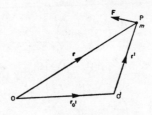

FIGURE 39

with position vector $\mathbf{r}_{o'}$, and let the particle P have position vector $\mathbf{r}'$ relative to it. The moment of momentum about O′ is

$$\mathbf{h}_{o'} = m\mathbf{r}' \times \mathbf{v}.$$

By the triangle law $\mathbf{r}' = \mathbf{r} - \mathbf{r}_{o'}$, so that

$$\mathbf{h}_{o'} = m(\mathbf{r} - \mathbf{r}_{o'}) \times \mathbf{v} = \mathbf{h}_o - m\mathbf{r}_{o'} \times \mathbf{v},$$

which clearly shows that generally $\mathbf{h}_o \neq \mathbf{h}_{o'}$. However, we still have

$$\frac{d\mathbf{h}_{o'}}{dt} = \frac{d}{dt}(m\mathbf{r}' \times \mathbf{v}) = \mathbf{r}' \times \mathbf{F},$$

the moment of the force about O′.

For a multi-particle system the moment of momentum is the sum of the individual moments. Let the particles have masses m_i, position vectors $\mathbf{r}_i$ referred to O and be subject to external forces $\mathbf{F}_i^{\text{ext}}$ and internal reactions $\mathbf{F}_i^{\text{int}}$, with $i = 1, 2,..., n$. The total force on particle i is $\mathbf{F}_i^{\text{ext}} + \mathbf{F}_i^{\text{int}}$ and the moment of momentum

$$\mathbf{h}_o = \sum_{i=1}^{n} m_i\mathbf{r}_i \times \dot{\mathbf{r}}_i.$$

Taking the time derivative,

$$\frac{d\mathbf{h}_o}{dt} = \frac{d}{dt}\left(\sum_{i=1}^{n} m_i\mathbf{r}_i \times \dot{\mathbf{r}}_i\right) = \sum_{i=1}^{n} m_i\dot{\mathbf{r}}_i \times \dot{\mathbf{r}}_i + \sum_{i=1}^{n} m_i\mathbf{r}_i \times \ddot{\mathbf{r}}_i$$

$$= \sum_{i=1}^{n} m_i\mathbf{r}_i \times \ddot{\mathbf{r}}_i = \sum_{i=1}^{n} \mathbf{r}_i \times (\mathbf{F}_i^{\text{ext}} + \mathbf{F}_i^{\text{int}}).$$

Every internal force must be balanced by an equal and opposite force acting in the same line with the result that the moments of these two forces must cancel. Consequently

$$\frac{d\mathbf{h}_o}{dt} = \sum_{i=1}^{n} \mathbf{r}_i \times \mathbf{F}_i^{\text{ext}},$$

that is the moment of the external forces about the origin equals the rate of change of moment of momentum about that point. If no external forces act on the system, $\dot{\mathbf{h}}_o = \mathbf{0}$ and hence $\mathbf{h}_o = $ a constant vector, and we say that the moment of momentum of the system is conserved.

The solar system (consisting of sun, planets and moons) is an example of such a situation since the only forces are the mutual gravitational attractions. The moment of momentum vector is fixed in direction relative to the stars and is consequently normal to an *invariant* plane called the *astronomical plane*. The plane of the earth's orbit (the ecliptic plane) is currently inclined at about $1.5°$ to the astronomical plane.

Note that moment of momentum is required in the analysis of the *rotation* of a body. We shall have more to say on this topic in chapter 8. A particle by its interpretation as a mass-point can have no sensible rotation. For this reason the motion of a system of particles is completely described by equation (4) of section 3.4 without the introduction of moment of momentum.

3.6 Gravitational force

So far we have discussed force in general terms without considering the nature of the force. One of the fundamental forces is gravity: any object in the universe experiences a force due to the presence of any other object. This is the Newtonian postulate of gravity which in detail states (in terms of particles) that *any particle attracts any other particle with a force which is proportional to the product of their masses and inversely proportional to the square of the distance between them.* This force, of course, acts along the line joining the two particles. Again the test of this postulate lies in its consistency with the laboratory and visible evidence available to us.

This result can be expressed symbolically most conveniently in vector terms. Let the particles A and B with masses m_A and m_B have position vectors $\mathbf{r}_A$ and $\mathbf{r}_B$ in an inertial frame (see figure 40). The vector

$$\overline{AB} = \mathbf{r}_B - \mathbf{r}_A$$

and the unit vector in the direction of $\overline{AB}$ is

$$\frac{\mathbf{r}_B - \mathbf{r}_A}{|\mathbf{r}_B - \mathbf{r}_A|}.$$

According to Newton's law of gravitation, the force acting on A due to B is given by F_A where

$$F_A = \frac{\gamma m_A m_B (r_B - r_A)}{|r_B - r_A|^3},$$

in which γ, the constant of proportionality, is called the *gravitational constant*. Although the gravitational force between two objects in a laboratory is very small, this force can be detected experimentally. The value of γ is found to be 6.67×10^{-11} m^3/kg s^2.

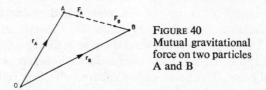

FIGURE 40
Mutual gravitational
force on two particles
A and B

By Newton's third law the force on B due to A is given by

$$F_B = -F_A = \frac{\gamma m_A m_B (r_A - r_B)}{|r_B - r_A|^3}.$$

Example 4   Estimate the mass of the earth, given that the acceleration induced by the gravity of the earth at its surface is 9·81 m/s^2, using a particle model for the earth. (Use the following data: mean radius of the earth = 6,400 km. $\gamma = 6.7 \times 10^{-11}$ m^3/kg s^2.)

We shall consider the earth as fixed in an inertial frame of reference. In our model the earth is contracted to a particle and we consider the behaviour of a *unit* mass 6,400 km from this point. The force required to produce an acceleration of 9·81 m/s^2 in a kg is 9·81 N. The gravitational force exerted on the unit mass is $\gamma M/a^2$ where M is the required mass and a is the radius of the earth. Hence $9.81 = \gamma M/a^2$ or

$$M = \frac{9.81 \times (6{,}400 \times 10^3)^2}{6.7 \times 10^{-11}} \text{ kg}$$

$$= 6.0 \times 10^{24} \text{ kg}.$$

This result does not take account of the oblateness of the earth nor that the earth has bulk but it compares very well with the currently adopted value of 5.98×10^{24} kg.

For spherical or nearly spherical bodies good estimates of the gravitational attraction *outside* the body can be obtained by replacing the body by a particle of equivalent mass at its centre. For arbitrary shapes the gravitational effects are much more complicated. The gravitational force *within* a body is also more elaborate and is beyond the scope of this book.

3.7 Fields of force

If at every point of a region of space a particle is acted upon by a force then there is said to exist a *field of force* in that region. The force will depend on position, in which case we would have $F(x,y,z)$ in Cartesian coordinates, and possibly on time too in which case we would have $F(x,y,z,t)$. The earth is an example of the first form of the force field; it generates a gravitational field of force throughout space which with our particle model is directed towards the centre of the earth. This force obeys an inverse square law and takes the form, for a particle of mass m,

$$\mathbf{F} = -\frac{\gamma m M \mathbf{r}}{r^3} \qquad (5)$$

if we treat the centre of the earth as a fixed point and measure r from the centre of the earth (M is the mass of the earth).

The law of gravitation for a sphere can be replaced by a simpler one when we are dealing with phenomena which occur within a 'small' area of the earth's surface (say about 300 km across and within a few tens of kilometres of the earth's surface). Within such a region the gravitational force will be substantially constant and parallel. We can confirm this by two quick calculations.

Two points 300 km apart on the earth's surface subtend an angle of 300/6,400 radians or 2·7° at the centre of the earth, if we take the radius of the earth to be 6,400 km. At the extremities of this distance the force directions will deviate from the parallel by about 2·7°.

Suppose at the surface of the earth $g = 9\cdot81$ m/s^2, then we have

$$g = \frac{\gamma M}{a^2}, \qquad (6)$$

where $a = 6,400$ km. At a height of 150 km let the acceleration due to gravity be g' so that

$$g' = \frac{\gamma M}{(a + 150)^2}.$$

Division of this equation by (6) gives

$$\frac{g'}{g} = \frac{a^2}{(a + 150)^2} = \left(1 + \frac{150}{a}\right)^{-2}$$

$$\simeq 1 - \frac{2 \times 150}{a} = 0\cdot95,$$

using the first two terms of the binomial expansion. Therefore,

$$g' = 0\cdot95 \times 9\cdot81 = 9\cdot3 \text{ m/s}^2.$$

Within the region indicated these two results show that the force is almost uniform in magnitude and direction. We can replace (5) by the uniform force field

$$\mathbf{F} = -\frac{\gamma mM}{a^2}\mathbf{k} = -mg\mathbf{k},$$

where $\mathbf{k}$ is the upward unit vector and $g = 9 \cdot 81 \text{ m/s}^2$. With a new frame of reference with origin on the earth's surface and z-axis vertically upwards, Newton's second law gives

$$\ddot{\mathbf{r}} = -g\mathbf{k}$$

for the particle of unit mass. This equation separates into the three scalar equations

$$\ddot{x} = \ddot{y} = 0, \qquad \ddot{z} = -g, \tag{7}$$

which imply that the particle moves with constant velocity parallel to the surface of the earth and with constant acceleration vertically. We shall examine motion in a uniform force field in the next section in the context of projectiles.

Other examples of fields of force are provided by a magnetic field and the force it exerts on a charged particle moving in it, or the wind in the atmosphere and its effect on an aircraft passing through it. Force fields may also depend on velocity or higher time-derivatives of displacement in addition to position and time.

3.8 Projectiles

The motion of a projectile near the earth's surface is governed by equations (7) above and provides a simple illustration of motion in a uniform field of force. Suppose that a particle is fired from a point on the earth's surface with speed V in a direction making angle α to the horizontal (the particle could be interpreted as a shell fired from a gun whose barrel is inclined at an angle α). Take the origin O at the point of projection, the z-axis vertical and the x-axis horizontal in the vertical plane through the initial velocity vector, with the y-axis completing the triad. The equations of motion are given by (7):

$$\ddot{x} = \ddot{y} = 0, \qquad m\ddot{z} = -mg,$$

where m is the mass of the particle.

Initially (at time $t = 0$), $x = y = z = 0$, $\dot{x} = V\cos\alpha$, $\dot{y} = 0$, $\dot{z} = V\sin\alpha$. We first observe that since $\dot{y} = 0$ initially it must remain so throughout the motion since $\ddot{y} = 0$. The particle must therefore move in the xz-plane as indicated in figure 41. Similarly since $\dot{x} = V\cos\alpha$ initially, the horizontal component of the velocity must remain $V\cos\alpha$. Thus our equations of motion reduce to

$$\dot{x} = V\cos\alpha, \qquad \ddot{z} = -g$$

(we can ignore the y-coordinate henceforward). These two elementary differential equations have solutions

$$x = Vt\cos\alpha + A, \qquad z = B + Ct - \tfrac{1}{2}gt^2,$$

where A, B and C are constants to be determined from the initial conditions.

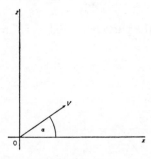

FIGURE 41

Note that motion in the z-direction is one of constant acceleration which has been examined in detail in section 2.3. Using the given initial conditions, we see that $A = 0$, $B = 0$, $C = V\sin\alpha$, so that the horizontal and vertical displacements are given by

$$x = Vt\cos\alpha, \tag{8}$$
$$z = Vt\sin\alpha - \tfrac{1}{2}gt^2, \tag{9}$$

in terms of the time t.

From (9), we observe that $z = 0$ when

$$t(V\sin\alpha - \tfrac{1}{2}gt) = 0,$$

which has two solutions $t = 0$ and $t = 2V\sin\alpha/g$. The former solution refers to the initial condition whilst the latter gives the time when the particle meets the horizontal through the point of projection, in other words it gives the *time of flight* of the particle over horizontal ground. Denoting this time by T, we see that

$$T = \frac{2V}{g}\sin\alpha.$$

During this time the particle covers a horizontal distance, called the horizontal *range* and denoted by R, of

$$R = VT \cos \alpha = \frac{2V^2}{g} \sin \alpha \cos \alpha = \frac{V^2}{g} \sin 2\alpha, \qquad (10)$$

from equation (8) and the trigonometric identity $\sin 2\alpha = 2 \sin \alpha \cos \alpha$. The *maximum* range for a *fixed* projection speed but variable projection angle occurs where $\sin 2\alpha$ takes its maximum value. For $0 \leqslant \alpha \leqslant \frac{1}{2}\pi$, the maximum value of $\sin 2\alpha$ is 1 when $\alpha = 45°$. Thus

$$R_{max} = \frac{V^2}{g},$$

which is achieved when the particle is fired at 45° to the horizontal.

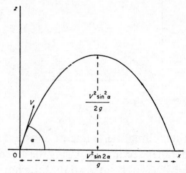

FIGURE 42   Range and maximum height for a projectile

It should be acknowledged that the range represents that of a particle *in vacuo* and ignores the effects, which can be significant, of air resistance.

The particle attains its greatest height where z has its maximum value. This occurs at the time when dz/dt vanishes. From equation (9)

$$\frac{dz}{dt} = V \sin \alpha - gt$$

and $dz/dt = 0$ when $t = V \sin \alpha/g = \frac{1}{2}T$. This is a maximum since $d^2z/dt^2 = -g < 0$. We note that the maximum is reached after half the total time of flight. The greatest height attained, H, is obtained by substituting the time back into equation (9) so that

$$H = \frac{V^2 \sin^2 \alpha}{g} - \frac{V^2 g \sin^2 \alpha}{2g^2} = \frac{V^2 \sin^2 \alpha}{2g}. \qquad (11)$$

Equations (8) and (9) are parametric equations of the *path* or *trajectory* of the particle in space in terms of the parameter t. The equation of the path is obtained by eliminating t between the equations:

$$z = x \tan \alpha - \frac{gx^2}{2V^2} \sec^2 \alpha. \tag{12}$$

This path is a parabola with its vertex upward as shown in figure 42. The path is symmetric about a vertical line through the maximum point of the path.

Example 5   A man finds that he can throw a ball less easily upwards than horizontally and that the speed of projection of the ball varies approximately as 25 cos ½α m/s, where α is the angle of projection. Find the maximum values of the range and height, and the angles at which the ball should be projected to attain these.

The equations of motion of the ball, (8) and (9), become

$$x = 25t \cos \tfrac{1}{2}\alpha \cos \alpha,$$

$$z = 25t \cos \tfrac{1}{2}\alpha \sin \alpha - \tfrac{1}{2}gt^2,$$

since $V = 25 \cos \tfrac{1}{2}\alpha$. The range

$$R = \frac{25^2}{g} \cos^2 \tfrac{1}{2}\alpha \sin 2\alpha \tag{13}$$

from (10). The range is a maximum when $\cos^2 \tfrac{1}{2}\alpha \sin 2\alpha$ is a maximum, which occurs where $dR/d\alpha$ vanishes. Now

$$\frac{dR}{d\alpha} = \frac{25^2}{g}(2 \cos^2 \tfrac{1}{2}\alpha \cos 2\alpha - \cos \tfrac{1}{2}\alpha \sin \tfrac{1}{2}\alpha \sin 2\alpha)$$

and $dR/d\alpha = 0$ when

$$2 \cos^2 \tfrac{1}{2}\alpha \cos 2\alpha = \cos \tfrac{1}{2}\alpha \sin \tfrac{1}{2}\alpha \sin 2\alpha.$$

Using the identities $2 \cos^2 \beta = 1 + \cos 2\beta$ and $\sin 2\beta = 2 \sin \beta \cos \beta$, this equation can be written

$$(1 + \cos \alpha)(2 \cos^2 \alpha - 1) = \sin \alpha \cdot \sin \alpha \cos \alpha = (1 - \cos^2 \alpha) \cos \alpha,$$

or as

$$(1 + \cos \alpha)(3 \cos^2 \alpha - \cos \alpha - 1) = 0,$$

of which there are three solutions:

$$\cos \alpha = -1, \qquad \cos \alpha = \tfrac{1}{6}(1 \pm \sqrt{13}).$$

We reject the two negative roots since we are interested only in the range $0 \leqslant \alpha \leqslant \tfrac{1}{2}\pi$. Thus the required angle is given by $\cos \alpha = \tfrac{1}{6}(1 + \sqrt{13}) = 0.7676$ so that $\alpha = 39° \, 51'$. The maximum range from (13) works out to be about 55·4 m.

The maximum height for *fixed* α is given by (11):

$$H = \frac{25^2}{2g} \cos^2 \tfrac{1}{2}\alpha \sin^2 \alpha. \tag{14}$$

The maximum possible height as α varies occurs when $dH/d\alpha$ vanishes. Now

$$\frac{dH}{d\alpha} = \frac{25^2}{2g}(2\cos^2 \tfrac{1}{2}\alpha \sin \alpha \cos \alpha - \cos \tfrac{1}{2}\alpha \sin \tfrac{1}{2}\alpha \sin^2 \alpha),$$

which vanishes when

$$2\cos^2 \tfrac{1}{2}\alpha \sin \alpha \cos \alpha = \cos \tfrac{1}{2}\alpha \sin \tfrac{1}{2}\alpha \sin^2 \alpha.$$

By using the trigonometric identities again,

$$(1 + \cos \alpha) \sin \alpha \cos \alpha = \tfrac{1}{2} \sin \alpha \sin^2 \alpha = \tfrac{1}{2} \sin \alpha (1 - \cos^2 \alpha),$$

or

$$\sin \alpha(1 + \cos \alpha)(3 \cos \alpha - 1) = 0,$$

giving the three roots $\sin \alpha = 0$, $\cos \alpha = -1$, $\cos \alpha = \tfrac{1}{3}$. The first two roots give the minimum heights. The third root is the one we require and gives an angle of 70° 32'. On substituting this angle back into (14) the maximum height is about 18·9 m, achieved when the ball is thrown at an angle of 70° 32' to the horizontal.

Example 6   Find the range of a projectile which is fired with speed V at angle α to an inclined plane which is itself inclined at an angle β to the horizontal. For fixed V, what is the maximum range?

The particle is assumed to be projected in the vertical plane through the line of greatest slope on the inclined plane. It is convenient in this problem to choose a modified coordinate system. Take the x-axis up the plane and the z-axis perpendicular to it as indicated in figure 43. The acceleration components in the x- and z-directions become respectively $-g \sin \beta$ and $-g \cos \beta$ resulting in the equations of motion

$$\ddot{x} = -g \sin \beta, \qquad \ddot{z} = -g \cos \beta.$$

The initial conditions for the problem are

$$x = z = 0, \qquad \dot{x} = V \cos \alpha, \qquad \dot{z} = V \sin \alpha \quad \text{at } t = 0.$$

Integrating the equations twice and using the initial conditions, the reader may verify that

$$x = Vt \cos \alpha - \tfrac{1}{2}gt^2 \sin \beta, \tag{15}$$
$$z = Vt \sin \alpha - \tfrac{1}{2}gt^2 \cos \beta. \tag{16}$$

When the projectile hits the plane, $z = 0$, which, from (16), occurs after a time T where

$$T = \frac{2V \sin \alpha}{g \cos \beta}.$$

The inclined range R at this time is, from (15),

$$R = VT\cos\alpha - \tfrac{1}{2}gT^2\sin\beta$$

$$= \frac{2V^2}{g}\frac{\sin\alpha}{\cos^2\beta}(\cos\alpha\cos\beta - \sin\alpha\sin\beta)$$

$$= \frac{2V^2\sin\alpha\cos(\alpha+\beta)}{g\cos^2\beta} = \frac{V^2[\sin(2\alpha+\beta) - \sin\beta]}{g\cos^2\beta},$$

by employing two standard trigonometric identities. For fixed V and β but variable α, the range will be a maximum where $\sin(2\alpha+\beta)$ has its maximum. The greatest value of the sine function is 1, which corresponds to $2\alpha+\beta = \tfrac{1}{2}\pi$, that is to $\alpha = \tfrac{1}{4}\pi - \tfrac{1}{2}\beta$. The maximum range

$$R_{max} = \frac{V^2(1-\sin\beta)}{g\cos^2\beta} = \frac{V^2(1-\sin\beta)}{g(1-\sin^2\beta)} = \frac{V^2}{g(1+\sin\beta)}.$$

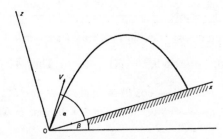

FIGURE 43   Projectile fired up an inclined plane

Example 7   Mud is thrown off the rim of a wheel, of radius a, on a car travelling with speed v. If $v^2 \geqslant ga$ show that no mud can be thrown higher than

$$a + \frac{v^2}{2g} + \frac{ga^2}{2v^2}$$

above the ground.

Figure 44 shows the wheel rolling along a straight line Ox with angular speed $\omega = v/a$. Suppose at time t the point of contact between the wheel and road is distance s from O and that mud is being thrown from the wheel at P through which the radius makes an angle θ with the downward vertical. If $\mathbf{r} = x\mathbf{i} + z\mathbf{k}$ is the position vector of P then, in terms of s and θ,

$$\mathbf{r} = (s - a\sin\theta)\mathbf{i} + a(1 - \cos\theta)\mathbf{k}.$$

The velocity of P

$$\dot{\mathbf{r}} = (\dot{s} - a\cos\theta\dot{\theta})\mathbf{i} + a\sin\theta\dot{\theta}\mathbf{k}$$
$$= v(1 - \cos\theta)\mathbf{i} + v\sin\theta\mathbf{k},$$

since $\dot{s} = v$ and $\dot{\theta} = \omega = v/a$. This is the velocity with which the mud is thrown from the wheel.

The vertical equation of motion of a particle of mud is

$$\ddot{z} = -g,$$

which has a solution

$$z = A + Bt - \tfrac{1}{2}gt^2.$$

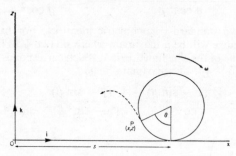

FIGURE 44   Coordinate scheme for Example 7

Initially for fixed θ, $\dot{z} = v \sin \theta$, $z = a(1 - \cos \theta)$. Thus $A = a(1 - \cos \theta)$ and $B = v \sin \theta$ and

$$z = a(1 - \cos \theta) + vt \sin \theta - \tfrac{1}{2}gt^2.$$

The maximum height reached occurs when $\dot{z} = 0$, that is when $t = v \sin \theta/g$. Thus the maximum height

$$H = a(1 - \cos \theta) + \frac{v^2 \sin^2 \theta}{2g}.$$

For varying θ this height has an overall maximum where $\mathrm{d}H/\mathrm{d}\theta = 0$.

$$\frac{\mathrm{d}H}{\mathrm{d}\theta} = a \sin \theta + \frac{v^2}{g} \sin \theta \cos \theta$$

which vanishes where $\sin \theta = 0$ or $\cos \theta = -ag/v^2$. If $v^2 < ag$, there is one real root: $\sin \theta = 0$ giving $\theta = 0$ and π. The first of these corresponds to the point of contact which is at rest and is clearly a minimum whilst the second corresponds to the mud being thrown off at the highest point of the wheel which will be the highest point of its path. If $v^2 \geqslant ag$, the second root, $\cos \theta = -ag/v^2$, gives an overall maximum height of

$$H_{\mathrm{max}} = a\left(1 + \frac{ag}{v^2}\right) + \frac{v^2}{2g}\left(1 - \frac{a^2 g^2}{v^4}\right)$$

$$= a + \frac{a^2 g}{2v^2} + \frac{v^2}{2g},$$

as required. To achieve this maximum mud is thrown off in the range $\tfrac{1}{2}\pi \leqslant \theta \leqslant \pi$.

For a wheel of radius 0·3 m travelling at 45 km/h, $H_{max} = 8·27$ m approximately. Remember however that the mud is more likely to be thrown off in the range $0 \leqslant \theta \leqslant \frac{1}{2}\pi$ since adhesion will generally not hold the mud to the wheel beyond this range.

Example 8   A gun can fire a shell with speed V in any direction. Show that a shell can reach any target within the surface

$$g^2r^2 = V^4 - 2gV^2z,$$

where z is the height of the target and r is the horizontal distance of the target from the gun.

The shell can be fired in any vertical plane through the gun and in such a plane the trajectory of the shell is given by equation (12) with r replacing x:

$$z = r \tan \alpha - \frac{gr^2}{2V^2} \sec^2 \alpha.$$

Using the identity $\sec^2 \alpha = 1 + \tan^2 \alpha$, this equation can be rewritten in the form

$$\frac{gr^2}{2V^2} \tan^2 \alpha - r \tan \alpha + z + \frac{gr^2}{2V^2} = 0. \tag{17}$$

Interpret (r,z) now as the coordinates of a target. Equation (17) is a quadratic equation in $\tan \alpha$ with the two roots

$$\tan \alpha = \frac{1}{gr}[V^2 \pm (V^4 - 2gzV^2 - g^2r^2)^{\frac{1}{2}}].$$

These two roots will be real if the discriminant

$$V^4 - 2gzV^2 - g^2r^2 \geqslant 0$$

and a shell will reach a target with coordinates (r,z) only if this inequality is satisfied. The *critical* surface is therefore given by

$$V^4 - 2gzV^2 - g^2r^2 = 0,$$

a *paraboloid of revolution*, sometimes called the paraboloid of safety. Any target on or within this paraboloid can be reached by a shell. Note also that for any target within the paraboloid there are *two* possible directions in which the barrel of the gun can be inclined; for a target on the paraboloid there is just one.

3.9 Rigid Bodies

The results obtained so far tacitly assume that 'bodies' can be approximated to by particles. Indeed the basic laws of Newtonian mechanics refer only to particles. However it would not be realistic to exclude all consideration of bodies of finite dimension. Probably the simplest type

of body is the *rigid body*. The rigidity can be expressed by the condition
that the distance between any two points of the body remains constant,
no matter what forces are applied to the body. By using this essentially
geometric constraint, we can avoid examining the local forces or *stresses*
within the body since the stresses in a rigid body must always be such as
to maintain its rigidity. If the body is composed of deformable material
and exhibits elastic or fluid properties, we must postulate the nature of the
internal stresses and examine the consequent deformation suffered by the
body. For many practical purposes the assumption of rigidity is a useful
model. This is not to say, however, that all bodies which appear rigid
can be treated as rigid bodies. Certain hard rubber balls show characteristics at variance with their predicted behaviour when a rigid body model
is used.

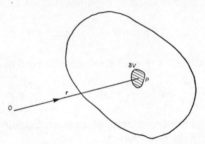

FIGURE 45   Position vector **r** of an element δV of the rigid body

The fundamental assumption concerning the nature of a rigid body is
that every subdivision of it has mass. In other words we may cut the body
into as many pieces as we please but each portion will have mass. This is
contrary to the usual molecular concept of matter but is sufficient for most
problems in the physical and engineering sciences where we are dealing
with matter in bulk. In figure 45, **r** is the position vector of a point P
of a rigid body. The point P is enclosed by a small region of volume
δV and mass δm. The ratio $\delta m/\delta V$ is the mean density of this region.
The limit of this ratio as δV collapses to the point is the density at P.
Symbolically, the density

$$\rho = \lim_{\delta V \to 0} \frac{\delta m}{\delta V}.$$

We note that ρ can be a function of position in the body.

The mass-centre $\bar{\mathbf{r}}$ of the rigid body is defined by

$$M\bar{\mathbf{r}} = \int \mathbf{r} \, dm = \int \mathbf{r}\rho \, dV,$$

where M is the total mass, and the integration is performed throughout the volume. Interpreting integration as a summation this definition is in line with that for multi-particle systems: it is the 'sum' of the product of elements of mass and **r**.

Example 9   Find the mass-centre of a solid hemisphere of uniform density ρ and radius a.

The radius perpendicular to the face is an axis of symmetry of the hemisphere. Since the density is uniform the mass-centre will lie on this line. The mass of the hemisphere is $\frac{2}{3}\pi a^3 \rho$.

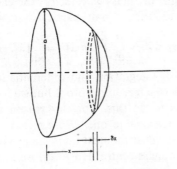

FIGURE 46   Integration scheme for the calculation of the mass-centre of a hemisphere

Consider now a disc of thickness δx which is parallel to the face and distance x from it (see figure 46). The mass of this disc is approximately $\rho\pi(a^2 - x^2)\delta x$. If $\bar{x}$ is the distance of the mass-centre from the face, we have

$$\bar{x} \cdot \tfrac{2}{3}\pi a^3 \rho = \int_0^a \rho\pi(a^2 - x^2)x \, \mathrm{d}x$$

$$= \rho\pi\left[\frac{a^2 x^2}{2} - \frac{x^4}{4}\right]_0^a$$

$$= \tfrac{1}{4}\rho\pi a^4.$$

Therefore $\bar{x} = 3a/8$.

The application of Newton's laws of motion for *particles* to rigid bodies presents serious technical difficulties since obviously a rigid body cannot be considered strictly speaking as an agglomeration of particles. It is possible to produce a plausible line of argument by imagining a rigid body subdivided into a large number of small elements of mass δm and then to replace these elements by particles of equal mass. This amounts to the assertion that a rigid body is a collection of particles held together by mass-less ties. This conflicts with our definition of a body having within it a continuous distribution of mass. In fact, in the same way that we had to redefine the mass-centre of a rigid body so must we also extend the Newtonian postulates and, in particular, the second law of motion.

The *linear momentum* **p** of a rigid body is defined by

$$\mathbf{p} = \int \dot{\mathbf{r}} \, dm = \int_V \dot{\mathbf{r}}\rho \, dV,$$

the integration being performed throughout the body (refer back to figure 45). Again this is 'sum' of 'mass × velocity' for each element δm and accords with the definition for a multi-particle system. Further

$$\mathbf{p} = \int_V \dot{\mathbf{r}}\rho \, dV = \frac{d}{dt} \int_V \mathbf{r}\rho \, dV = \frac{d}{dt}(M\bar{\mathbf{r}}) = M\dot{\bar{\mathbf{r}}}, \tag{18}$$

where the operations of integration and differentiation have been interchanged. This is a step which requires proof but we have not available the necessary mathematics to do this. For this reason we shall accept this operation as being a reasonable one. We conclude, as with the multi-particle system, that the linear momentum is the product of the total mass and the velocity of the mass-centre. However, we shall verify (18) in the following example.

Example 10   A wheel of radius a, mass M and density ρ rolls along a straight line with constant speed U. Verify that

$$\int_V \dot{\mathbf{r}}\rho \, dV = \frac{d}{dt} \int_V \mathbf{r}\rho \, dV = MU\mathbf{i}.$$

Assume that the wheel has negligible thickness so that the density is mass per unit area and the element of volume can be interpreted as an element of area. Let the x-axis be the line along which the wheel rolls with the z-axis vertical. If ω is the angular speed of the wheel, then $U = a\omega$. Consider at time t a point P of the wheel distance R from the centre and such that the radius through P makes an angle θ with the downward vertical (see figure 47). Clearly the position vector of P is given by

$$\mathbf{r} = (s - R\sin\theta)\mathbf{i} + (a - R\cos\theta)\mathbf{k},$$

and, consequently,

$$\dot{\mathbf{r}} = (\dot{s} - R\cos\theta\dot{\theta})\mathbf{i} + R\sin\theta\dot{\theta}\mathbf{k} = \left(U - \frac{RU}{a}\cos\theta\right)\mathbf{i} + \frac{RU}{a}\sin\theta\mathbf{k},$$

since R is a constant for a particular point P, $\dot{s} = U$ and $\dot{\theta} = \omega$. An element of area is $R\delta R\delta\theta$ (the shaded area in figure 47). Thus

$$\int_V \dot{\mathbf{r}}\rho \, dV = \int_0^a \int_0^{2\pi} \left[\left(U - \frac{RU}{a} \cos\theta \right)\mathbf{i} + \frac{RU}{a} \sin\theta\mathbf{k} \right]\rho \, d\theta R \, dR$$

$$= \int_0^a \left[\left(U\theta - \frac{RU}{a} \sin\theta \right)\mathbf{i} - \frac{RU}{a} \cos\theta\mathbf{k} \right]_{\theta=0}^{\theta=2\pi} \rho R \, dR$$

$$= \int_0^a 2\pi\rho UR \, dR\mathbf{i} = 2\pi\rho U[\tfrac{1}{2}R^2]_{R=0}^{R=a} \, \mathbf{i}$$

$$= \pi a^2 \rho U\mathbf{i} = MU\mathbf{i}.$$

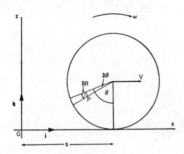

FIGURE 47

Similarly

$$\frac{d}{dt}\int_V \mathbf{r}\rho \, dV = \frac{d}{dt}\int_0^a \int_0^{2\pi} [(s - R\sin\theta)\mathbf{i} + (a - R\cos\theta)\mathbf{k}]\rho \, d\theta R \, dR$$

$$= \frac{d}{dt}\int_0^a (2\pi s\mathbf{i} + 2\pi a\mathbf{k})\rho R \, dR$$

$$= \frac{d}{dt}(\pi a^2 \rho s\mathbf{i} + \pi a^3 \rho\mathbf{k})$$

$$= \pi a^2 \rho\dot{s}\mathbf{i} = MU\mathbf{i}.$$

The forces which a rigid body may experience can be classified under two headings: the *body forces* which apply to every point of the body, as for example in the case of gravity, and the *applied surface forces* which may be either point loads, $\mathbf{F}_1$, $\mathbf{F}_2$,... in figure 48, or pressure applied over a section of the surface (the hatched surface S in the figure). Suppose a rigid body is subject to a body force $\mathbf{Q}$ per unit mass, point loads $\mathbf{F}_1$, $\mathbf{F}_2$, $\mathbf{F}_3$,..., $\mathbf{F}_n$ and pressure p over the surface S. The total force $\mathbf{F}$ acting on the body (internal reactions in the body cancel one another out) is given by

$$F = \int_V \mathbf{Q}\rho \, \mathrm{d}V + \sum_{i=1}^{n} \mathbf{F}_i - \int_S p\mathbf{n} \, \mathrm{d}S,$$

where $\mathbf{n}$ is the unit outward vector normal to the surface of the body. The last term represents the total effect of the pressure over the surface S (remember that pressure is force per unit area and acts normal to the surface).

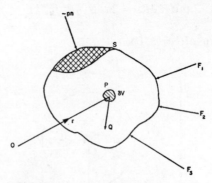

FIGURE 48   Different forms of force which a rigid body may experience

Newton's second law of motion modified for bodies asserts that the total force on the body equals the rate of change of linear momentum, that is

$$F = \frac{\mathrm{d}\mathbf{p}}{\mathrm{d}t} = \frac{\mathrm{d}}{\mathrm{d}t}\int_V \dot{\mathbf{r}}\rho \, \mathrm{d}V$$

$$= \frac{\mathrm{d}}{\mathrm{d}t}(M\dot{\bar{\mathbf{r}}}) = M\ddot{\bar{\mathbf{r}}} \qquad (19)$$

by equation (18). There results the important principle: the total force acting on a rigid body balances the product of total mass and the acceleration of the mass-centre. This statement reveals the added importance of particle dynamics since the mass-centre of a rigid body behaves as a particle.

Example 11   A rigid body moves in a uniform gravitational field. Show that the equation of motion of its mass-centre is

$$\ddot{\bar{\mathbf{r}}} = -g\mathbf{k},$$

where $-\mathbf{k}$ *is a unit vector in the direction of the force.*

In this case the body force $\mathbf{Q}$ is $-g\mathbf{k}$ where g, the acceleration due to gravity, is constant. The total force

$$\mathbf{F} = -\int g\mathbf{k}\, dm = -g\mathbf{k}\int dm = -Mg\mathbf{k}.$$

By the equation of motion

$$M\ddot{\mathbf{r}} = -Mg\mathbf{k},$$

or $\ddot{\mathbf{r}} = -g\mathbf{k}$.

We note from (19) that if the total force $\mathbf{F}$ vanishes the linear momentum of the body is conserved and its mass-centre moves in a straight line with constant speed.

The position of the mass-centre at any time does not tell us anything about the *orientation* of the body about its mass-centre. For example in figure 49 we can say nothing about the inclination of the uniform rod AB

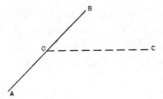

FIGURE 49

from the knowledge that its centre O moves along OC. Our second postulate for rigid bodies asserts that the moment of all the forces acting on the body about the origin of an inertial frame balances the rate of change of moment of momentum about the same point. The moment of momentum of a body subject to the forces indicated in figure 48 is defined as

$$\mathbf{h} = \int_V \mathbf{r} \times \dot{\mathbf{r}}\rho\, dV;$$

again this is a natural extension of the definition for a multi-particle sytem. The moment of the forces acting on the body

$$\mathbf{M} = \int_V \mathbf{r} \times \mathbf{Q}\rho\, dV + \sum_{i=1}^n \mathbf{r}_i \times \mathbf{F}_i - \int_S p\mathbf{r} \times \mathbf{n}\, dS,$$

where $\mathbf{r}_1$, $\mathbf{r}_2$,... are the position vectors of the points where the forces $\mathbf{F}_1$, $\mathbf{F}_2$,... act. Our second postulate says that

$$\mathbf{M} = \frac{d\mathbf{h}}{dt}. \tag{20}$$

Thus the *six* scalar equations governing the motion of a rigid body are contained in the two vector equations

$$\mathbf{F} = \frac{d\mathbf{p}}{dt}, \qquad \mathbf{M} = \frac{d\mathbf{h}}{dt}. \tag{21}$$

The two postulates for bodies replace Newton's three laws of motion for particles. They are particularly important since they can be generalized to non-rigid bodies, for example to fluids and elastic bodies.

We have emphasized that the general motion of a rigid body is beyond our task in this book and we shall not pursue equation (20) further. However, we shall note some results applicable to statics. Suppose the rigid body is at rest, that is, $\dot{\mathbf{r}} = 0$. The linear momentum and moment of momentum must vanish with the result that the equations of *static equilibrium* are, from (21),

$$\mathbf{F} = \mathbf{0}, \qquad \mathbf{M} = \mathbf{0},$$

that is, the total force and the total moment of the forces must each balance.

Suppose now that the body is translating but not rotating, which means that every point of the body must have the same velocity as that of the mass-centre, that is $\dot{\mathbf{r}} = \dot{\bar{\mathbf{r}}}$. The angular momentum

$$\mathbf{h} = \int_V \mathbf{r} \times \dot{\mathbf{r}} \rho \, dV = \int_V \mathbf{r} \times \dot{\bar{\mathbf{r}}} \rho \, dV = \int_V \mathbf{r} \rho \, dV \times \dot{\bar{\mathbf{r}}},$$

since $\dot{\bar{\mathbf{r}}}$ is independent of the volume integration. By the definition of mass-centre,

$$\mathbf{h} = M\bar{\mathbf{r}} \times \dot{\bar{\mathbf{r}}},$$

and consequently

$$\frac{d\mathbf{h}}{dt} = M\bar{\mathbf{r}} \times \ddot{\bar{\mathbf{r}}} = \bar{\mathbf{r}} \times \mathbf{F}$$

by (19). Now

$$\mathbf{M} = \frac{d\mathbf{h}}{dt} = \bar{\mathbf{r}} \times \mathbf{F} = \int_V \bar{\mathbf{r}} \times \mathbf{Q}\rho \, dV + \sum_{i=1}^{n} \bar{\mathbf{r}} \times \mathbf{F}_i - \int_S p\bar{\mathbf{r}} \times \mathbf{n} \, dS,$$

and by the definition of $\mathbf{M}$ (see equation prior to equation (20)),

$$\int_V (\mathbf{r} - \bar{\mathbf{r}}) \times \mathbf{Q}\rho \, dV + \sum_{i=1}^{n} (\mathbf{r}_i - \bar{\mathbf{r}}) \times \mathbf{F}_i - \int_S p(\mathbf{r} - \bar{\mathbf{r}}) \times \mathbf{n} \, dS = \mathbf{0}.$$

In other words, for a body simply translating, the moment of the external forces about the *mass-centre* must vanish. The moment about any *fixed* point, of course, will not generally be zero.

Example 12   A uniform bar of mass m and length 2a is supported in a horizontal position at a point distance $\frac{1}{2}a$ from one end at a point distance $\frac{1}{4}a$ from the other end of the bar. How is the weight distributed between the supports?

We are only interested in the vertical forces P and Q acting on the bar at the supports (see figure 50). The rod is in static equilibrium so that the vertical forces

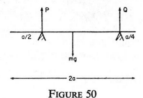

FIGURE 50

must balance:

$$P + Q = mg. \tag{22}$$

The moments of the forces about a fixed point, say the mid-point of the bar, must balance. Thus

$$\tfrac{1}{2}aP = \tfrac{3}{4}aQ, \tag{23}$$

since the weight mg acts through the mid-point. Solving (22) and (23), we obtain

$$P = \tfrac{3}{5}mg, \quad Q = \tfrac{2}{5}mg.$$

Example 13   A wagon of length 10 m, width 2 m and depth 3 m can move along a horizontal track on wheels whose axles are 2 m from the ends of the wagon. The wagon contains material of density 10^3 kg/m³. The maximum safe working load of the axles is that occurring when the wagon is full and stationary. If the wagon is drawn by a coupling which exerts a constant horizontal pull of 8×10^4 N on the floor of the wagon, find the maximum safe load assuming that it is evenly distributed.

A sketch of the wagon together with the two vertical reactions R and S on the axles is shown in figure 51.

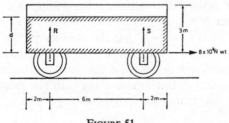

FIGURE 51

4

When full the wagon contains $10 \times 3 \times 2 \times 10^3 = 6 \times 10^4$ kg. By symmetry each axle can support a load not greater than 3×10^4 kg. Suppose the load reaches a height d m above the floor of the wagon when it moves: the mass-centre will be at height $\frac{1}{2}d$ above the centre of the floor. The load will now be $10 \times d \times 2 \times 10^3 = 2 \times 10^4 d$ kg. Since the wagon does not rotate and moves horizontally the total vertical force and the moment of the forces about the mass-centre must vanish:

$$R + S = 2 \times 10^4 \, dg$$
$$8 \times 10^4 \times \tfrac{1}{2}d + 3S = 3R$$

From the second of these equations we note that $R > S$ and therefore we need only determine R, the greater load. Eliminating S between these equations:

$$6 \times 10^4 \, dg + 4 \times 10^4 d - 3R = 3R$$

and, therefore,

$$d = \frac{3R}{(2 + 3g)} 10^4 \, \text{m}$$

The maximum value R can take is $3 \times 10^4 \, g$ N with the result that the maximum value of d is 2·8 m. Thus the maximum safe load is

$$5{\cdot}6 \times 10^4 \, \text{kg}$$

approximately.

3.10 Impulsive motion

A golf ball struck by a golf club achieves a velocity in a relatively short span of time. When the collision or impact occurs the ball is deformed and large internal stresses are created. These stresses tend to restore the ball to its original shape and it is the combined effect of these stresses which cause the ball to be projected from the face of the club. The precise behaviour of the ball will depend on the *elasticity* of the material of which the ball is composed. If the ball starts from rest, a typical graph of speed v against time t is shown in figure 52. The ball accelerates from zero speed to speed v_1 in a 'small' time interval t_1. The mathematical analysis of large scale deformation of bodies is a very complicated subject and it is theoretically much simpler to imagine that the velocity jumps suddenly at time $t = 0$ from zero to speed v_1. In this way we need not consider the details of the impact. The collision between the club and ball creates linear momentum mv_1 in the ball where m is the mass of the ball. The momentum so created is called the *impulse* which we shall denote by I. Thus

$$I = mv_1.$$

We can interpret I in a different sense if we return to the real situation. Suppose F is the resultant force which acts on the ball so that

$$F = m\frac{dv}{dt}.$$

Integrate with respect to time over the time interval t_1:

$$\int_{t=0}^{t=t_1} F \, dt = m \int_{t=0}^{t=t_1} \frac{dv}{dt} \, dt = m \int_{v=0}^{v=v_1} dv = mv_1.$$

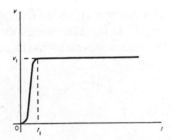

FIGURE 52   Typical velocity response of a body subjected to an impulse

We observe that the impulse is the time integral of the force; in a sense, it is the total effect of the elastic force on the ball. Note also that impulse is not a force and if mass is in kg and speed is in m/s, impulse will be measured in kg m/s.

In general, if a particle of mass m moving with velocity v_1 experiences an impulse I which produces a final velocity v_2 in the particle, then

$$I = m(v_2 - v_1). \tag{24}$$

That is: the impulse is the vector difference of the final and initial linear momenta. We note that in any direction in which the component of I vanishes, the linear momentum in that direction is conserved.

Since it is assumed that the impulse is created instantaneously, the integrals of other forces which are acting on the body do not enter into equation (24). It is often assumed, however, that impulses are transmitted along strings joining two bodies, see example 17 which follows, but again this really represents the integral of a very large force over a very short time. Such impulses are often referred to as impulsive tensions, although strictly they are not tensions which have the dimensions of force.

The form of the balance of momentum change and impulse follows naturally for a rigid body. Suppose a rigid body is subject to impulses

$I_1, I_2,..., I_n$ acting at the same instant of time (see figure 53). As explained in the previous section the linear momentum

$$p = \int_V \dot{r}\rho \, dV = \frac{d}{dt} \int_V r\rho \, dV = M\dot{r},$$

where M is the mass of the body. For rigid bodies the total impulse balances the change in linear momentum. Thus

$$\sum_{i=1}^n I_i = p_1 - p_2 = M(\dot{r}_1 - \dot{r}_2),$$

where suffixes 1 and 2 refer respectively to the state of the body before and after the impulses are applied. In other words, the mass-centre behaves as though it is a particle of mass M with all the impulses acting on it.

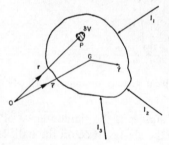

FIGURE 53

If we wish to examine the angular velocity created by the application of impulses we equate the moment of the impulses to the jump in angular momentum.

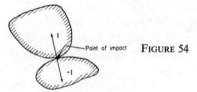

Point of impact   FIGURE 54

When two bodies collide, as in figure 54, each body will experience an impulsive reaction due to the impact of the other, I and $-I$ in the figure. If friction is negligible, we assume that the impulsive reactions act along the normals to the surfaces at the point of impact (if friction must be taken into account there will, in addition, be an impulsive tangential reaction on the bodies). For each of the bodies the balance of impulse and jump of linear momentum still hold, whilst for the system as a whole, since no external impulse acts, the impulsive reactions must be equal and opposite. For this reason also the linear momentum of the whole system must be conserved.

Returning to our illustration of the golf ball, we noted that the total propulsive force exerted by the internal stresses will depend very much on the material of which a golf ball is made. We must specify the elastic law empirically. The simplest law is *Newton's law of restitution*. This states that when two bodies collide their relative parting velocity in the direction of the common normal at the point of impact is − *e* times their relative approach velocity in this direction. We shall assume that for any two materials, the *coefficient of restitution e* is a positive constant. The reason for the minus sign prefixing *e* in the statement of the law is that the two relative velocities are taken in the same direction and that bodies usually rebound on impact.

Example 14   A steel ball is released from rest 1 m above a horizontal steel plate. On rebound it is found to reach a height of 81 cm. Find e for steel against steel.

Since the ball falls with constant acceleration g it hits the plate with speed $\sqrt{200g}$ cm/sec. Since the ball reaches a height of 81 cm, it must rebound with speed $\sqrt{(2g \times 81)}$ cm/sec upwards. By Newton's law

$$\sqrt{162g} = e\sqrt{200g}.$$

Therefore

$$e = \left(\frac{81}{100}\right)^{\frac{1}{2}} = 0.90.$$

There are no units for e since it is a ratio of two speeds.

This example provides a simple experimental method of determining e.

Example 15   Two spheres of masses m and M moving in the same straight line with velocities u_1 and v_1 collide. Find their subsequent speeds if the coefficient of restitution is e.

In any impact between spheres the impulsive reactions will act along the line joining the centres of the spheres. Assume that sphere m overtakes sphere M, that is, $u_1 > v_1$. Let u_2 and v_2 be the corresponding final velocities of the spheres in the same sense. For the system as a whole the linear momentum will be conserved, that is the initial momentum balances the final momentum:

$$mu_1 + Mv_1 = mu_2 + Mv_2. \tag{25}$$

Newton's law gives (taking care with the signs)

$$v_2 - u_2 = - e(v_1 - u_1). \qquad (26)$$

Solving equations (25) and (26), we find that

$$u_2 = \frac{1}{m + M}[Mv_1(1 + e) + u_1(m - eM)],$$

$$v_2 = \frac{1}{m + M}[mu_1(1 + e) + v_1(M - em)],$$

the final velocities of the two spheres. All velocities which appear may be positive or negative: if a velocity is negative it will be in the opposite sense to that drawn in figure 55.

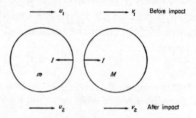

FIGURE 55   Velocity scheme for the direct impact of two spheres

If $e = 0$ for the two spheres, $u_2 = v_2$ and the two bodies adhere after impact: we say that they are *inelastic*. If $e = 1$, the relative velocity before impact equals in *magnitude* the relative velocity after impact. In this ideal case we describe the bodies as *perfectly elastic*. For real substances $0 < e < 1$. Steel against steel has a high value for e (Example 14) whereas dough, for instance, is almost inelastic.

Example 16   A sphere sliding on a smooth table (that is, frictionless) with speed u hits a smooth vertical wall at angle θ to the wall. If e is the coefficient of restitution between the sphere and wall, find the velocity of the sphere after impact.

Let the sphere rebound from the wall with speed v in a direction ϕ to the wall (figure 56). Since the wall is smooth the impulsive reaction on the sphere will be perpendicular to the wall. Thus the linear momentum of the sphere parallel to the wall will be conserved:

$$u \cos \theta = v \cos \phi. \qquad (27)$$

Newton's law gives

$$v \sin \phi = eu \sin \theta. \qquad (28)$$

From (27) and (28):

$$v = u(e^2 \sin^2 \theta + \cos^2 \theta)^{\frac{1}{2}} \quad \text{and} \quad \tan \phi = e \tan \theta.$$

The ball rebounds from the wall with speed $u(e^2 \sin^2 \theta + \cos^2 \theta)^{\frac{1}{2}}$ in a direction $\tan^{-1}(e \tan \theta)$ to the wall.

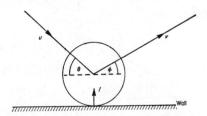

FIGURE 56   Oblique impact of a sphere with a vertical wall

Example 17   A tug of mass m is attached to a ship of mass M by a cable of negligible mass. Initially the cable is slack. The tug moves off and attains a speed u_1 before the cable becomes taut and the ship is jerked into motion. If $e = \frac{1}{2}$ for the cable, find, neglecting any impulsive resistance of the water, the speed imparted to the ship. If $m = 5 \times 10^5 \, kg, M = 1.5 \times 10^7 \, kg$ and $u_1 = 1 \, m/s$, find the mean tension in the cable supposing the jerk takes 2s.

Let u_2 and v_2 be respectively the final speeds of the tug and ship. The momentum of the whole system is conserved. Thus

$$mu_1 = mu_2 + Mv_2. \tag{29}$$

Newton's law gives

$$u_2 - v_2 = -eu_1 = -\tfrac{1}{2}u_1. \tag{30}$$

Solving (29) and (30) for v_2, we obtain

$$v_2 = \frac{3mu_1}{2(m + M)},$$

the final speed of the ship. Note that, after the jerk in the cable,

$$u_2 = v_2 - \tfrac{1}{2}u_1 < v_2,$$

which implies that the cable becomes slack again since the ship moves off more quickly than the tug.

The above analysis assumes that the jerk takes place instantaneously. In order to investigate the tension in the cable we must look at the integral of the equation of motion for the system. Let T be the tension in the cable. Whilst the cable is taut the equation of motion for the tug is

$$-T = m\frac{dv}{dt}.$$

Integrate over the time interval of 2 sec, so that

$$-\int_0^2 T \, \mathrm{d}t = m \int_{u_1}^{u_2} \mathrm{d}v = m(u_2 - u_1).$$

If the mean tension is $\overline{T}$ we can say approximately that

$$\int_0^2 T \, \mathrm{d}t = 2\overline{T},$$

so that

$$\overline{T} = -\tfrac{1}{2}m(u_2 - u_1) = \tfrac{1}{2}Mv_2 \quad [\text{by } (29)]$$

$$= \frac{3mMu_1}{4(m + M)}.$$

Thus

$$\overline{T} = \frac{3 \times 5 \times 10^5 \times 1{\cdot}5 \times 10^7 \times 1}{4 \times 155 \times 10^5}$$

$$= 3{\cdot}6 \times 10^5 \, \mathrm{N}$$

Example 18   Two particles A and B of the same mass are connected by a taut string and lie at rest on a horizontal table. Particle A is struck a blow of magnitude I in a direction inclined at 45° to BA. Find the initial velocities of the particles.

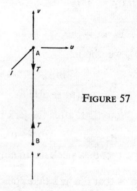

FIGURE 57

When A is struck, an impulsive tension T will be created in the string since this is taut (we assume the string is inextensible). Let A move off with velocity components u perpendicular to the string and v parallel to the string (figure 57). Since A and B are connected by a taut string, B must move off in the direction BA with the same speed v. B will have no velocity component perpendicular to

AB since the only impulse acting on B is the impulsive tension acting along the string. If m is the mass of each particle, we have for A

$$\frac{I}{\sqrt{2}} = mu, \qquad \frac{I}{\sqrt{2}} - T = mv,$$

and for B

$$T = mv.$$

Eliminating T, the velocity components are given by

$$u = I/m\sqrt{2}, \qquad v = I/2m\sqrt{2}.$$

Remember these are the *initial* velocities; subsequently the system moves as two connected particles.

Exercises

1. What force in poundals is required to give a car of mass 10^3 kg an acceleration of 2 m/s^2?

2. A particle of unit mass has position vector $\mathbf{r} = t\mathbf{i}$ in one inertial frame of reference. A second frame is translating with respect to the inertial frame such that its origin has a position vector $a\mathbf{i} + b\mathbf{j} + t^2\mathbf{k}$ where a and b are constants. Find the path the particle takes relative to the second frame and show that it will appear to be subject to a force $-2\mathbf{k}$.

3. Atwood's machine consists of two weights fastened to the end of light string which passes over a light free pulley. If the two weights have masses 7 kg and 9 kg, find their acceleration.

4. A proton moving in a horizontal path in vacuo at a speed of 3×10^6 m/s enters a uniform electric field which exerts a downward force of 6×10^{-15} N on it. The mass of the proton is $1 \cdot 66 \times 10^{-27}$ kg. If the field extends over a region $0 \cdot 5$ m long, through what angle is the particle deflected?

5. A particle is projected vertically upwards under gravity with a speed of 16 m/s. One second later another particle is fired upwards from the same point. Find the initial speed of this particle in order that the two particles will collide when the first particle has reached its highest point.

6. A balloon of total mass M descends with a downward acceleration f_1. Assuming no air resistance, find what mass of ballast should be thrown out in order that the balloon should rise with acceleration f_2.

7. A circular face of a solid circular cylinder of radius a and height a is attached to the circular face of a solid hemisphere of radius a and of the same density. Find the mass-centre of the composite body.

8. An object falls vertically past a window 2 m high in $\frac{1}{12}$ s. Find the height above the bottom of the window from which the object was dropped.

9. A stone is dropped from a balloon rising at 10 m/s and reaches the ground in 8s. How high was the balloon when the stone was dropped?

10. Find the mass of the sun given that the gravitational constant $\gamma = 6.67 \times 10^{-11}$ m^3/kgs^2 and that the earth's orbit is a circle of radius 1.5×10^8 km which it completes in 365 days.

11. A locomotive can keep a train of mass 3×10^6 kg moving up an incline of 1 (vertically) in a 100 (horizontally) at a constant speed. How long will it take to accelerate the locomotive to 45 km/h from rest on the level? If the drawbar weighs 150 kg, how much harder will the locomotive pull the drawbar than the drawbar pulls the train?

12. A barge whose deck is 4 m below the level of a dock is pulled in by means of a cable attached to a ring on the dock, the cable being hauled in by a windlass on the deck of the barge at the rate of 2 m/min. Find the tension in the cable when the windlass is 5 m horizontally from the dock given that the barge has a mass of 10^5 kg.

13. An aircraft flies along the upper arc of a circle of radius 8,000 m in order to simulate weightlessness in the cabin. Obtain the speed of the aircraft for this to be achieved at the highest point of the path.

14. A rectangular gate of mass M and width $2b$ is supported by two hinges symmetrically placed on the side of the gate and distance l apart. The upper hinge provides no vertical support. Find the magnitude of the support at both hinges.

15. A car has a wheelbase of 1·8 m and runs on wheels of radius 0·3 m. The car weighs 1,000 kg and its mass-centre is centrally placed with respect to the wheels at a height 0·45 m above the road. The car accelerates at 1m/s². Assuming that the propulsive force can be interpreted as a horizontal force acting on the rear axle, find the distribution of the weight between the axles.

16. A particle is projected with speed 20 m/sec in a direction inclined at 30° to the horizontal. Calculate the horizontal range of the particle and the maximum height it reaches.

17. A gun emplacement is on the edge of a cliff of height h. Prove that the greatest horizontal distance at which a shell from the emplacement can hit the ship is $2\sqrt{[k(k + h)]}$, and that the greatest horizontal distance at which a gun in the ship can hit the emplacement is $2\sqrt{[k(k - h)]}(k > h)$, if $\sqrt{(2gk)}$ is the firing speed of a shell in each case.

18. A particle is thrown from the highest point of a hemispherical mound of radius 100 m. Find the minimum throwing speed necessary for it to clear the mound.

19. A particle is fired at an inclination $\alpha + \beta$ to the horizontal with a speed u. Show that the particle will strike, at right angles, a plane through the point of projection inclined at angle β to the horizontal if $\cot \beta = 2 \tan \alpha$. If the particle strikes the plane with speed $\frac{1}{2}u$, show that the range is $u^2 \sqrt{21}/8g$.

20. It is required to hit a squash ball from a given point with a given speed v so as to strike a vertical wall above a horizontal line on the wall. It is found that when the ball is projected in the vertical plane perpendicular to the wall, the ball just hits the line if its *initial projected direction* is inclined at θ_1 or θ_2 $(\theta_1 > \theta_2)$ to the horizontal. Show that the ball can reach any point on the wall within a circle of radius

$$v^2 \sin (\theta_1 - \theta_2)/g \sin (\theta_1 + \theta_2).$$

21. The line joining the net and the point of projection of a netball makes an angle α with the horizontal. If the net is at height h above the point of projection, show that to score the initial speed of the ball must be not less than

$$[gh(1 + \operatorname{cosec} \alpha)]^{\frac{1}{2}}.$$

22. A shell bursting on the ground throws fragments in all directions with speeds up to 30 m/s. Find for what period of time a man standing 30 m from the explosion is in danger.

23. A baseball is hit from 1 m above the ground and attains a maximum height of 21 m and a horizontal range of 100 m. A fielder can catch the ball between the ground and 3 m. Over what horizontal distance would a fielder be capable of catching the ball?

24. Two parallel vertical walls have height h_0 and h_1 and the distance between these top edges is l (see figure 58). A particle is projected from the ground in a plane perpendicular to both walls. Show that the minimum speed of projection necessary for the particle to clear both walls is $[g(h_0 + h_1 + l)]^{\frac{1}{2}}$.

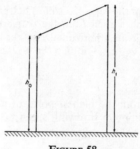

FIGURE 58

25. A boy of mass 40 kg moving at 16 km/h jumps on to a toboggan of mass 10 kg, sliding at 32 km/h in the same direction, as it passes him. What is the final speed of the toboggan?

26. A particle of mass m falls freely a distance h and then jerks into motion a mass M ($M > m$) connected to m by a light string which passes over a frictionless pulley. Find the time which elapses before M returns to its original position.

27. A ball is projected vertically upwards from the ground with a speed of 29 m/s. Simultaneously a similar ball is dropped from the highest point that the first ball would reach. If the coefficient of restitution between the balls is 0·6, calculate the time which elapses between the balls hitting the ground.

28. A set of n wagons, each of mass m, standing in a railway siding is set in motion by a locomotive of mass rm starting with speed V. Initially the couplings between the wagons are slack, as is the coupling between the first wagon and the locomotive, and each wagon moves a distance s before it jerks the succeeding

wagon into motion. The coefficient of restitution of the coupling is e. Find the time which ensues between the movement of the first and last wagons, neglecting the effect of friction and assuming that each coupling does not remain taut until the last wagon moves.

29. One smooth sphere hits another smooth sphere which is at rest. The two spheres are perfectly elastic. After the collision they move off at right angles to each other. Show that their masses are equal.

30. Four particles A, B, C, D, each of mass M, are connected by equal light strings AB, BC, DC, DA and lie at rest on a smooth horizontal table with the strings taut so that ABCD is a rhombus and $B\hat{A}D \doteq 2\alpha\,(\alpha < 45°)$. The particle A is given a velocity U in the direction CA. Find the initial velocities of B, C, D.

31. Two small spheres P and Q of equal mass lie touching each other in a smooth circular horizontal groove of radius a. Sphere P is projected away from Q with speed U. Assuming no resistance to motion in the groove, ascertain

    (i) the speeds of P and Q after the nth collision,
    (ii) the time that elapses before the nth collision
if the coefficient of restitution for each collision is e.

32. A ball of mass 110 gm is struck by a club, the contact lasting 1/100th of a second The ball is given a speed of 10 m/s. Assuming that the force increases from zero linearly with time for 1/200th of a second and decreases linearly to zero again, find the impulse of the blow and the maximum force on the ball.

33. A child throws a ball at a vertical wall 3 m in front of him. The ball hits the wall when at the highest point of its path, rebounds and bounces on to a table, height 1 m above the ground, at such a distance from the wall that the child can catch it when it is at the highest point of its first bounce. If the point at which he catches it is exactly the same point as the one from which he threw it at an angle of 45° to the horizontal, and the coefficient of restitution between ball and wall is $\frac{1}{2}$, find

    (i) the coefficient of restitution between the ball and the table,
    (ii) the height at which he throws (and catches) the ball,
    (iii) the height at which the ball hits the wall,
    (iv) the distance from the wall of the first bounce.

34. A man weighing 80 kg stands 1 m from the bow of a boat which is just touching the shore of a lake, the line of the boat being perpendicular to the shore. The boat weighs 40 kg. Assuming that the resistance to motion of the boat in the water is negligible, find:

   (i) the distance the man would be from the bank if he moved to the bow of the boat,
  (ii) whether it would be feasible for him to jump to the bank (a man could expect to jump about 2 m from a standing position on firm ground),
 (iii) what impulse he would impart horizontally to the boat if he did jump.

35. A projectile of mass m, carrying a small wire attached to the firing site, is fired with speed V. If we assume that the effect of the wire on the projectile is a force $\alpha^2 m r$ directed towards the origin (the firing site), show that the maximum range is attained when

$$\cos 2\beta = \alpha^2 V^2/(\alpha^2 V^2 + 2g^2),$$

where β is the angle of projection.

4

Differential equations and their applications in mechanics

4.1 General comments

Problems in particle and rigid body mechanics reduce generally to the solution of one or more differential equations. Newton's law of motion for a particle—force equals the product of mass and acceleration:

$$\mathbf{F} = m\ddot{\mathbf{r}}$$

—is a differential equation. This vector equation is equivalent to the three scalar equations

$$F_x = m\frac{d^2x}{dt^2}, \qquad F_y = m\frac{d^2y}{dt^2}, \qquad F_z = m\frac{d^2z}{dt^2}$$

where $\mathbf{F} = F_x\mathbf{i} + F_y\mathbf{j} + F_z\mathbf{k}$. Whenever possible our aim is to *solve* these three equations for x, y and z in terms of the time, given the behaviour of the force components.

Any equation involving derivatives is a differential equation. Thus

$$\frac{dx}{dt} = x + t, \qquad \frac{d^2x}{dt^2} = 2\frac{dx}{dt} + x^2,$$

$$\frac{d^3x}{dt^3} = \frac{dx}{dt}, \qquad e^t\frac{dx}{dt} = \sin x,$$

are all examples of differential equations. In these equations x *depends* on the single variable t; in this case the equations are called ordinary differential equations to distinguish them from partial differential equations in which partial derivatives appear, indicating that the variable depends on two or more further variables. A significant feature of rigid-body dynamics is that the principles governing it lead usually to ordinary differential equations. For this reason we shall deal exclusively with them.

The *order* of a differential equation is the order of the derivative of highest order in the equation. Thus, in

$$\frac{dx}{dt} = t \quad \text{and} \quad \frac{d^3x}{dt^3} = x + \sin t,$$

the first equation is of the first order and the second equation is of the third order.

Example 1   *A particle of mass m moving with velocity* **v** *is subject to a force m***r** **× v**. *Write down the Cartesian components of the equation of motion.*

The equation of motion is

$$m\mathbf{r} \times \mathbf{v} = m\ddot{\mathbf{r}}.$$

Since **v** = **ṙ**, this becomes

$$\mathbf{r} \times \dot{\mathbf{r}} = \ddot{\mathbf{r}}.$$

Evaluating the vector product, we obtain

$$y\frac{dz}{dt} - z\frac{dy}{dt} = \frac{d^2x}{dt^2},$$

$$z\frac{dx}{dt} - x\frac{dz}{dt} = \frac{d^2y}{dt^2},$$

$$x\frac{dy}{dt} - y\frac{dx}{dt} = \frac{d^2z}{dt^2}.$$

There result three ordinary differential equations each of the second order. Notice however that x, y and z appear in each equation so that we must solve the equations *simultaneously* for x, y and z in terms of t.

Any relation between the variables which does not contain derivatives and satisfies a differential equation is called a *solution* of the differential equation. For example, it is easy to verify that

$$x = C\,e^{5t} \tag{1}$$

satisfies the first-order differential equation

$$\frac{dx}{dt} = 5x \tag{2}$$

for all values of the constant *C*. Since the *arbitrary constant C* appears in (1), we describe (1) as a *general solution* of (2). In mechanics we are usually more interested in particular solutions of differential equations, that is solutions which satisfy one or more *initial* or *end* conditions. Thus the solution of (2) which is such that $x = 4$ when $t = 0$ is obviously the particular solution

$$x = 4 e^{5t},$$

in other words we must put $C = 4$. The number of conditions required will be the same as the number of available constants in the general solution which is usually equal to the order of the equation.

We shall first examine a number of techniques which apply to special classes of differential equations. The reader should be warned that only very restricted classes of equations have solutions which can be expressed in terms of elementary solutions.

We have already encountered one simple second-order equation, namely that governing the vertical motion of a particle under uniform gravity. If *z* is measured upwards and *g* is the acceleration due to gravity

$$\ddot{z} = - g.$$

By direct verification the displacement of the particle is given by

$$z = A + Bt - \tfrac{1}{2}gt^2,$$

where *A* and *B* are constants which can be determined from the initial displacement and velocity of the particle.

4.2 First-order equations: variables separable

An equation of the form

$$\frac{\mathrm{d}x}{\mathrm{d}t} = f(x, t) \tag{3}$$

is a first-order differential equation. If $f(x, t)$ can be written as the quotient of two expressions each of which contains only one of the variables (the variables separate) we can frequently solve (3) explicitly. Thus if

$$f(x, t) = g(t)/h(x),$$

(3) becomes

$$\frac{\mathrm{d}x}{\mathrm{d}t} = \frac{g(t)}{h(x)}.$$

Expressing the equation formally as

$$h(x)\, \mathrm{d}x = g(t)\, \mathrm{d}t,$$

we can integrate both sides to give the general solution

$$\int h(x)\, dx = \int g(t)\, dt + C,$$

where the integrals are indefinite integrals and C is a constant. It is assumed that $h(x)$ and $g(t)$ are sufficiently 'well-behaved'.

Example 2   Solve

$$x\frac{dx}{dt} = e^{-t}.$$

By the method outlined above

$$\int x\, dx = \int e^{-t}\, dt + C,$$

or

$$\tfrac{1}{2}x^2 = -e^{-t} + C,$$

which is the general solution.

Neither the differential equation nor the solution may be defined for all values of x and t. For example

$$\frac{dx}{dt} = (1 - x)^{\frac{1}{2}},$$

is only defined in real terms for $x \leqslant 1$. Equally the solution

$$-2(1 - x)^{\frac{1}{2}} = t + C$$

exists only for $x \leqslant 1$.

Example 3   Radium decays at a rate proportional to the mass of radium present. The half-life of radium is about 17 centuries (this is the time taken for radium to have half its mass transformed). Determine how much of 100 gm of radium will remain after 10 centuries.

Let m be the mass of radium present at time t. The differential equation governing the decay is

$$\frac{dm}{dt} = -km,$$

where k is a constant, the minus sign being present since the mass decays. The solution is given by

$$\int \frac{dm}{m} = -k \int dt + C,$$

or

$$\ln m = -kt + C,$$

the integration presenting no difficulty since $m > 0$. If we take exponentials of both sides,

$$m = m_0 e^{-kt}, \qquad m_0 = e^C,$$

where m_0 is the mass present at time $t = 0$. The mass falls to $\frac{1}{2}m_0$ in a time of 17 centuries so that

$$\tfrac{1}{2} = e^{-17k},$$

or

$$k = \frac{1}{17} \ln 2.$$

Using tables of natural logarithms,

$$k = 0{\cdot}041 \ (\text{centuries})^{-1}.$$

After 10 centuries, the mass remaining of 100 gm will be $100 e^{-10 \times 0{\cdot}041} = 66$ gm approximately. This is an example of *exponential* decay with time.

Example 4 *A particle of mass m is subject to a force kx. At $x = 0$ its velocity is v_0. Find its velocity when $x = 2$.*

The equation of motion is

$$kx = m\frac{d^2x}{dt^2},$$

which is a second-order equation. However its velocity $v = dx/dt$, so that the equation can be written

$$kx = m\frac{dv}{dt}.$$

We now consider velocity as dependent on displacement x rather than time t:

$$kx = m\frac{dx}{dt}\frac{dv}{dx} = mv\frac{dv}{dx},$$

which is a first-order equation of the variables separable type. The solution is

$$\tfrac{1}{2}kx^2 = \tfrac{1}{2}mv^2 + C.$$

Since $v = v_0$ at $x = 0$, $C = -\tfrac{1}{2}mv_0^2$ so that

$$\tfrac{1}{2}kx^2 = \tfrac{1}{2}m(v^2 - v^2_0).$$

At $x = 2$,

$$\tfrac{1}{2}mv^2 = \tfrac{1}{2}mv^2_0 + 2k,$$

or

$$v^2 = v^2_0 + \frac{4k}{m}.$$

This is a useful method of dealing with motion in which the force is dependent on displacement only.

Example 5   A body of mass m falls from rest in a uniform gravitational field through the atmosphere which exerts on the body a drag mkv^2, where v is the velocity of the body and k is a positive constant. Find the variation of velocity with time for the body.

The equation of motion is

$$- m\frac{dv}{dt} = - mkv^2 + mg,$$

where v is the upward velocity. This is an equation in which the variables separate so that the solution is

$$\int \frac{dv}{g - kv^2} = - \int dt + C,$$

or

$$\frac{1}{2(gk)^{\frac{1}{2}}} \ln \left[\frac{(g/k)^{\frac{1}{2}} + v}{(g/k)^{\frac{1}{2}} - v} \right] = - t + C.$$

Rearranging this equation, we obtain

$$v = \left(\frac{g}{k}\right)^{\frac{1}{2}} \frac{A\, e^{-2\sqrt{(gk)t}} - 1}{A\, e^{-2\sqrt{(gk)t}} + 1},$$

where A is now the unknown constant. At time $t = 0$, $v = 0$ so that $A = 1$. The particular solution required is

$$v = \left(\frac{g}{k}\right)^{\frac{1}{2}} \frac{e^{-2\sqrt{(gk)t}} - 1}{e^{-2\sqrt{(gk)t}} + 1}.$$

As $t \to \infty$, the velocity approaches a *limiting* value $- (g/k)^{\frac{1}{2}}$ (negative because velocity is measured upwards). In fact this velocity, called the limiting or terminal velocity, is the velocity at which the air resistance balances gravity, as can be seen by putting the acceleration to zero in the equation of motion.

Example 6   *Determine the lowest speed with which a rocket must be fired from the earth's surface in order that it should escape the earth's gravitational field. Neglect air resistance and the earth's spin. Take* $\gamma = 6\cdot7 \times 10^{-11} \, m^3/kg \, s^2$, *mass of earth,* $M = 6\cdot0 \times 10^{24} \, kg$ *and radius of earth* $a = 6,400 \, km$.

When at a distance r from the centre of the earth, the rocket is subject to a force per unit mass of $\gamma M/r^2$ towards the centre of the earth. The equation of motion is therefore

$$- \frac{\gamma M}{r^2} = \ddot{r}.$$

If V is the projection speed, we see that initially the velocity $v = V$ at $r = a$. The equation of motion can be rewritten as

$$- \frac{\gamma M}{r^2} = \frac{dv}{dt} = \frac{dr}{dt}\frac{dv}{dr} = v\frac{dv}{dr},$$

an equation of the variables separable type. The solution is

$$- \gamma M \int \frac{dr}{r^2} = \int v \, dv + C;$$

that is,

$$\frac{\gamma M}{r} = \tfrac{1}{2}v^2 + C.$$

From the initial condition we see that $C = (\gamma M/a) - \tfrac{1}{2}V^2$, resulting in the required particular solution

$$\gamma M\left(\frac{1}{r} - \frac{1}{a}\right) = \tfrac{1}{2}(v^2 - V^2).$$

The rocket just escapes from the earth's gravitational field if $v \to 0$ as $r \to \infty$: the rocket then just reaches 'infinity' with zero velocity. For this to be the case, we must have

$$\frac{\gamma M}{a} = \tfrac{1}{2}V^2,$$

or

$$V = \left(\frac{2\gamma M}{a}\right)^{\frac{1}{2}} = \left(\frac{2 \times 6\cdot7 \times 10^{-11} \times 6\cdot0 \times 10^{24}}{6\cdot4 \times 10^{6}}\right)^{\frac{1}{2}} \text{m/s}$$

$$= 1\cdot1 \times 10^{4} \text{ m/s}$$

$$= 40{,}000 \text{ km/h},$$

approximately. This is called the *escape velocity* for the earth.

4.3 First-order equations: homogeneous

The first-order equation

$$\frac{dx}{dt} = f(x, t)$$

can be reduced to an equation of the variables separable type if $f(x, t)$ is dependent only on the ratio x/t. In the equation

$$\frac{dx}{dt} = g\left(\frac{x}{t}\right), \tag{4}$$

we make the substitution $x = vt$. Now

$$\frac{dx}{dt} = t\frac{dv}{dt} + v,$$

so that equation (4) becomes the separable equation

$$t\frac{dv}{dt} = g(v) - v$$

for the new variable v. When v has been found in terms of t the substitution can be reversed to find x.

Example 7   Solve

$$2t^2\frac{dx}{dt} = x^2 + t^2$$

for $t \geqslant 1$ given that $x = 1$ at $t = 1$.

This is a homogeneous first-order equation. Put $x = vt$. We have

$$2t^2\left(t\frac{dv}{dt} + v\right) = v^2 t^2 + t^2,$$

or

$$2\left(t\frac{dv}{dt} + v\right) = v^2 + 1.$$

By separating the variables, the solution is given by

$$2\int \frac{dv}{(v-1)^2} = \int \frac{dt}{t} + C, \tag{5}$$

so that

$$-\frac{2}{v-1} = \ln|t| + C.$$

Putting $v = x/t$, the general solution becomes

$$-2t = (x - t)(\ln|t| + C).$$

Putting $x = 1$ when $t = 1$ we see that, according to this equation, no solution is possible for these initial conditions. The reason for this apparent breakdown in the method can be seen if we retrace our steps to equation (5). The integral on the left-hand side of (5) is meaningless (we say that it does not converge) in any interval containing $v = 1$ because of the singularity there in the integrand $1/(v - 1)^2$. We note also that $v = 1$ initially. However there is, in fact, a solution satisfying the initial conditions since if $v = 1$, it follows that $x = t$. It is a simple matter to verify that $x = t$ satisfies the original equation and is such that $x = 1$ when $t = 1$. Thus $x = t$ is the required solution.

This example is significant since it reveals that differential equations may have isolated particular solutions which are not displayed by the formal evaluation of the indefinite integrals.

4.4 First-order equations: integrating factor method

The integrating factor method is applicable to first-order equations of the type

$$\frac{dx}{dt} + p(t)x = q(t), \tag{6}$$

where $p(t)$ and $q(t)$ are sufficiently well-behaved functions of t. We attempt to write the left-hand side of (6) as the derivative of a product:

$$\frac{d}{dt}[r(t)x] = r(t)\frac{dx}{dt} + xr'(t). \tag{7}$$

Multiply both sides of (6) by $r(t)$:

$$r(t)\frac{dx}{dt} + r(t)p(t)x = r(t)q(t). \tag{8}$$

If we put

$$r(t)p(t) = r'(t) \qquad (9)$$

and use the identity (7), equation (8) may be expressed as

$$\frac{d}{dt}[r(t)x] = r(t)q(t),$$

an equation essentially of separable type. On integration

$$r(t)x = \int r(t)q(t)\, dt + C,$$

which will be the solution. The unknown $r(t)$ is given by (9):

$$\frac{r'(t)}{r(t)} = p(t),$$

which can be integrated to give

$$\ln|r(t)| = \int p(t)\, dt + D,$$

where D is a constant. If we take the exponential of both sides

$$r(t) = e^D\, e^{\int p(t)\, dt}.$$

We can drop the modulus sign since the exponential on the right-hand side must be positive. The constant e^D can also be ignored since each term in the differential equation is multiplied by $r(t)$.

Example 8   Solve

$$\frac{dx}{dt} + 2x = t.$$

In this case $p(t) = 2$ and $q(t) = t$, and the integrating factor

$$r(t) = e^{\int 2\, dt} = e^{2t}.$$

The differential equation can be rewritten in the form

$$\frac{d}{dt}(e^{2t}x) = t\, e^{2t}.$$

Integrating,

$$x\, e^{2t} = \int t\, e^{2t}\, dt + C$$

$$= \tfrac{1}{2}t\, e^{2t} - \tfrac{1}{4}e^{2t} + C,$$

or

$$x = \tfrac{1}{2}t - \tfrac{1}{4} + C\, e^{-2t}.$$

Example 9   *A train of total mass m is moved from rest by the engine which exerts a time-dependent force $mk(1 - e^{-t})$ on the train. The resistance to motion is mcv where v is the speed of the train and c is a constant. Find the subsequent speed of the train.*

The equation of motion is given by

$$m\frac{dv}{dt} = mk(1 - e^{-t}) - mcv,$$

or

$$\frac{dv}{dt} + cv = k(1 - e^{-t}).$$

The integrating factor is obviously e^{ct}. The equation can now be written in the separable form

$$\frac{d}{dt}(v\,e^{ct}) = k[e^{ct} - e^{(c-1)t}].$$

Integrating,

$$v\,e^{ct} = k \int [e^{ct} - e^{(c-1)t}]\,dt + C.$$

$$= \frac{k}{c}e^{ct} - \frac{k}{c-1}e^{(c-1)t} + C$$

When $t = 0$, $v = 0$, so that

$$C = -\frac{k}{c} + \frac{k}{c-1} = \frac{k}{c(c-1)}.$$

By multiplying through by e^{-ct}, the speed of the train is given by

$$v = \frac{k}{c} - \frac{k}{(c-1)}e^{-t} + \frac{k}{c(c-1)}e^{-ct}.$$

The limiting speed of the train, obtained by letting $t \to \infty$, is k/c, a result which can be deduced directly from the original differential equation.

4.5 Linear differential equations of the second order

The differential equation

$$\frac{d^2x}{dt^2} + a_1\frac{dx}{dt} + a_0x = f(t) \tag{10}$$

is called a linear differential equation of the second order. In this equation, a_1 and a_0 may depend on t but we shall be solely concerned here with those equations in which a_1 and a_0 are constants. The properties of equation (10) are closely related to those of the *homogeneous* second-order equation

$$\frac{d^2x}{dt^2} + a_1\frac{dx}{dt} + a_0x = 0, \tag{11}$$

that is equation (10) with 0 replacing $f(t)$ on the right-hand side. Suppose x_1 and x_2 are two solutions of (11). It is a simple matter to verify by direct substitution that

$$x = C_1 x_1 + C_2 x_2 \tag{12}$$

is also a solution of (11) for any two constants C_1 and C_2. This explains the significance of *linear* in describing these equations: a further solution can be obtained by *adding* together two solutions. However x_1 could be equal to or proportional to x_2 in which case x would be essentially x_1 apart from a constant. We would say that x_1 depends on x_2. We wish to find the most general solution of (11) and this will be so if x_1 and x_2 are *independent* in (12) [this is covered by a theorem, which we shall not prove here, which states that the general solution of (11) is (12) if x_1 and x_2 are independent]. Two variables x_1 and x_2 are said to be *linearly independent* if for a range of values of t,

$$\alpha_1 x_1 + \alpha_2 x_2 = 0$$

implies $\alpha_1 = \alpha_2 = 0$. For example $x_1 = e^{-t}$ and $x_2 = 2 e^{-t}$ would not be independent since we could choose $\alpha_1 = -2\alpha_2$ for any number α_2.

Example 10   Verify that $x_1 = e^t$ and $x_2 = e^{-t}$ are two solutions of

$$\frac{d^2 x}{dt^2} - x = 0.$$

In this case $a_1 = 0$ and $a_0 = -1$. By differentiating x_1 and x_2 twice with respect to t

$$\frac{d^2 x_1}{dt^2} = e^t = x_1, \qquad \frac{d^2 x_2}{dt^2} = e^{-t} = x_2,$$

thus verifying that they are solutions. It is not difficult to see that they are independent, with the result that the general solution of the equation is

$$x = A e^t + B e^{-t}$$

for any two constants A and B.

The general solution in the previous example could have been derived in the following way. Rewrite

$$\frac{d^2 x}{dt^2} - x = 0$$

as

$$\left(\frac{d^2x}{dt^2} - \frac{dx}{dt}\right) + \left(\frac{dx}{dt} - x\right) = 0.$$

Making the substitution,

$$z = \frac{dx}{dt} - x, \tag{13}$$

which then becomes

$$\frac{dz}{dt} + z = 0.$$

This is an equation of the variables separable type with solution

$$z = C_1 e^{-t}.$$

Substituting back for z in equation (13), we obtain the second first-order equation

$$\frac{dx}{dt} - x = z = C_1 e^{-t},$$

to which the method of the integrating factor can be applied. The integrating factor is e^{-t}, so that

$$\frac{d}{dt}(x e^{-t}) = C_1 e^{-2t}.$$

On integration

$$x e^{-t} = -\tfrac{1}{2}C_1 e^{-2t} + C_2.$$

If we insert new arbitrary constants A and B intead of C_1 and C_2, the general solution becomes

$$x = A e^{t} + B e^{-t}.$$

In general it would be difficult to spot how to rewrite a linear second-order differential equation in terms of two first-order differential equations, but we can be helped in this by a method known as the *operator* method.

Formally we rewrite the differential equation of the previous section as

$$\left(\frac{d^2}{dt^2} - 1\right)x = 0 \tag{14}$$

and treat d/dt as an algebraic quantity. We can then 'factorize' equation (14) and write it as

$$\left(\frac{d}{dt} + 1\right)\left[\left(\frac{d}{dt} - 1\right)x\right] = 0.$$

The operation, of course, must be performed in the order indicated. We again put

$$z = \left(\frac{d}{dt} - 1\right)x = \frac{dx}{dt} - x,$$

as in equation (13), and proceed as before.

Clearly the method can be extended to any second-order homogeneous equation. The operator

$$\frac{d^2}{dt^2} + a_1\frac{d}{dt} + a_0$$

can always be factorized as follows:

$$\frac{d^2}{dt^2} + a_1\frac{d}{dt} + a_0 = \left(\frac{d}{dt} - m_1\right)\left(\frac{d}{dt} - m_2\right),$$

where m_1 and m_2 are the roots of the quadratic equation

$$m^2 + a_1m + a_0 = 0. \tag{15}$$

We then put $z = (d/dt - m_2)x$, which results in the equation

$$\frac{dz}{dt} - m_1z = 0,$$

with solution

$$z = C_1 e^{m_1 t}.$$

Substituting back, we obtain

$$\frac{dx}{dt} - m_2x = C_1 e^{m_1 t},$$

which has the integrating factor $e^{-m_2 t}$ and solution

$$x e^{-m_2 t} = \frac{C_1}{m_1 - m_2} e^{(m_1 - m_2)t} + C_2,$$

or

$$x = A e^{m_1 t} + B e^{m_2 t}, \tag{16}$$

provided $m_1 \neq m_2$. If $m_1 = m_2$ the method still works but the result is different.

We have thus found the general solution of all equations of this type: it is always given by (16) where m_1 and m_2 are the roots of equation (15) which is called the *auxiliary equation*.

Example 11   Solve

$$\frac{d^2x}{dt^2} - \frac{dx}{dt} - 2x = 0$$

with initial conditions $x = 0$, $dx/dt = 1$ at $t = 0$.

The auxiliary equation is

$$m^2 - m - 2 = 0 \quad \text{or} \quad (m-2)(m+1) = 0.$$

We can take $m_1 = 2$, $m_2 = -1$. The general solution is therefore

$$x = A\,e^{2t} + B\,e^{-t}. \tag{17}$$

In order to find the constants A and B we need

$$\frac{dx}{dt} = 2A\,e^{2t} - B\,e^{-t}. \tag{18}$$

Inserting the initial conditions into (17) and (18), we obtain

$$A + B = 0,$$
$$2A - B = 1,$$

whence $A = \frac{1}{3}$ and $B = -\frac{1}{3}$. The required solution is therefore

$$x = \tfrac{1}{3}\,e^{2t} - \tfrac{1}{3}\,e^{-t}.$$

Note that a second-order linear equation requires *two* initial conditions.

Example 12   Solve

$$\frac{d^2x}{dt^2} - 2\frac{dx}{dt} + 2 = 0$$

with the initial conditions $x = 0$ and $dx/dt = 2$ at $t = 0$.

The auxiliary equation is

$$m^2 - 2m + 2 = 0,$$

with solutions

$$m_1, m_2 = \tfrac{1}{2}[2 \pm \sqrt{(4-8)}] = 1 \pm \sqrt{(-1)} = 1 \pm i.$$

The roots are now *complex* but the method continues as before. The general solution is

$$x = A\,e^{(1+i)t} + B\,e^{(1-i)t}.$$

From the initial conditions, A and B must satisfy

$$0 = A + B, \qquad 2 = A(1 + i) + B(1 - i).$$

The elimination of B leads to

$$2 = A(1 + i) - A(1 - i),$$

whence $A = 1/i = -i$ and $B = i$. The solution is therefore

$$x = -i\, e^{(1+i)t} + i\, e^{(1-i)t} = -i\, e^{t}(e^{it} - e^{-it}),$$

which is expressed in complex terms. The complex number i can be eliminated by using the following results from complex numbers:

$$e^{it} = \cos t + i \sin t, \qquad e^{-it} = \cos t - i \sin t,$$

or

$$\cos t = \tfrac{1}{2}(e^{it} + e^{-it}), \qquad \sin t = \frac{1}{2i}(e^{it} - e^{-it}).$$

By the last result, the real form of the solution is

$$x = 2\, e^{t} \sin t.$$

For the non-homogeneous second-order equation (10),

$$\frac{d^2 x}{dt^2} + a_1 \frac{dx}{dt} + a_0 x = f(t),$$

the method of approach is now clear. First we factorize the operator:

$$\frac{d^2}{dt^2} + a_1 \frac{d}{dt} + a_0 = \left(\frac{d}{dt} - m_1\right)\left(\frac{d}{dt} - m_2\right),$$

where m_1 and m_2 are the roots of the quadratic equation

$$m^2 + a_1 m + a_0 = 0.$$

We then reduce the equation to one of first-order by the substitution $z = (d/dt - m_2)x$, resulting in

$$\frac{dz}{dt} - m_1 z = f(t).$$

Using the integrating factor method, this equation becomes

$$\frac{d}{dt}(e^{-m_1 t} z) = f(t)\, e^{-m_1 t},$$

with the general solution

$$z = C_1 e^{m_1 t} + e^{m_1 t} \int e^{-m_1 t} f(t)\, dt$$

$$= C_1 e^{m_1 t} + g(t),$$

say, where

$$g(t) = e^{m_1 t} \int e^{-m_1 t} f(t) \, dt.$$

We now obtain a further first-order equation

$$\frac{dx}{dt} - m_2 x = C_1 e^{m_1 t} + g(t),$$

with solution

$$x = C_2 e^{m_2 t} + C_1 e^{m_2 t} \int e^{(m_1 - m_2)t} \, dt + e^{m_2 t} \int e^{-m_2 t} g(t) \, dt.$$

If $m_1 \neq m_2$, the solution can be written

$$x = (A e^{m_1 t} + B e^{m_2 t}) + h(t),$$

and, if $m_1 = m_2$, it can be written

$$x = (A + Bt) e^{m_1 t} + h(t).$$

Note that the first term in each case (called the *complementary function*) is the general solution of the corresponding homogeneous equation, whilst the second term is a *particular solution or integral* of the non-homogeneous equation.

The complementary function can easily be written down for any non-homogeneous second-order differential equation and it is this term which contains the two arbitrary constants.

A particular integral is any function which satisfies the original differential equation. Once we have found such a function, by guessing or otherwise, we may write down the general solution even though many other different particular integrals can still be found. We illustrate this by solving

$$\frac{d^2 x}{dt^2} - x = 2.$$

In Example 10, *et seq.* we found that the complementary function was

$$x = A e^t + B e^{-t}.$$

We also see by inspection that $x = -2$ satisfies the differential equation and is therefore a particular integral. The general solution would thus be

$$x = A e^t + B e^{-t} - 2,$$

since it both satisfies the differential equation and contains two arbitrary constants. Other particular integrals could be $(4 e^{-t} - 2)$ or $(15 e^t - 2)$ or any other multiple of $e^{\pm t}$ the reader might care to add to -2. Such particular integrals add nothing new to the general solution above since the additional terms become absorbed by the arbitrary constants A and B.

Such informed guesses are perfectly acceptable methods for finding the particular integral and the reader, after practice, can develop rules such as 'if $f(t)$ has the form e^{at}, try for a particular integral a function of the form $\alpha\, e^{at}$,' α being determined by substitution. There are difficulties in some cases however as is illustrated by the discussion following Example 15.

There also exist a number of operator techniques for obtaining a particular integral when the function $f(t)$ takes special forms. These methods are given in most elementary textbooks on ordinary differential equations. Whilst all these methods often shorten the analysis we shall exclude them here and obtain solutions using the more general approach outlined above.

Example 13   Solve

$$\frac{d^2x}{dt^2} - 2\frac{dx}{dt} + x = t.$$

The auxiliary equation is

$$m^2 - 2m + 1 = 0,$$

with the repeated root $m = 1$. In operator form the equation becomes

$$\left(\frac{d}{dt} - 1\right)\left(\frac{d}{dt} - 1\right)x = t.$$

Put $z = (dx/dt) - x$. The equation

$$\frac{dz}{dt} - z = t$$

has solution

$$z\, e^{-t} = C_1 + \int t\, e^{-t}\, dt = C_1 - t\, e^{-t} + \int e^{-t}\, dt$$

$$= C_1 - t\, e^{-t} - e^{-t},$$

or

$$z = C_1\, e^{t} - t - 1.$$

Writing z in terms of x again, we see that

$$\frac{dx}{dt} - x = C_1\, e^{t} - t - 1.$$

The solution of this equation is given by

$$x\,e^{-t} = C_2 + C_1 \int dt - \int (t+1)\,e^{-t}\,dt$$

$$= C_2 + C_1 t + (t+1)\,e^{-t} + e^{-t},$$

so that the general solution of the original equation is

$$x = (C_2 + C_1 t)\,e^t + (t+2).$$

Example 14 *Solve*

$$\frac{d^2 x}{dt^2} + \omega^2 x = 0.$$

The auxiliary equation is

$$m^2 + \omega^2 = 0,$$

giving $m_1 = \omega i$ and $m_2 = -\omega i$. The solution is therefore

$$x = C_1\,e^{\omega i t} + C_2\,e^{-\omega i t}.$$

By expressing the exponentials in terms of cos and sin,

$$x = C_1(\cos \omega t + i \sin \omega t) + C_2(\cos \omega t - i \sin \omega t)$$

$$= (C_1 + C_2) \cos \omega t + i(C_1 - C_2) \sin \omega t$$

$$= A \cos \omega t + B \sin \omega t,$$

in its real form. It can be written differently if we put

$$A = C \sin \varepsilon, \qquad B = C \cos \varepsilon,$$

where $C = \sqrt{(A^2 + B^2)}$ and $\tan \varepsilon = A/B$. Thus

$$x = C(\sin \varepsilon \cos \omega t + \cos \varepsilon \sin \omega t)$$

$$= C \sin (\omega t + \varepsilon), \tag{19}$$

using an elementary trigonometric identity.

The motion represented by (19) is called simple harmonic motion. More will be said about oscillations in general in chapter 7, together with further applications of second-order linear differential equations.

5

4.6 Higher order linear differential equations

The methods of the previous section can be readily extended to higher order linear differential equations with constant coefficients. The operator in the nth order equation

$$\frac{d^n x}{dt^n} + a_{n-1}\frac{dx^{n-1}}{dt^{n-1}} + \dots + a_1\frac{dx}{dt} + a_0 x = f(t)$$

is factorized so that the equation can be written

$$\left(\frac{d}{dt} - m_1\right)\left(\frac{d}{dt} - m_2\right)\dots\left(\frac{d}{dt} - m_n\right)x = f(t),$$

where $m_1, m_2, \dots, m_n$ are the roots of the auxiliary equation

$$m^n + a_{n-1}m^{n-1} + \dots + a_0 = 0.$$

The equation is reduced to a first-order equation by the substitution

$$z = \left(\frac{d}{dt} - m_2\right)\dots\left(\frac{d}{dt} - m_n\right)x.$$

This equation is solved by the integrating factor method, and the whole process is continued by making repeated substitutions. If the equation is homogeneous ($f = 0$) and $m_1, m_2, \dots, m_n$ are distinct, the equation has the general solution

$$x = A_1 e^{m_1 t} + A_2 e^{m_2 t} + \dots + A_n e^{m_n t},$$

where $A_1, A_2, \dots, A_n$ are constants.

We can most easily explain the method by considering an example.

Example 15   Solve

$$\frac{d^4 x}{dt^4} - x = e^{-t}.$$

The auxiliary equation is

$$m^4 - 1 = 0,$$

with solutions $m_1 = 1$, $m_2 = -1$, $m_3 = i$, $m_4 = -i$. Write the equations as

$$\left(\frac{d}{dt} - 1\right)\left(\frac{d}{dt} + 1\right)\left(\frac{d}{dt} - i\right)\left(\frac{d}{dt} + i\right)x = e^{-t}.$$

Put $z_1 = [(d/dt) + 1][(d^2/dt^2) + 1]x$, so that z_1 satisfies

$$\left(\frac{d}{dt} - 1\right)z_1 = e^{-t}.$$

The solution of this first-order equation is

$$z_1 = -\tfrac{1}{2}e^{-t} + C_1 e^t.$$

Put $z_2 = [(d^2/dt^2) + 1]x$, so that z_2 satisfies

$$\left(\frac{d}{dt} + 1\right)z_2 = -\tfrac{1}{2}e^{-t} + C_1 e^t,$$

with solution

$$z_2 = -\tfrac{1}{2}t\,e^{-t} + \tfrac{1}{2}C_1 e^t + C_2 e^{-t}.$$

Put $z_3 = [(d/dt) + i]x$, so that

$$\left(\frac{d}{dt} - i\right)z_3 = -\tfrac{1}{2}t\,e^{-t} + \tfrac{1}{2}C_1 e^t + C_2 e^{-t},$$

which has the general solution

$$z_3 = \frac{t}{2(1+i)}e^{-t} + \frac{1}{2(1+i)^2}e^{-t} + \frac{C_1}{2(1-i)}e^t - \frac{C_2}{(1+i)}e^{-t} + C_3 e^{it}.$$

Finally, x satisfies

$$\left(\frac{d}{dt} + i\right)x = \frac{t}{2(1+i)}e^{-t} + \frac{1}{2(1+i)^2}e^{-t} + \frac{C_1 e^t}{2(1-i)} -$$

$$\frac{C_2}{(1+i)}e^{-t} + C_3 e^{it},$$

which has the general solution

$$x = -\frac{t\,e^{-t}}{2(1+i)(1-i)} - \frac{e^{-t}}{2(1+i)(1-i)^2} - \frac{e^{-t}}{2(1+i)^2(1-i)}$$

$$+ A\,e^t + B\,e^{-t} + C\,e^{it} + D e^{-it},$$

after changing the arbitrary constants to A, B, C, D. Simplification leads to

$$x = -\tfrac{1}{4}t\,e^{-t} - \tfrac{1}{4}e^{-t} + A\,e^t + B\,e^{-t} + C\,e^{it} + D\,e^{-it},$$

or, in real form,

$$x = -\tfrac{1}{4}t\,e^{-t} + (A\,e^t + B'\,e^{-t} + C'\cos t + D'\sin t),$$

where the last two terms have been expressed in terms of cos and sin, and $-\tfrac{1}{4}e^{-t}$ has been absorbed by $B\,e^{-t}$ to form the new term $B'\,e^{-t}$. In the above working, the reader can check the individual integrations for himself.

An alternative technique is based to some extent on trial and error. The lengthy analysis displayed above can be replaced by the following. The complementary function given in the brackets of the last equation can be written down immediately once the auxiliary equation has been solved. Since the right-hand side of the differential equation is e^{-t}, this strongly suggests that we try to find a constant K such that $K\,e^{-t}$ is a particular integral. Substitution of $K\,e^{-t}$ into the differential equation quickly shows that there is no constant K for which this is true. The reason for this failure is not difficult to find: e^{-t} satisfies the homogeneous equation (the method would have worked had this not been the case). We now attempt to find a constant K such that $Kt\,e^{-t}$ is a particular integral. Substitution this time gives

$$-4Ke^{-t}=e^{-t},$$

which implies that $K = -\frac{1}{4}$. The solution above then follows.

This method can be used widely for exponential and trigonometric functions. For example, if $f(t) = \cos \omega t$, try the particular integral $K_1 \cos \omega t + K_2 \sin \omega t$. Practice develops the ability to make intelligent guesses for particular integrals.

4.7 Simultaneous differential equations

Many problems in mechanics require the solution for two or more variables contained in two or more ordinary differential equations. For example, the two equations

$$\frac{dx}{dt} - 3x + 2y = 0, \tag{20}$$

$$4x + \frac{dy}{dt} - y = 0, \tag{21}$$

each contain x and y. In order to solve these equations *simultaneously* for x and y, we attempt to eliminate one of the variables. From the second equation, we see that

$$x = \frac{1}{4}\left(y - \frac{dy}{dt}\right). \tag{22}$$

Substituting x back into (20), we have

$$\frac{d}{dt}\left[\frac{1}{4}\left(y - \frac{dy}{dt}\right)\right] - \frac{3}{4}\left(y - \frac{dy}{dt}\right) + 2y = 0,$$

or

$$\frac{d^2y}{dt^2} - 4\frac{dy}{dt} - 5y = 0,$$

a second-order equation containing only y. The auxiliary equation is

$$m^2 - 4m - 5 = 0,$$

with solutions $m_1 = 5$ and $m_2 = -1$. The general solution is therefore

$$y = A e^{5t} + B e^{-t}.$$

We pause here to consider how many constants we would expect to find in the solution of (20) and (21). Each involves effectively one integration with the result that the solutions for x and y will contain two constants. We already have two constants in the solutions for y, and therefore y should be expressible in terms of these constants. Substituting for y in (22) we have

$$x = \tfrac{1}{4}(A e^{5t} + B e^{-t} - 5A e^{5t} + B e^{-t}),$$
$$= -A e^{5t} + \tfrac{1}{2}B e^{-t}.$$

If instead we substitute for y in (20), we find that x satisfies a first-order equation which, when solved, introduces apparently a third arbitrary constant. However this third constant would not be independent of the other two since we must ensure that the x and y so found still satisfy equation (21). This requirement provides a relation between the three constants. Always make sure the number of constants does not exceed the number of integrations involved: a straightforward verification that the solutions do satisfy the given equations is always a certain test.

Example 16   A particle moves in the force field $k^2(y\mathbf{i} + x\mathbf{j})$ per unit mass, where k is a constant. If it starts from the origin with velocity $V\mathbf{i}$, find the subsequent path of the particle.

If $\mathbf{r}$ is the position vector of the particle at time t, the equation of motion is

$$k^2(y\mathbf{i} + x\mathbf{j}) = \ddot{\mathbf{r}},$$

or, in scalar form,

$$\frac{d^2x}{dt^2} = k^2y, \qquad \frac{d^2y}{dt^2} = k^2x, \qquad \frac{d^2z}{dt^2} = 0. \tag{23}$$

The initial conditions at $t = 0$ are

$$x = y = z = 0, \qquad \frac{dy}{dt} = \frac{dz}{dt} = 0, \qquad \frac{dx}{dt} = V.$$

From the third of equations (23),

$$z = A_1t + A_2,$$

and, if $z = dz/dt = 0$, at $t = 0$, we must have $A_1 = A_2 = 0$. Throughout the motion $z = 0$ and the particle moves in the (x,y)-plane.

The first two members of (23) are simultaneous equations in x and y. Eliminating y, we find that x satisfies

$$\frac{d^4x}{dt^4} - k^4 x = 0.$$

The general solution of this is (Example 15),

$$x = A\,e^{kt} + B\,e^{-kt} + C\cos kt + D\sin kt,$$

whilst

$$y = \frac{1}{k^2}\frac{d^2x}{dt^2} = A\,e^{kt} + B\,e^{-kt} - C\cos kt - D\sin kt.$$

The initial conditions give the following four equations for A, B, C and D:

$$A + B + C = 0, \tag{24}$$
$$A - B + D = V/k, \tag{25}$$
$$A + B - C = 0, \tag{26}$$
$$A - B - D = 0. \tag{27}$$

Subtracting (26) from (24), $C = 0$. From (25) and (27), $D = V/2k$. Equations (24) and (27) become

$$A + B = 0, \qquad A - B - V/2k = 0.$$

Therefore $A = V/4k$, $B = -V/4k$. The required solution is

$$x = V(e^{kt} - e^{-kt} + 2\sin kt)/4k$$
$$= V(\sinh kt + \sin kt)/2k,$$

and

$$y = V(e^{kt} - e^{-kt} - 2\sin kt)/4k$$
$$= V(\sinh kt - \sin kt)/2k.$$

These are the parametric equations of the path in the (x,y)-plane.

In some cases it is not always obvious how to eliminate one variable. For example, in

$$\frac{dx}{dt} + 2x - \frac{dy}{dt} - y = e^{-t}, \tag{28}$$

$$2\frac{dx}{dt} - x - \frac{dy}{dt} + 3y = 4\,e^{-t}, \tag{29}$$

it is not possible to eliminate either y or x directly. Suppose we wish to find the equation for x. First eliminate dy/dt by subtraction:

$$-\frac{dx}{dt} + 3x - 4y = -3\,e^{-t},$$

or

$$y = \frac{1}{4}\left(-\frac{dx}{dt} + 3x + 3\,e^{-t} \right).\tag{30}$$

Substitute y back into (28):

$$\frac{dx}{dt} + 2x - \frac{1}{4}\left(-\frac{d^2x}{dt^2} + 3\frac{dx}{dt} - 3\,e^{-t} \right) - \frac{1}{4}\left(-\frac{dx}{dt} + 3x + 3\,e^{-t} \right) = e^{-t},$$

or

$$\frac{1}{4}\frac{d^2x}{dt^2} + \frac{1}{2}\frac{dx}{dt} + \frac{5}{4}x = e^{-t}.$$

This equation can be solved in the usual way for x, and then y found from equation (30).

In many problems in mechanics the ordinary differential equations governing the system are not linear nor is the method of solution obvious. One can only resort to *ad hoc* techniques. The equations of motion of a satellite circling the earth in a plane orbit are given, using polar coordinates (r, θ), by

$$\frac{d^2r}{dt^2} - r\left(\frac{d\theta}{dt}\right)^2 = -\frac{\gamma M}{r^2}, \qquad \frac{d}{dt}\left(r^2\frac{d\theta}{dt} \right) = 0,\tag{31}$$

where γ is the gravitational constant and M is the mass of the earth (the polar components of acceleration were derived in section 1.10). The second equation can be integrated once to give

$$r^2\frac{d\theta}{dt} = h, \quad \text{a constant.}\tag{32}$$

We shall attempt to construct a differential equation relating r and θ rather than r and t. Eliminate $d\theta/dt$ between the first of equations (31) and (32):

$$\frac{d^2r}{dt^2} - \frac{h^2}{r^3} = -\frac{\gamma M}{r^2}.\tag{33}$$

Let $u = 1/r$ and consider the derivatives dr/dt and d^2r/dt^2:

$$\frac{dr}{dt} = \frac{dr}{d\theta}\cdot\frac{d\theta}{dt} = \frac{h}{r^2}\frac{dr}{d\theta} = -h\frac{du}{d\theta},$$

$$\frac{d^2r}{dt^2} = \frac{d}{dt}\left(\frac{dr}{dt}\right) = \frac{d\theta}{dt}\cdot\frac{d}{d\theta}\left(\frac{dr}{dt}\right) = -\frac{h}{r^2}\cdot h\frac{d^2u}{d\theta^2} = -h^2u^2\frac{d^2u}{d\theta^2},$$

where (32) has to be used twice. Equation (33) can now be expressed as

$$- h^2 u^2 \frac{d^2 u}{d\theta^2} - h^2 u^3 = - \gamma M u^2,$$

or

$$\frac{d^2 u}{d\theta^2} + u = \frac{\gamma M}{h^2},$$

a second-order linear differential equation with constant coefficients. The solution is

$$u = \frac{1}{r} = A \cos \theta + B \sin \theta + \frac{\gamma M}{h^2},$$

which is the equation of a conic. The constants A, B and h will be determined by the initial conditions imposed on the satellite. We shall discuss the solution to these equations in further detail in chapter 9.

4.8 Miscellaneous problems

Example 17   Show that the equation of motion of a simple pendulum of length a is

$$a\ddot{\theta} = - g \sin \theta,$$

where θ is the inclination of the string from the downward vertical.

A simple pendulum is a particle (called the bob) suspended from a fixed point by a string which moves in a vertical plane through the point of suspension. If the bob has mass m, the forces acting on it are its weight mg and the tension T in the string which acts towards the point of suspension O (see figure 59). The transverse component of acceleration (that is in the direction perpendicular to the string) of the bob is $a\ddot{\theta}$. Equating this to the transverse force, we obtain

$$mg \sin \theta = - ma\ddot{\theta}$$

as required.

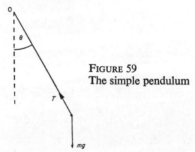

FIGURE 59
The simple pendulum

To integrate this equation once, we introduce the identity

$$\frac{d^2\theta}{dt^2} = \frac{d}{dt}\left(\frac{d\theta}{dt}\right) = \frac{d\theta}{dt}\frac{d}{d\theta}\left(\frac{d\theta}{dt}\right) = \dot{\theta}\frac{d\dot{\theta}}{d\theta},$$

so that θ now satisfies the separable equation

$$g \sin \theta = -a\dot{\theta}\frac{d\dot{\theta}}{d\theta},$$

with solution

$$-g \cos \theta = -\tfrac{1}{2}a\dot{\theta}^2 + C.$$

This equation can be integrated again but the answer requires knowledge of elliptic functions.

However we can obtain some information about the motion by assuming that the deviation of the string from the downward vertical is small (say, less than 20°). The function $\sin \theta$ can be expanded as a power series in θ:

$$\sin \theta = \theta - \tfrac{1}{6}\theta^3 + \ldots,$$

and for small θ we can say that θ is a reasonably good approximation to $\sin \theta$ (compare θ with $\sin \theta$ for small θ using tables of $\sin \theta$). With this approximation the equation of motion can be written

$$g\theta = -a\ddot{\theta},$$

or

$$\ddot{\theta} + \frac{g}{a}\theta = 0,$$

the equation for simple harmonic motion. As we have seen, the solution is

$$\theta = C \sin\left[\sqrt{\left(\frac{g}{a}\right)}t + \varepsilon\right]$$

(see equation 19).

The treatment of projectiles in section 3.8 assumed that the resistance of the air was negligible, or that the projectile was moving in a vacuum. In practice the frictional effects of air can make significant changes from the ideal parabolic trajectory. The magnitude of the resistance depends largely on two factors: the dimensions of the projectile perpendicular to the direction of motion, and the speed. It is found usually that the resistance varies as the speed for low speeds and as the square of the speed for high speeds. In still air the resistance opposes the motion and acts in a direction opposite to that of the velocity. If the projectile is moving in a wind the resistance will be in a direction determined in part by the velocity of the wind.

In still air, suppose the resistance $\mathbf{R}$ is proportional in magnitude to some power of the speed:

$$R = |\mathbf{R}| = mkv^n,$$

where $v = |\mathbf{v}|$, k is a constant and m is the mass of the projectile. The vector

$$\mathbf{R} = - mkv^n \frac{\mathbf{v}}{v} = - mkv^{n-1}\mathbf{v}.$$

For the projectile moving in still air under gravity its equation of motion is

$$- mg\mathbf{k} - mkv^{n-1}\mathbf{v} = m\frac{d\mathbf{v}}{dt}, \qquad (34)$$

where $\mathbf{k}$ is the upward unit vector. Since the resistance opposes the direction of motion the projectile will move in the vertical plane through the point of projection which contains the initial velocity vector.

First let us consider vertical motion. Equation (34) takes the one-dimensional form

$$\frac{dw}{dt} = - g - k|w|^{n-1}w, \qquad (35)$$

where w is the vertical velocity component, positive being upwards. This differential equation does not generally have a simple solution except, for example, in the cases $n = 1$ and $n = 2$. In resisted motion n usually lies in the range $1 \leqslant n \leqslant 2$. As the body falls the resistance increases as its speed increases until the resistance ultimately balances the force due to gravity. This occurs when the acceleration vanishes. The body then falls with constant speed—the so-called *terminal speed*. On putting $dw/dt = 0$ in (35), the terminal speed

$$w_\tau = \left(\frac{g}{k}\right)^{1/n}.$$

Once we know w_τ and n, the magnitude of k can be determined.

Example 18   A man falling with speed 50 m/s at a height of 200 m opens his parachute. With resistance proportional to velocity the terminal speed of the parachutist is 5 m/s. Estimate his time of descent. (Take $g = 9.8$ m/s².)

With z upwards with origin at ground level, the equation of motion is

$$\frac{d^2z}{dt^2} = - g - k\frac{dz}{dt},$$

with the initial conditions at $t = 0$:

$$z = 200 \text{ m}, \qquad \frac{dz}{dt} = -50 \text{ m/s}.$$

The terminal speed must equal g/k so that

$$k = g/5 = 9{\cdot}8/5 = 1{\cdot}96 \text{ s}^{-1}.$$

The differential equation

$$\frac{d^2z}{dt^2} + k\frac{dz}{dt} = -g$$

is of the second order with auxiliary equation $m(m + k) = 0$. It is easy to guess that $-gt/k$ is a particular integral of this equation. The general solution is therefore

$$z = A + B\,e^{-kt} - \frac{gt}{k}.$$

The initial conditions give

$$200 = A + B,$$

$$-50 = -Bk - \frac{g}{k}.$$

Thus

$$B = \frac{1}{k}\left(50 - \frac{g}{k}\right) = \frac{1}{1{\cdot}96}(50 - 5) = \frac{45}{1{\cdot}96} = 22{\cdot}96$$

and

$$A = 200 - 22{\cdot}96 = 177{\cdot}04.$$

The required solution is

$$z = 177{\cdot}04 + 22{\cdot}96\,e^{-1{\cdot}96t} - 5t.$$

After 3s we get approximately that the value of the second term is

$$23\,e^{-1{\cdot}96t} = 23\,e^{-5{\cdot}88}. = 23 \times 0{\cdot}003 \simeq 0{\cdot}07$$

using tables of the exponential function. This term is very small compared with the first term. The man reaches the ground $z = 0$ when

$$177{\cdot}04 + 22{\cdot}96\,e^{-1{\cdot}96t} - 5t = 0$$

or, since the second term is negligible, when

$$177{\cdot}04 - 5t = 0$$

which gives a time of descent of approximately 35s.

Example 19 *A projectile with a terminal speed of 30·5 m/s is fired with an initial speed of 30·5 m/s at an inclination of 45° to the horizontal. If the resistance is proportional to velocity find the path taken by the projectile.*

Let V be initial speed and α the angle of projection to the horizontal: we will insert the numerical values later. The equations of motion are

$$\frac{d^2x}{dt^2} = -k\frac{dx}{dt},$$

$$\frac{d^2z}{dt^2} = -g - k\frac{dz}{dt}.$$

These are two standard second-order equations with solutions

$$x = A + B\,e^{-kt},$$

$$z = C + D\,e^{-kt} - \frac{g}{k}t,$$

where A, B, C and D are constants. With the origin at the point of projection the initial conditions are

$$x = 0, \qquad \dot{x} = V\cos\alpha,$$

$$z = 0, \qquad \dot{z} = V\sin\alpha,$$

at $t = 0$. The constants consequently take the values

$$A = -B = \frac{V}{k}\cos\alpha, \qquad C = -D = \frac{1}{k^2}(Vk\sin\alpha + g),$$

giving the required solution:

$$x = \frac{V}{k}(1 - e^{-kt})\cos\alpha, \tag{36}$$

$$z = \frac{1}{k^2}(Vk\sin\alpha + g)(1 - e^{-kt}) - \frac{g}{k}t. \tag{37}$$

These are the parametric equations of the path of the projectile. Since the terminal speed is 30·5 m/s,

$$k = \frac{g}{30\cdot5} = 0\cdot322\ \text{s}^{-1}.$$

The values of x and z from (36) and (37) have been computed at time intervals 0·5 sec and the results are shown in the table to the nearest half metre.

t seconds	x metres	z metres
0	0	0
0·5	10·0	8·5
1·0	18·5	14·0
1·5	25·5	16·0
2·0	31·5	16·0
2·5	37·0	13·0
3·0	41·5	8·5
3·5	44·0	2·5

A sketch of the trajectory is shown in figure 60 using the data from the table. The path for resisted motion is characterized by a steep descent to the ground. The horizontal range is about 45 m compared with a range of about 95 m for the same problem with no resistance.

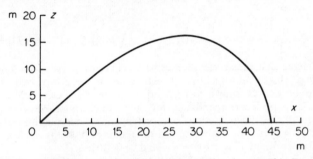

FIGURE 60   Projectile's path for resistance proportional to speed in Example 19

The equation of the path of the projectile can be found explicitly where the resistance is proportional to the velocity, but this is not the case, in general, if the resistance depends on the square of the speed. Suppose $n = 2$ in equation (34) so that the equations of motion of the projectile are

$$\frac{du}{dt} = -k(u^2 + w^2)^{\frac{1}{2}}u, \qquad (38)$$

$$\frac{dw}{dt} = -g - k(u^2 + w^2)^{\frac{1}{2}}w, \qquad (39)$$

where $u = \dot{x}$ and $w = \dot{z}$. We cannot integrate these equations explicitly but we can obtain a specific solution by a method of successive approximation. We will illustrate the technique by repeating Example 19 with a square-law resistance.

Example 20   A projectile with a terminal speed of 30·5 m/s is fired with an initial speed of 30·5 m/s at an inclination of 45° to the horizontal. If the resistance is proportional to the square of the speed in magnitude estimate the total range.

We now have to solve the equations of motion, equations (38) and (39), by a numerical technique. There is a considerable literature on numerical methods for solving differential equations and any reader who is interested in following up such methods should look for further details elsewhere. In this chapter we illustrate one such elementary method and comment on the accuracy involved.

Firstly we need the magnitude of k. If the body is falling vertically with its terminal speed, we get

$$(30\cdot5)^2 = g/k \text{ or } k = 0\cdot0105$$

At time $t = 0$, $u = w = 30\cdot5/\sqrt{2} = 21\cdot57$ m/s so that initially the accelerations are

$$\frac{du}{dt} = -0\cdot0105 \times 30\cdot5 \times 21\cdot57 = 6\cdot91 \text{ m/s}^2,$$

$$\frac{dw}{dt} = -9\cdot81 - 0\cdot0105 \times 30\cdot5 \times 21\cdot57 = -16\cdot71 \text{ m/s}^2.$$

We now assume that the acceleration remains constant at this value during the first time step. This is known as Euler's method and the error involved in making this assumption may be shown to be $\frac{1}{2}h^2(d^2w/dt^2)$ in the w calculation, where h is the time step, and correspondingly for the u calculation. We may evaluate d^2w/dt^2 at $t = 0$ after differentiating equation (39) and we find that the error is then approximately $4\cdot5h^2$. Thus the error, if a time step of 0·1s was used, is roughly 0·045 m/s. The corresponding error in u would be 0·030 m/s.

Carrying out this procedure we obtain the velocities at $t = 0\cdot1$:

$$u = 21\cdot57 + 0\cdot1(-6\cdot90) = 20\cdot88 \text{ m/s},$$

$$w = 21\cdot57 + 0\cdot1(-16\cdot7) = 19\cdot90 \text{ m/s}.$$

We are now in a position to use a more accurate iteration formula. Formally it may be written as

$$u_{r+1} = u_{r-1} + 2h\left(\frac{du}{dt}\right)_r,$$

$$w_{r+1} = w_{r-1} + 2h\left(\frac{dw}{dt}\right)_r,$$

where the subscript r refers to the rth step. This may be shown to have an accuracy of $\frac{1}{3}h^3(d^3u/dt^3)$, $\frac{1}{3}h^3(d^3w/dt^3)$ in u and w respectively. This is known as the 'leapfrog' method since we do not use the velocity at the previous time step but only the acceleration, and assume that the latter has remained constant throughout the previous two time intervals.

Since

$$\left(\frac{du}{dt}\right)_1 = -0.0105 \times [(20.9)^2 + (19.9)^2]^{\frac{1}{2}} \times 20.88 = -6.33 \text{ m/s}^2,$$

and

$$\left(\frac{dw}{dt}\right)_1 = -9.81 - 0.0105[(20.9)^2 + (19.9)^2]^{\frac{1}{2}} \times 19.9 = -15.84 \text{ m/s}^2,$$

we obtain the velocities at $t = 0.2$ as

$$u_2 = 21.57 + 0.2(-6.3) = 20.31 \text{ m/s},$$

$$w_2 = 21.57 + 0.2(-15.8) = 18.41 \text{ m/s}.$$

We may now increase the time step to 0.2s, since the accuracy of the leapfrog method is proportional to h^3 instead of h^2 (d^3w/dt^3 varies over the total range considered but an average estimate of the error of each step is 0.01 m/s), and obtain the values in the following table. After $t = 0.6$s, intermediate steps are left out of the table but the velocity profiles are shown in full in figure 61.

t seconds	u m/s	w m/s	x metres	z metres
0	21.6	21.6	0	0
0.1	20.9	19.9	2.2	2.2
0.2	20.3	18.4	4.2	4.0
0.4	19.2	15.5	8.1	7.4
0.6	18.3	12.9	11.9	10.2
1.0	16.8	8.1	18.9	14.3
1.4	15.6	3.8	25.3	16.7
1.8	14.6	−0.2	31.4	17.4
2.2	13.8	−4.0	37.1	16.6
2.6	12.9	−7.6	42.5	14.3
3.0	12.1	−10.8	47.5	10.6
3.4	11.3	−13.8	52.2	5.6
3.8	10.4	−16.5	56.6	−0.5

The final two columns of the table for horizontal distance x and height z are evaluated by again using the leapfrog scheme after an initial time step using the Euler method. That is

$$x_{r+1} = x_r + 2hu_r,$$

$$z_{r+1} = z_r + 2hw_r.$$

From this we can plot the trajectory, figure 62, and obtain an estimate of the range of the projectile. This estimate would be 56 m, which may be shown to be accurate to within 1 m. More complicated numerical methods may be used to improve this

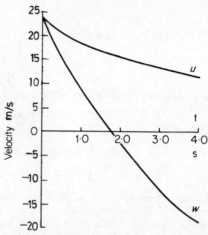

FIGURE 61 Horizontal and vertical velocity components for projectile moving under the influence of square-law resistance in Example 20

accuracy but, since the objective in this example has been to introduce the reader to a
reasonably accurate method of solving the relevant differential equations by a simple
scheme, they will not be discussed.

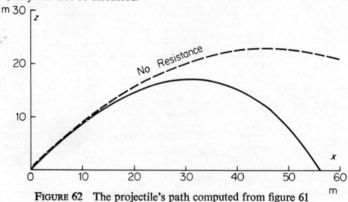

FIGURE 62   The projectile's path computed from figure 61

We note that the horizontal range of 56 m is greater than the 45 m which occurred
when the resistance was proportional to the velocity. This greater range occurs
because for the same terminal velocity the squared law gives relatively less drag at
lower speeds.

*Example 21   An aircraft flying horizontally with constant speed V_1 at height h
flies over a missile launching site. At this moment a missile, which can maintain
a constant speed V_2, is launched to intercept the aircraft. The guidance system of
the missile locks it on to the aircraft in such a way that it is always pointing in the
direction of the aircraft. Find the missile's path.*

This is an example of a pursuit curve. Take an origin fixed in the aircraft with polar coordinates (r, θ) as shown in figure 63. Relative to the aircaft the missile has polar velocity components $(\dot{r}, r\dot{\theta})$. Its actual velocity components are $(\dot{r} + V_1 \cos \theta, r\dot{\theta} - V_1 \sin \theta)$. Since the missile, when viewed from the aircraft, appears to be moving towards the aircraft these velocity components must equal $(- V_2, 0)$. Thus

$$\frac{dr}{dt} = - (V_2 + V_1 \cos \theta),$$

$$r\frac{d\theta}{dt} = V_1 \sin \theta.$$

The initial conditions are $r = h$, $\theta = \frac{1}{2}\pi$ at $t = 0$.

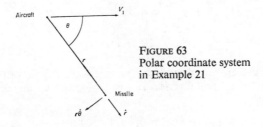

FIGURE 63
Polar coordinate system
in Example 21

In order to find the path we need r in terms of θ. Dividing the first of these equations by the second, we obtain

$$\frac{dr}{r d\theta} = - k \operatorname{cosec} \theta - \cot \theta,$$

where $k = V_2/V_1$. The equation is of the separable type with solution

$$\ln r = - \int (\operatorname{cosec} \theta + \cot \theta) \, d\theta + C$$
$$= k \ln (\operatorname{cosec} \theta + \cot \theta) - \ln \sin \theta + C.$$

From the initial conditions, $C = \ln h$. The path is therefore given by

$$r = h(\operatorname{cosec} \theta + \cot \theta)^k \operatorname{cosec} \theta = h \cot^k \tfrac{1}{2}\theta \operatorname{cosec} \theta,$$

relative to the aircraft.

To find where the interception takes place (V_2 must be greater than V_1 for interception to take place at all, of course) we require the time of flight of the missile so that we can then easily find the position of the aircraft at this time. Interception takes place when $r = 0$ which can only occur when $\theta = \pi$. The required time

$$T = \int_0^T dt = \int_{\frac{1}{2}\pi}^{\pi} \frac{dt}{d\theta} \, d\theta = \int_{\frac{1}{2}\pi}^{\pi} \frac{r}{V_1 \sin \theta} \, d\theta$$
$$= \frac{h}{V_1} \int_{\frac{1}{2}\pi}^{\pi} \frac{d\theta}{\tan^k \tfrac{1}{2}\theta \sin^2 \theta}.$$

Using the substitution $u = \tan \frac{1}{2}\theta$ where $\sin \theta = 2u/(1 + u^2)$ and

$$2\frac{du}{d\theta} = (1 + u^2),$$

then

$$
\begin{aligned}
T &= \frac{h}{V_1} \int_1^\infty \frac{(1 + u^2)\,du}{2u^{k+2}} = \frac{h}{2V_1} \int_1^\infty (u^{-k-2} + u^{-k})\,du \\
&= \frac{h}{2V_1}\left[-\frac{u^{-k-1}}{(k+1)} - \frac{u^{-k+1}}{(k-1)} \right]_1^\infty \\
&= \frac{h}{2V_1}\left(\frac{1}{k+1} + \frac{1}{k-1} \right) \\
&= \frac{hk}{V_1(k^2 - 1)}. \qquad (k > 1)
\end{aligned}
$$

For $k > 1$ interception takes place: for $k < 1$ the missile will never reach the aircraft since the integral diverges. If $k = 1$ we must reexamine the integral for T. In this case

$$
\begin{aligned}
T &= \frac{h}{2V_1} \lim_{q \to \infty} \int_1^q \left(\frac{1}{u^3} + \frac{1}{u} \right) du \\
&= \frac{h}{2V_1} \lim_{q \to \infty} \left(-\frac{1}{2u^2} + \ln u \right)_1^q \\
&= \infty,
\end{aligned}
$$

and the missile will not intercept the aircraft.

Exercises

1. Obtain general solutions of the following first-order differential equations.

(i) $\dfrac{dx}{dt} = t^3 x^2$,

(ii) $\dfrac{dx}{dt} = e^{-x} \sin t$,

(iii) $(2t - x)\dfrac{dx}{dt} = 2x - t$,

(iv) $t\dfrac{dx}{dt} = (x^2 + t^2)^{\frac{1}{2}} + x$,

(v) $t\dfrac{dx}{dt} - 3x = t^5,$

(vi) $\dfrac{dx}{dt} - tx = t.$

2. A body cools according to Newton's law of cooling

$$\frac{d\theta}{dt} = -k\theta,$$

where θ is the temperature difference between the body and the surrounding air, and k is a constant. Initially the body has a temperature of 90°C (Centigrade) and the air is at 16°C. Ten minutes later the body has a temperature of 72°C. Estimate the time taken for the temperature to drop to 20°C.

3. A particle moving in space is subject to a time-varying force

$$\mathbf{F} = e^{-t}\,\mathbf{i} + \sin t\mathbf{j} + \cos t\mathbf{k}$$

per unit mass. If the particle starts from rest, find its velocity at any subsequent time.

4. In a straight river of width $2a$ the water flows parallel to the banks with speed $V_0(1 - y^2/a^2)$ where y is measured from the centre of the river (this is a *parabolic* velocity distribution: the water is at rest at the banks and has a maximum value V_0 at the centre). A man, who can maintain a speed V in still water, swims across the river directly towards the opposite bank. Find where he reaches the opposite bank.

5. Obtain general solutions of

(i) $\dfrac{d^2x}{dt^2} + 4x = 0,$

(ii) $\dfrac{d^2x}{dt^2} + 7\dfrac{dx}{dt} + 12x = 0,$

(iii) $\dfrac{d^2x}{dt^2} + 6\dfrac{dx}{dt} + 9x = 0.$

6. Obtain general solutions of

(i) $\dfrac{dx}{dt} + x = t^3,$

(ii) $\dfrac{d^2x}{dt^2} - \dfrac{dx}{dt} - 2x = 44 - 76t - 48t^2$,

(iii) $\dfrac{d^2x}{dt^2} + 6\dfrac{dx}{dt} + 25x = 104\,e^{3t}$,

(iv) $\dfrac{d^2x}{dt^2} - k^2x = \sinh kt$,

(v) $\dfrac{d^2x}{dt^2} + 8\dfrac{dx}{dt} + 25x = 48\cos t - 16\sin t$.

7. Find the solution of

$$5\dfrac{dx}{dt} + 4x - 2\dfrac{dy}{dt} - y = e^{-t},$$

$$\dfrac{dx}{dt} + 8x - 3y = 5\,e^{-t},$$

such that $x = 2$, $y = 4$ when $t = 0$.

8. Find the solution of

$$m\dfrac{d^2x}{dt^2} = Ve - He\dfrac{dy}{dt},$$

$$m\dfrac{d^2y}{dt^2} = He\dfrac{dx}{dt},$$

where m, V, H and e are constants, such that $dx/dt = 0$, $dy/dt = 0$, $x = 0$ and $y = 0$ when $t = 0$.

9. A particle moves in the force-field

$$F = y^2\mathbf{i} - \mathbf{j}$$

per unit mass. If the particle starts from rest at the origin, obtain the equation of its path.

10. A falling raindrop increases its mass at a rate proportional to the product of its surface area and speed v. Show that its radius is proportional to its distance s below a fixed level.

Assuming that the rate of change of linear momentum is equal to the force applied, show that the acceleration is $g - 3v^2/s$. Show also that the acceleration eventually approaches $\frac{1}{7}g$.

11. A body is projected vertically upwards in a medium for which the resistance is $k \times$ (speed)^2 per unit mass. If the initial speed is v_0 show that the body returns to the point of projection with speed v_1, where

$$v_1^2 = \frac{gv_0^2}{g + kv_0^2}.$$

12. A particle of mass m moves in the plane $z = 0$ under the attractive force $2m\pi^2 r$ towards the origin, r being its distance from the origin. In addition there is a force of magnitude $m\pi v$ in the direction $\mathbf{v} \times \mathbf{k}$, where $\mathbf{v}$ is the velocity of the particle and $\mathbf{k}$ a unit vector perpendicular to $z = 0$. If the particle is projected from the origin at $t = 0$ with velocity $3\mathbf{i}$, find its position at $t = 3$.

13. A cyclist exerts a constant propulsive force and is subject to air resistance which is proportional to the square of his speed. He can ride at a maximum speed of 36 km/h on the level and of 18 km/h up a slope of 1 in 20. Show that he can attain a speed of 20 km/h on the level, when starting from rest, in about 31 m.

14. A body having a mass of 45×10^5 kg is acted on by a force of $10^4(6 - v)$ N where v is its speed in m/s and experiences a resistance proportional to the square of its speed. If its maximum speed is 2 m/s show that it attains a speed of 1·5 m/s from rest in approximately 161 s and find the distance it has travelled to the nearest metre.

15. A body of mass 150 kg is dropped by parachute with negligible initial velocity. While the parachute is opening the motion is resisted by a force of $30v$ N, where v m/s is the velocity of the body. If the parachute is fully open at the end of 5 sec, prove that the velocity will then be

$$5g(1 - e^{-1}) \text{ m/s.}$$

The subsequent motion is resisted by a force of $10v^2$ N. Find the minimum safe dropping height (subject to the parachute opening fully), given that the impact velocity must not exceed $(20g)^{\frac{1}{2}}$ m/s.

16. The force exerted on a charged particle by the constant magnetic field $\mathbf{H}$ is $Q\mathbf{H} \times \dot{\mathbf{r}}$ where Q is a constant. If $\dot{\mathbf{r}}$ is perpendicular to $\mathbf{H}$ at some instant show that the particle describes a circle with constant speed. (Neglect gravity.)

17. A man rows a boat across a river of width d m, always rowing in the direction of a point directly opposite to his starting point. He can row the boat at a rate of v m/s and the river flows at w m/s. Show that the differential equation of the path is

$$\frac{\mathrm{d}y}{\mathrm{d}x} = \frac{y - k(x^2 + y^2)^{\frac{1}{2}}}{x}, \qquad k = \frac{w}{v},$$

where the origin of coordinates is on the opposite bank and y points downstream. Solve this equation and find the path of the boat. Show that the boat will reach the opposite bank if $k < 1$.

18. A projectile is fired with initial velocity $V_0 \cos \alpha \mathbf{i} + V_0 \sin \alpha \mathbf{k}$ into a wind of velocity $- V\mathbf{i}$. The resistance is proportional to the vector difference of projectile velocity and wind velocity and opposes the motion. If the terminal speed of the projectile is 60 m/s, $V_0 = 30$ m/s, $\alpha = 30°$ and $V = 3$ m/s, find the horizontal range of the particle. What wind speed would cause the projectile to return to its firing point?

19. A hydrofoil starts a journey with its hull submerged in the water, called stage (a), and when an appropriate speed is reached its hull is raised out of the water, called stage (b). In stage (a) the resistance to motion is of magnitude $3mkv$, where m is the mass of the boat, v its speed and k a constant, and the boat is subject to a constant force which would enable it to reach a maximum speed V. In stage (b) the resistance to motion has a magnitude mkv and it is subject to a different constant force which would enable it to achieve a speed $2V$ in the limit. Find at what speed the hull of the hydrofoil should be raised in order that a minimum time should be used in attaining a speed V_1, where $2V > V_1 \geqslant V$, and show that to attain a speed V the minimum time would be $(1/3k) \ln (27/4)$.

20. A rabbit is running with speed v along a straight hedge. A dog, which is at a distance d from the hedge and which runs at speed $2v$ sees the rabbit when it is at its nearest point. The dog then chases the rabbit by running in such a direction that it is always pointing at the moving rabbit. By using polar coordinates relative to the rabbit, or otherwise, to find the equation of the path of the dog, show that the rabbit runs a distance $\frac{2}{3}d$ before it is caught. [Use the result

$$\int_0^{\frac{1}{2}\pi} \frac{\mathrm{d}\theta}{(1 + \sin \theta)^2} = \frac{2}{3}\Bigg].$$

21. A body is released from rest at a height of 61 m above the ground. The resistance to motion is proportional to $v^{\frac{1}{2}}$ where v is the speed of the body and its terminal speed is 33·5 m/s. Use a time step of 0·25 s in the Euler method and then a time step of 0·5 s in the leapfrog method to obtain an estimate of the time of descent of the body.

5

Work and energy

5.1 Work

The *work* done on a particle by a constant force F when the particle is moved a distance s in the direction of the force is defined to be Fs—the product of force and distance. For example, if a man carries a 30 kg load up a vertical ladder through a height of 10 m, the work done by the man in lifting the load will be $30 \times 10 \times g = 300g$ Nm since he lifts the load against the gravitational attraction of the earth. As its name suggests, work is a measure of the effort expended by the man: it does not describe how or at what rate the load is lifted.

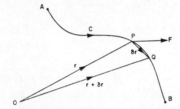

FIGURE 64   Path of integration of the line integral defining work

This simple description of work must now be generalized to include variable forces and situations in which the particle does not move in a straight line. Suppose a particle has a position vector $\mathbf{r}$ and moves in a field of force $\mathbf{F}$. The work $\mathcal{W}$ done by the force-field $\mathbf{F}$ on the particle as it moves from point A to point B on a specified curve C (figure 64) is defined by the line integral

$$\mathcal{W} = \int_C \mathbf{F} \cdot d\mathbf{r}. \tag{1}$$

We can show that this agrees with simpler ideas of work given above. Suppose A is at the origin and B is the point $(1, 0, 0)$, and C is the straight line joining A and B. If $\mathbf{F} = F_0\mathbf{i}$, a constant force,

$$\mathcal{W} = \int_C F_0\mathbf{i} \cdot d\mathbf{r} = \int_0^1 F_0 \, dx = F_0 \times 1,$$

that is, it is the product of force and distance moved.

131

Alternatively we can think of

$$\delta \mathcal{W} = \mathbf{F} \cdot \delta \mathbf{r}$$

as approximately the increment of work done as the point P moves to the neighbouring point Q in figure 64. If θ is the angle between $\mathbf{F}$ and $\overline{PQ}$,

$$\delta \mathcal{W} = |\mathbf{F}|\,|\delta \mathbf{r}| \cos \theta$$

by the definition of the scalar product; it is the product of the component of $\mathbf{F}$ in the direction $\overline{PQ}$ and the distance moved.

Remember that integral (1) is a line integral and must be evaluated as outlined in section 1.12.

The S.I. unit of work is the joule (J) which represents 1 N acting through a distance of 1 m.

Example 1 *Find the total work done in moving a particle in a force field given by* $\mathbf{F} = 3xy\mathbf{i} - 2yz\mathbf{j} + y\mathbf{k}\ N$ *along the curve* $x = t$, $y = 2t^2$, $z = 1 + t$ *from* $t = 1$ *to* $t = 2$ *where* x, y, z *are measured in metres.*

The work done

$$\mathcal{W} = \int_C \mathbf{F} \cdot \mathbf{dr} = \int_C (3xy\mathbf{i} - 2yz\mathbf{j} + y\mathbf{k}) \cdot (\mathbf{i}\,dx + \mathbf{j}\,dy + \mathbf{k}\,dz)$$

$$= \int_C (3xy\,dx - 2yz\,dy + y\,dz)$$

$$= \int_{t=1}^{t=2} [3(t)(2t^2)\,dt - 2(2t^2)(1 + t)\,d(2t^2) + 2t^2\,d(1 + t)]$$

$$= \int_1^2 (6t^3 - 16t^3 - 16t^4 + 2t^2)\,dt$$

$$= \int_1^2 (-16t^4 - 10t^3 + 2t^2)\,dt$$

$$= \left(-\frac{16t^5}{5} - \frac{5t^4}{2} + \frac{2t^3}{3} \right)_1^2$$

$$= -\frac{3961}{30}\ \text{J}.$$

The symbol t in this example is not necessarily time but merely a parameter which describes the path C.

5.2 Conservative and non-conservative forces

If the man of the preceding section carries the 30 kg load up an inclined ladder to a height of 10 m, he still performs work of $300g$ Nm. For, if the ladder is inclined at an angle θ to the horizontal, the work done is $30g \cos \theta \times (10/\cos \theta) = 300g$ Nm: the first term is the component of weight along the ladder and the second term is the length of the ladder. In fact, whatever path the man climbs in reaching 10 m the work done is unchanged because

$$\mathscr{W} = \int_C 30g\mathbf{k} \cdot d\mathbf{r},$$

where C is any path joining a point at zero height and a point at a height of 10 m. Thus

$$\mathscr{W} = \int_0^{10} 30g \, dz = 300g \text{ Nm};$$

the work done is *independent* of the path taken. We say that the uniform gravitational field is a *conservative* field of force.

More generally, if the work done by a force on a particle which is moved from A to B is independent of the path joining the two points, the force is said to be conservative. A force which is not conservative is called a *non-conservative* force.

The contents of section 1.13 are relevant here. We showed there that if a line integral was independent of the path joining the two points, then curl $\mathbf{F} = 0$, provided certain conditions were satisfied. This implies that $\mathbf{F}$ can be expressed as the gradient of a scalar potential function i.e. $\mathbf{F} = -\text{grad } \phi$. Thus, under the action of a conservative field of force, the work done depends only on the values of ϕ at the end points of the path of integration, and if a particle moves round a closed curve the total work done is zero. A consequence of this is that the work done is recoverable.

The definition of work so far refers only to points or particles and not to bodies with finite dimensions. Suppose a rigid body occupying position 1 in a field of force $\mathbf{F}$ per unit mass in figure 65 is moved into position 2 which involves a translation and a rotation. Consider a small element $\rho \delta V$ of the body which moves from position 1 to 2 along the path C. We adopt the following plausible reasoning. The work done in moving the element $\rho \delta V$ is

$$\int_C \mathbf{F} \cdot d\mathbf{r} \rho \delta V,$$

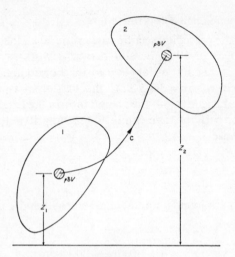

since $F\rho\delta V$ is the force on this element. The total work done will be the sum of these elements through the volume:

$$\mathscr{W} = \int_V \int_C \mathbf{F} \cdot d\mathbf{r}\rho \, dV \tag{2}$$

which is a multiple integral involving a line integral and a volume integral. In general, this integral cannot be simplified greatly. Suppose the field of force is now a uniform gravitational one, $\mathbf{F} = -g\mathbf{k}$. Then

$$\mathscr{W} = \int_V \int_C (-g) \, dz\rho \, dV$$

$$= \int_V (z_1 - z_2)\rho \, dV$$

$$= g \int_V z_1\rho \, dV - g \int_V z_2\rho \, dV$$

$$= Mg\bar{z}_1 - Mg\bar{z}_2$$

$$= Mg(\bar{z}_1 - \bar{z}_2), \tag{3}$$

where $\bar{z}_1$ and $\bar{z}_2$ are the initial and final heights of the mass-centre of the body. The work done is therefore the product of the weight of the body and height through which its mass-centre rises. Note that any rotation of the body does not affect the work done.

Let us consider now a particular non-conservative force. Suppose a block slides along a rough horizontal table. Any motion of the block will be opposed by the *friction* between the block and the table and we assume that the frictional force F acts in a direction opposite to the direction of motion of the block. Thus if, in figure 66, the block is moving in a straight line A to B, the frictional force F on the block acts from B to A. The mathematical description of F is a matter for definition based, in part, on experimental evidence. It may depend on such properties as the nature of the surfaces in contact, the weight of the block and the speed of the block. In one of its simplest forms F is a constant multiple of the reaction (in this case the weight of the block), the constant depending on the two surfaces in contact.

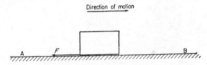

Direction of motion

FIGURE 66   A block sliding on a rough horizontal plane

In the example under consideration F will be constant so that the work done on the block by the frictional force will be $-F \cdot AB$ (negative sign because F opposes the motion). If now the block is slid back to A the total work done will be $-2F \cdot AB$ since F will act in the opposite direction in the return motion of the block. The work done is not recoverable because it is transformed principally into heat by the friction.

Conservative systems are important for the good theoretical reason that they are usually simpler to handle mathematically. This explains why so many problems in dynamics assume smooth bodies, frictionless pulleys, etc. For example, as we saw in section 3.8, the motion of projectiles under a constant gravitational field without air resistance is reasonably easy to analyse. The same problem with air resistance (which is a non-conservative force acting on the projectile) considered in section 4.8 is much more complicated.

A body may experience simultaneously conservative and non-conservative forces in which case only part of the work done will be recoverable.

Example 2   A particle of mass m at rest at the origin generates a gravitational force field

$$\mathbf{F} = -\frac{\gamma m \mathbf{r}}{r^3}$$

(*this is the force of attraction which a particle of unit mass placed at* $\mathbf{r}$ *would experience*). *Show that* $\mathbf{F}$ *is conservative.*

By the definition of curl (section 1.13):

$$\text{curl}\left(-\frac{\gamma m \mathbf{r}}{r^3}\right) = -\gamma m\left\{\mathbf{i}\left[\frac{\partial}{\partial y}\left(\frac{z}{r^3}\right) - \frac{\partial}{\partial z}\left(\frac{y}{r^3}\right)\right] + \mathbf{j}\left[\frac{\partial}{\partial z}\left(\frac{x}{r^3}\right) - \frac{\partial}{\partial x}\left(\frac{z}{r^3}\right)\right] + \mathbf{k}\left[\frac{\partial}{\partial x}\left(\frac{y}{r^3}\right) - \frac{\partial}{\partial y}\left(\frac{x}{r^3}\right)\right]\right\}$$

$$= 3\gamma m\left[\mathbf{i}\left(\frac{yz}{r^5} - \frac{zy}{r^5}\right) + \mathbf{j}\left(\frac{zx}{r^5} - \frac{xz}{r^5}\right) + \mathbf{k}\left(\frac{yx}{r^5} - \frac{xy}{r^5}\right)\right]$$

$$= \mathbf{0}.$$

Thus curl $\mathbf{F} = \mathbf{0}$, $\mathbf{F}$ is conservative and there exists a scalar function ϕ such that $\mathbf{F} = -\text{grad } \phi$. The reader should verify that the *gravitational potential* is

$$\phi = -\frac{\gamma m}{r}.$$

Example 3 *Consider a model of a hurricane in which the wind field is given by* $\mathbf{v} = g(r)\mathbf{e}_\theta$, *where* $\mathbf{e}_\theta$ *is a unit vector in the direction of* θ *increasing and* (r, θ) *are polar coordinates with the centre of the hurricane as origin. Suppose that a ship in such a hurricane is subjected to a force* $\alpha\mathbf{v}$ *due to the action of the wind with* α *a constant. Is such a field of force conservative?*

Expressed in Cartesian coordinates, the force on the ship,

$$\alpha\mathbf{v} = \alpha g(r)\mathbf{e}_\theta = \alpha[-g(r)\sin\theta\,\mathbf{i} + g(r)\cos\theta\,\mathbf{j}]$$

$$= \alpha\left[-\frac{g(r)}{r}y\mathbf{i} + \frac{g(r)}{r}x\mathbf{j}\right],$$

where $r^2 = x^2 + y^2$. Consequently

$$\text{curl}\,(\alpha\mathbf{v}) = \alpha\mathbf{k}\left\{\frac{\partial}{\partial x}\left[\frac{xg(r)}{r}\right] + \frac{\partial}{\partial y}\left[\frac{yg(r)}{r}\right]\right\}$$

$$= \alpha\mathbf{k}\left\{\frac{g(r)}{r} + \frac{x^2}{r}\frac{d}{dr}\left[\frac{g(r)}{r}\right] + \frac{g(r)}{r} + \frac{y^2}{r}\frac{d}{dr}\left[\frac{g(r)}{r}\right]\right\},$$

noting that $\dfrac{\partial}{\partial x}(r) = \dfrac{x}{r}$ and $\dfrac{\partial}{\partial y}(r) = \dfrac{y}{r}$. Thus

$$\text{curl}\,(\alpha\mathbf{v}) = \alpha\mathbf{k}\left\{\frac{2g(r)}{r} + r\frac{d}{dr}\left[\frac{g(r)}{r}\right]\right\},$$

which will vanish only if

$$\frac{2g(r)}{r} + r\frac{d}{dr}\left[\frac{g(r)}{r}\right] = 0.$$

Putting $z = g(r)/r$, we find that the equation is of separable type

$$2z + r\frac{dz}{dr} = 0,$$

with solution

$$z = \frac{A}{r^2} \quad \text{or} \quad g(r) = \frac{A}{r},$$

where A is a constant. Thus, if $g(r) \neq A/r$, the wind field will certainly be non-conservative. In the particular case $g(r) = A/r$, which is not much different from the wind field exterior to the central core of a hurricane, then the comment made in section 1.13 becomes applicable. We have curl $\mathbf{F} = \mathbf{0}$ but for a path enclosing the centre of the hurricane one of the two conditions for the theorem

$$`\int_C \mathbf{F} \cdot d\mathbf{r} = 0 \text{ implies curl } \mathbf{F} = \mathbf{0} \text{ and conversely'}$$

is not satisfied. If the origin is included in the region then $\mathbf{F}$ is not well-behaved there; if the origin is excluded by surrounding it with an interior contour, then the region is not simply-connected (see section 1.13 for this definition). If we integrate the line integral around a circle of constant radius r_0 we get

$$\int_C \mathbf{F} \cdot d\mathbf{r} = \int_C \frac{A}{r}\mathbf{e}_\theta \cdot (dr\mathbf{e}_r + r\,d\theta\mathbf{e}_\theta)$$

$$= \int_0^{2\pi} A\,d\theta = 2\pi A,$$

confirming the point just made. If however the path does *not* include the origin, the conditions of the theorem are satisfied and the value of any such line integral is zero.

5.3 Potential energy

We have seen that a force $\mathbf{F}$ is conservative if curl $\mathbf{F} = \mathbf{0}$ throughout an appropriate region and that, if this is so, there must exist a scalar function of position ϕ such that $\mathbf{F} = -\text{grad }\phi$. Suppose that a particle of mass m is moved from position A to B in a conservative force field $\mathbf{F} = -\text{grad }\phi$ (remember that $\mathbf{F}$ is the force which a particle of unit mass would experience) along a curve C. The negative of the work done is called the *potential energy* $\mathscr{V}$ relative to the first position, A. Thus

$$\mathscr{V} = -\mathscr{W} = -m\int_A^B \mathbf{F} \cdot d\mathbf{r} = m\int_A^B \text{grad }\phi \cdot d\mathbf{r}$$

$$= m(\phi_B - \phi_A),$$

which is proportional to the difference in the potentials at the two points. Energy can be described as the capacity for doing work and is distinguished in conservative systems from work in general since the work is mechanically recoverable. Much confusion often arises between the meaning of potential and potential energy. The potential of a force may be thought of as an abstraction: if a particle of unit mass is placed at a point it experiences a force which is the negative gradient of the potential. The potential energy of an actual particle is a quantity associated with the position in space of that particle.

Whilst potential and potential energy are simply related for particles, they are not so for bodies. The potential energy of a body in moving it from position 1 to 2 (figure 65) is, from equation (2):

$$
\mathscr{V} = -\mathscr{W} = -\int_V \int_C \mathbf{F} \cdot \mathrm{d}\mathbf{r}\rho \, \mathrm{d}V
$$

$$
= \int_V \int_C \mathrm{grad}\, \phi \cdot \mathrm{d}\mathbf{r}\rho \, \mathrm{d}V
$$

$$
= \int_V (\phi_2 - \phi_1)\rho \, \mathrm{d}V,
$$

where ϕ_1 and ϕ_2 are the values of the potential at the end-points of the path C. For bodies, the potential energy involves the volume integral of the potential initially and finally. Such general treatments are beyond the scope of this book and we restrict our attention to bodies in uniform gravitational fields.

From equation (3) we see that if the mass-centre of a body is raised through a height h in a uniform gravitational field $-g\mathbf{k}$, the body acquires potential energy

$$
\mathscr{V} = Mgh,
$$

where M is the mass of the body. In any specific problem all potential energies must be referred to the *same* reference level.

5.4 Power and kinetic energy: conservation of energy

Suppose a particle is subject to a force $\mathbf{F}$. The work done by the force in moving the particle from $\mathbf{r}$ to the neighbouring point $\mathbf{r} + \delta\mathbf{r}$ is given by

$$
\delta\mathscr{W} = \mathbf{F} \cdot \delta\mathbf{r}
$$

approximately. The *rate of working* or *work-rate* $\dot{\mathscr{W}}$ is given by

$$
\dot{\mathscr{W}} = \lim_{\delta t \to 0} \frac{\delta\mathscr{W}}{\delta t} = \lim_{\delta t \to 0} \frac{\mathbf{F} \cdot \delta\mathbf{r}}{\delta t} = \mathbf{F} \cdot \dot{\mathbf{r}},
$$

which is the product of force and the velocity of the particle.

The work-rate is usually known by the more familiar name of *power*. The S.I. unit of power is the watt (W) which is 1 J/s. The unit of 1 kWh (kilowatt-hour) = 3.6×10^6 J is still an acceptable unit of energy and work. One British unit of power, which is gradually being superseded by the kilowatt, is the horse-power (hp) which is defined as 17,700 foot/poundals/s. In terms of S.I. units

$$1 \text{ hp} = 0.7457 \text{ kW}.$$

If the particle has mass m, $\mathbf{F} = m\ddot{\mathbf{r}}$ and the work-rate

$$\dot{W} = m\ddot{\mathbf{r}} \cdot \dot{\mathbf{r}} = \frac{\mathrm{d}}{\mathrm{d}t}(\tfrac{1}{2}m\dot{\mathbf{r}} \cdot \dot{\mathbf{r}})$$

$$= \frac{\mathrm{d}}{\mathrm{d}t}(\tfrac{1}{2}mv^2),$$

where v is the speed of the particle. The term $\tfrac{1}{2}mv^2$ is called the *kinetic energy* of the particle and denoted by the symbol $\mathscr{T}$. Suppose that the force $\mathbf{F}$ is the sum of conservative and non-conservative forces, the conservative part having potential ϕ. We can write

$$\mathbf{F} = \mathbf{F}' - m \operatorname{grad} \phi$$

where $\mathbf{F}'$ is the non-conservative force. Thus

$$\frac{\mathrm{d}\mathscr{T}}{\mathrm{d}t} = \mathbf{F} \cdot \dot{\mathbf{r}} = \mathbf{F}' \cdot \dot{\mathbf{r}} - m\dot{\mathbf{r}} \cdot \operatorname{grad} \phi.$$

The force $\mathbf{F}'$ will *not* do work during the motion of the particle only if $\mathbf{F}' \cdot \dot{\mathbf{r}} = 0$, that is, if this force always remains perpendicular to the motion. Let us assume that this is the case and also that ϕ is a function of position only. Then

$$\frac{\mathrm{d}\mathscr{T}}{\mathrm{d}t} = - m\dot{\mathbf{r}} \cdot \operatorname{grad} \phi = - m\left(\frac{\mathrm{d}x}{\mathrm{d}t}\frac{\partial \phi}{\partial x} + \frac{\mathrm{d}y}{\mathrm{d}t}\frac{\partial \phi}{\partial y} + \frac{\mathrm{d}z}{\mathrm{d}t}\frac{\partial \phi}{\partial z}\right)$$

$$= - m\frac{\mathrm{d}\phi}{\mathrm{d}t}.$$

But for a particle, $m\phi = \mathscr{V}$ where $\mathscr{V}$ is the potential energy of the particle. Thus

$$\frac{\mathrm{d}\mathscr{T}}{\mathrm{d}t} = - \frac{\mathrm{d}\mathscr{V}}{\mathrm{d}t} \quad \text{or} \quad \frac{\mathrm{d}}{\mathrm{d}t}(\mathscr{T} + \mathscr{V}) = 0,$$

which implies that

$$\mathcal{T} + \mathcal{V} = \text{constant.}$$

This is the energy principle for a conservative system, namely that the sum of the kinetic and potential energies remains constant throughout the motion. The meaning of conservative has been extended slightly to include systems in which there may occur non-conservative forces which do no work. The conservation of energy means that energy can be transferred continuously between its kinetic and potential states: if the particle slows down there must be a corresponding increase in its potential energy and vice-versa.

For a system of particles subject to *external* conservative forces and non-conservative forces which do no work the total kinetic energy and potential energy is conserved.

The units of energy are the same as those of work.

Example 4   A bead can slide on a smooth circular wire of radius a which is fixed in a vertical plane. The bead is displaced slightly from the highest point of the wire. Find the speed of the bead subsequently.

The bead experiences two forces—its weight and the reaction due to the wire. The weight mg acts vertically downwards and the reaction R acts radially outwards since there is no friction between the bead and the wire (figure 67).

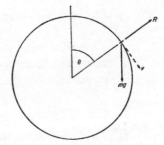

FIGURE 67   A bead sliding on a vertical wire

Since the bead is always moving tangentially, no work is done by R. The system is conservative and the energy is conserved. At time t let the radius to the bead make an angle θ to the vertical and let the speed of the bead be v. Let the lowest point of the wire represent zero potential energy. The kinematic and potential energies are

$$\mathcal{T} = \tfrac{1}{2}mv^2, \qquad \mathcal{V} = mga(1 + \cos \theta).$$

By the energy principle, $\mathscr{T} + \mathscr{V} = $ constant,

$$\tfrac{1}{2}mv^2 + mga(1 + \cos\theta) = \text{constant} = \text{initial value} = 2mga$$

since $v = 0$ and $\theta = 0$ initially. The speed at any angle θ is therefore

$$v = [2ga(1 - \cos\theta)]^{\tfrac{1}{2}}.$$

Note that the use of the energy principle avoids one integration of the equations of motion. Thus the tangential equation of motion is (see p. 19)

$$g\sin\theta = a\ddot\theta = a\dot\theta\frac{\mathrm{d}\dot\theta}{\mathrm{d}\theta},$$

and integration of this equation will give the energy equation and therefore the speed. Note also that if friction were present the energy equation would no longer hold and the equation of motion would then have to be solved to find the speed.

Following the usual extension of our postulates and definitions from particles to bodies, the kinetic energy of a body is given by the volume integral

$$\mathscr{T} = \tfrac{1}{2}\int_V \dot{\mathbf{r}} \cdot \dot{\mathbf{r}}\rho \, \mathrm{d}V.$$

If the body is rigid and translates without rotation every point of the body will have the same velocity $\mathbf{v} = \dot{\mathbf{r}}$. Thus, since $\mathbf{v}$ can only depend on time,

$$\mathscr{T} = \tfrac{1}{2}v^2 \int_V \rho \, \mathrm{d}V = \tfrac{1}{2}Mv^2,$$

where M is the mass of the body. If in addition the body rotates, then a further term will be included in the kinetic energy due to the rotational motion which the body has. We shall consider rotational effects in chapter 8.

Suppose a rigid body is subject to point forces $\mathbf{F}_1, \mathbf{F}_2,..., \mathbf{F}_n$ at $\mathbf{r}_1, \mathbf{r}_2,..., \mathbf{r}_n$ and moves without rotation in a uniform gravitational field $-g\mathbf{k}$ (since the body does not rotate the moment of the forces $\mathbf{F}_1,..., \mathbf{F}_n$ about the mass-centre must vanish). We know that the mass-centre $\bar{\mathbf{r}}$ moves as a particle with all the forces acting there. The rate of working of the forces is given by

$$\dot{\mathscr{W}} = \mathbf{F}_1 \cdot \dot{\mathbf{r}}_1 + \mathbf{F}_2 \cdot \dot{\mathbf{r}}_2 + ... + \mathbf{F}_n \cdot \dot{\mathbf{r}}_n - Mg\mathbf{k} \cdot \dot{\bar{\mathbf{r}}}$$
$$= (\mathbf{F}_1 + \mathbf{F}_2 + ... + \mathbf{F}_n - Mg\mathbf{k}) \cdot \dot{\bar{\mathbf{r}}},$$

since $\dot{\mathbf{r}}_i = \dot{\bar{\mathbf{r}}}$ ($i = 1, 2,..., n$). Therefore, since

$$M\ddot{\bar{\mathbf{r}}} = \mathbf{F}_1 + \mathbf{F}_2 + ... + \mathbf{F}_n - Mg\mathbf{k},$$

then

$$\dot{\mathscr{W}} = M\ddot{\bar{\mathbf{r}}} \cdot \dot{\bar{\mathbf{r}}} = \frac{\mathrm{d}}{\mathrm{d}t}(\tfrac{1}{2}M\dot{\bar{\mathbf{r}}} \cdot \dot{\bar{\mathbf{r}}}) = \frac{\mathrm{d}\mathscr{T}}{\mathrm{d}t},$$

and

$$\frac{\mathrm{d}\mathscr{T}}{\mathrm{d}t} = \mathbf{F}_1 \cdot \dot{\mathbf{r}}_1 + \mathbf{F}_2 \cdot \dot{\mathbf{r}}_2 + \ldots + \mathbf{F}_n \cdot \dot{\mathbf{r}}_n - Mg\mathbf{k} \cdot \dot{\mathbf{r}}.$$

Suppose now that the point forces do no work so that

$$\mathbf{F}_1 \cdot \dot{\mathbf{r}}_1 = \mathbf{F}_2 \cdot \dot{\mathbf{r}}_2 = \ldots = \mathbf{F}_n \cdot \dot{\mathbf{r}}_n = 0,$$

which implies that

$$\frac{\mathrm{d}\mathscr{T}}{\mathrm{d}t} = - Mg\mathbf{k} \cdot \dot{\mathbf{r}} = - Mg\frac{\mathrm{d}\bar{z}}{\mathrm{d}t}.$$

We conclude that

$$\frac{\mathrm{d}}{\mathrm{d}t}(\mathscr{T} + Mg\bar{z}) = 0,$$

or

$$\mathscr{T} + Mg\bar{z} = \text{constant},$$

which is the energy principle again since $Mg\bar{z}$ is the potential energy $\mathscr{V}$ of the body.

We must emphasize that the principle asserted above has been derived for non-rotating bodies; it is still true for rotating bodies if the rotational energy of the body is included in the kinetic energy. Rigid bodies *translating* in uniform force-fields are equivalent to particles.

Example 5 *A rocket is fired from the earth's surface with speed v at an angle α to the radius through the point of projection. Show that the rocket's subsequent greatest distance from the earth is the larger root of*

$$\left(v^2 - \frac{2\gamma M}{a}\right)r^2 + 2\gamma Mr - a^2 v^2 \sin^2 \alpha = 0,$$

if $v^2 < 2\gamma M/a$, where a is the radius and M the mass of the earth, and γ is the gravitational constant. Deduce that the escape velocity is independent of α. Assume that the earth is stationary.

Let the position of the rocket have polar coordinates (r, θ) referred to the centre of the earth as depicted in figure 68. If we treat the rocket as a particle of mass m, the total energy of the rocket is conserved. The gravitational potential energy of a particle of mass m distance r from the centre of the earth is

$$\mathscr{V} = - \frac{\gamma M m}{r},$$

and the kinetic energy is

$$\mathscr{T} = \tfrac{1}{2}m[\dot{r}^2 + (r\dot{\theta})^2].$$

The energy principle gives

$$\tfrac{1}{2}m[\dot{r}^2 + (r\dot{\theta})^2] - \frac{\gamma Mm}{r} = \tfrac{1}{2}mv^2 - \frac{\gamma Mm}{a}, \qquad (4)$$

the initial value of the energy.

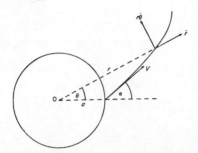

FIGURE 68   Coordinate scheme for the path of the rocket in figure 68

Secondly, since the only force on the rocket acts towards the centre of the earth, the transverse component of acceleration must vanish (section 1.10):

$$\frac{1}{r}\frac{\mathrm{d}}{\mathrm{d}t}(r^2\dot{\theta}) = 0,$$

or

$$r^2\dot{\theta} = \text{constant} = av\sin\alpha,$$

since $r = a$ and $r\dot{\theta} = v_0\sin\alpha$ initially. Substituting for $\dot{\theta}$ in (4):

$$\dot{r}^2 + \frac{a^2v^2\sin^2\alpha}{r^2} - \frac{2\gamma M}{r} = v^2 - \frac{2\gamma M}{a}. \qquad (5)$$

At the highest point of the rocket's path, $\dot{r} = 0$ so that the required height is a solution of the quadratic equation

$$\left(v^2 - \frac{2\gamma M}{a}\right)r^2 + 2\gamma Mr - a^2v^2\sin^2\alpha = 0.$$

If $v^2 < 2\gamma M/a$ the equation has two positive roots which correspond to furthest and nearest points of the orbit of the rocket from the centre of the earth. If $v = (2\gamma M/a)^{\frac{1}{2}}$, equation (5) becomes

$$\dot{r}^2 = \frac{1}{r^2}(2\gamma Mr - a^2v^2\sin^2\alpha)$$

$$= \frac{2\gamma M}{r^2}(r - a\sin^2\alpha),$$

and $\dot{r}$ has a real value for any value of $r \geqslant a$. In other words the rocket will just escape the earth's gravity since $\dot{r} \to 0$ as $r \to \infty$. The value of the initial speed is independent of α.

Example 6   Find the power required to pump 6 m³ of water per minute to a height of 20 m through a pipe of cross-sectional area 0·004 m². [The mass of 1 m³ of water is 10³ kg.]

The water must be raised through a height of 20 m. Volume ejected per second $= 6/60 = 0 \cdot 1$ m³. The speed of the water in the pipe

$$= \frac{\text{Volume ejected/s}}{\text{Cross-sectional area of pipe}}$$

$$= \frac{0 \cdot 1}{0 \cdot 004} = 25 \text{ m/s}.$$

Mass of water ejected per second $= 100$ kg. Hence kinetic energy is produced at a rate per second of

$$\tfrac{1}{2} \times 100 \times 25^2.$$

Each minute 6,000 kg of water must be lifted through 20 m. The rate of production of potential energy per second is therefore

$$\frac{6,000 \times 20 \times 9 \cdot 81}{60} = 19,620 \text{ J}$$

Therefore each second the total energy created

$$= 31,250 + 19,620$$

$$= 50,870 \text{ J}$$

The pump is working at 50,870 J/s or approximately 51 kW.

5.5 Springs and elastic strings

We may describe an elastic body as one which deforms when subjected to a load and resumes its original shape when the load is removed. We have discussed in section 3.10 the overall elastic behaviour of impact in very simple terms without examining in detail the actual nature of the elasticity within the body. We shall adopt the same procedure with springs.

Springs serve many purposes in engineering and are designed to have particular characteristics to suit what is required of them. They are used to store energy as in a clock or to absorb energy and so protect a mechanism which might otherwise be damaged by a sudden applied force as in a car which passes over a pot-hole.

We shall think principally in terms of the coil spring and the elastic string where the former can be extended and compressed along its length whilst the latter cannot sustain compression. The elastic string may become slack during the motion. The *ideal* spring or string is assumed to have no mass and also a *natural length* which it takes up when subject to no load. (The natural length of a heavy spring would be the length it took up if placed horizontally on a smooth horizontal table: a suspended heavy spring will be extended by its own weight.)

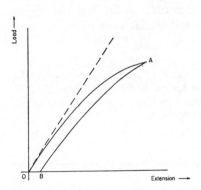

FIGURE 69   Typical load versus extension for a spring. The broken line shows a linear spring and OA a spring with non-linear characteristics

Consider an ideal spring suspended from a fixed point. By attaching loads to the free end we can measure the resulting extensions of the spring and plot graphically load versus extension. The solid line OA in figure 69 represents the typical behaviour of a coil spring. We shall approximate to the curve by a straight line (the broken line in the figure) which implies a linear relation between load and extension. Such an idealized spring is called a *linear* spring and is said to obey *Hooke's law*. It is a reasonable approximation for loads which do not produce excessive extensions of the spring. Excessive loads may also cause the spring to *yield* so that after unloading the spring does not return to its original length and is permanently extended. The curve AB shows an unloading curve for a spring which has yielded; the permanent extension is OB.

Our simple model for a spring can be summarized:

$$\text{load} \propto \text{extension},$$

or

$$F = \frac{\lambda x}{a}, \tag{6}$$

where F is the force or load applied, x is the extension, a is the natural length and λ is the *modulus of elasticity* of the spring, that is, that force which produces unit extension in a spring of unit length. The ratio $k = \lambda/a$ is called the *stiffness* of the spring. We shall assume that the spring under compression has similar properties to the extended spring so that relation (6) still holds with x negative for compression. On the other hand for an elastic string we must apply the restriction $x \geqslant 0$.

These remarks refer only to the static behaviour of springs but we assume that law (6) still applies when the spring is in motion.

Example 7   A bob of mass m is attached to the free end of a spring of natural length a and modulus λ, the other end of the spring being fixed. The bob is displaced from its position of equilibrium and moves in the vertical line of the spring. Determine the subsequent motion of the bob.

Let b be the extension of the spring when in equilibrium so that

$$mg = \frac{\lambda b}{a}. \tag{7}$$

Suppose at time t the spring has an *additional* extension x and that the tension is then T (figure 70). The equation of motion of the bob is

$$mg - T = m\ddot{x}, \tag{8}$$

where

$$T = \frac{\lambda(x + b)}{a}. \tag{9}$$

From (7), (8) and (9), we can easily see that the displacement x satisfies

$$\ddot{x} + \frac{\lambda}{am}x = 0. \tag{10}$$

From section 4.5, this is the equation for simple harmonic motion. The solution is

$$x = A \cos(\omega t + \varepsilon), \qquad \omega^2 = \lambda/am,$$

where the constants A and ε are to be determined by the initial displacement and velocity of the bob. If we add $2\pi/\omega$ on to the time t, the displacement x will return to its original value. This is called the *period* of the oscillation. The period of oscillation of the bob is $2\pi(am/\lambda)^{\frac{1}{2}}$.

The *amplitude* of the oscillation is the maximum displacement of the bob from its equilibrium position. Since $|\cos(\omega t + \varepsilon)| \leqslant 1$ the amplitude is $|A|$.

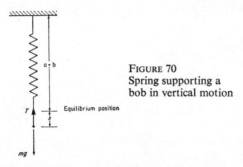

FIGURE 70
Spring supporting a
bob in vertical motion

If the spring is replaced by an elastic string the motion will be simple harmonic provided the string remains extended, that is provided the amplitude of the oscillation $|A| \leqslant b$. If $|A| > b$ the string will become slack for part of the motion and the bob will move as a particle vertically under gravity.

We shall have more to say about oscillations in general in chapter 7.

Obviously a spring stores energy when extended or compressed. The potential energy of a spring with extension x is the work done in extending the spring from its natural length. Thus

$$\mathscr{V} = \int_0^x T \, dy,$$

where T is the tension at extension y. Since $T = (\lambda/a)y$ for the linear spring,

$$\mathscr{V} = \int_0^x \frac{\lambda y}{a} \, dy = \frac{1}{2}\frac{\lambda}{a}x^2.$$

Since there is no energy dissipation in the ideal spring the energy principle must hold: $\mathscr{T} + \mathscr{V} =$ constant. In Example 8, we must have

$$\tfrac{1}{2}m\dot{x}^2 + \tfrac{1}{2}\frac{\lambda}{a}x^2 = \text{constant}, \tag{11}$$

which is, of course, a first integral of equation (10). Put another way, equation (10) is the time-derivative of (11).

5.6 Equilibrium and stability

Imagine a ball placed at the highest point of a fixed sphere and at the lowest point of a fixed hollow sphere (figure 71). We can balance the ball in both positions and we say that the ball is *in equilibrium*. The *stability* of the ball in both these positions is concerned with what happens to the ball when it is given a small push. Clearly in the first case the ball rolls off the sphere whilst in the second case the ball rolls to and fro across the equilibrium position. The former we would call *unstable* and the latter *stable* equilibrium. We now attempt to formulate mathematical definitions of stability.

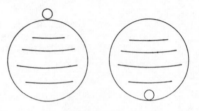

FIGURE 71

Equilibrium we have already encountered in section 3.9. A particle is in equilibrium if the forces acting on it balance and if it is at rest. A rigid body is in equilibrium if the forces balance and the moment of forces about any fixed point balance.

Stability can be defined in a variety of ways. For example, a position of stable equilibrium can be defined as one in which, in any disturbance from the position of equilibrium, the forces acting tend to restore the system to its position of equilibrium or as one in which any sufficiently small disturbance produces a bounded motion about the equilibrium position. It is largely a matter of translating into mathematical language what we think of intuitively as stable equilibrium. Here we shall adopt a definition which involves the kinetic energy.

Suppose a system is in equilibrium and is given any velocities consistent with the constraints acting on the system, and let the kinetic energy so imparted to the system be $\mathcal{T}_0$. Let $\mathcal{T}$ be the kinetic energy of the system when in any subsequent position other than the equilibrium position. If $\mathcal{T} < \mathcal{T}_0$ for all subsequent times for a sufficiently small $\mathcal{T}_0$, we say that the position is *stable*. If this condition is not universally satisfied the position is *unstable*. This means that equilibrium is stable if for any sufficiently small initial disturbance the kinetic energy away from the equilibrium position is less than the initial kinetic energy. $\mathcal{T}$ *may* equal $\mathcal{T}_0$ again at the equilibrium position.

Let us restrict our attention for the moment to a particle of mass m which moves along a curve. Let s denote distance along the curve and suppose that $s = 0$ is an equilibrium position. If the particle is given an initial speed v, $\mathcal{T}_0 = \frac{1}{2}mv^2$ and $\mathcal{T} = \frac{1}{2}m\dot{s}^2$. Our definition asserts that the equilibrium is stable if $\mathcal{T} < \mathcal{T}_0$ or $\dot{s}^2 < v^2$ which implies that the speed at any point must be less than the initial speed: this seems a plausible notion of stability.

The advantage of adopting this definition lies in its generality since it can apply equally to conservative and dissipative systems.

As with most definitions of stability one can construct critical cases in which the theory and experience do not quite match up to one another. Consider a particle placed on a smooth plane. Clearly the particle is in equilibrium. If any horizontal velocity is given to the particle the kinetic energy will be conserved, that is $\mathcal{T} = \mathcal{T}_0$, and by our definition this would be described as unstable equilibrium (this critical case is sometimes described as neutral equilibrium). In contrast, if the particle is placed on a rough horizontal plane any initial kinetic energy must be diminished by the action of friction and the equilibrium position will be stable according to the definition.

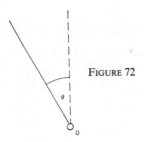

FIGURE 72

The description of energy of a mechanical system requires a recognition of the positions which the system can take up consistent with the *constraints* imposed upon it. For example, suppose the rod in figure 72 is hinged at O to a fixed point and moves in a fixed vertical plane. We say that the rod is *constrained* so that one end point is fixed and the rod moves in a plane. Every possible position of the rod can be described by the angle θ. This example requires one parameter or coordinate θ to describe every *configuration* of the system and for this reason we say that the body has one *degree of freedom*.

A particle moving in space has three degrees of freedom since three independent coordinates are required to fix its position. A rigid body moving freely has six degrees of freedom; three coordinates are needed to determine the translation and three the orientation of the body.

A simple method of testing whether sufficient coordinates have been selected is to fix them: if parts of the system can still be moved, more coordinates are needed. Figure 73 shows a hinged rod AB supported by a spring CB. Once the inclination of AB is fixed by θ the inclination of the spring is determined, and the system has one degree of freedom.

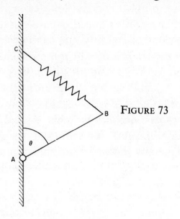

FIGURE 73

5.7 Conservative systems with one degree of freedom

For a system with one degree of freedom any point of the system can be expressed in terms of a single coordinate q. Then $\mathbf{r}(q)$ is the position vector of a point of the system. The velocity and acceleration of this point are given by

$$\dot{\mathbf{r}} = \frac{d\mathbf{r}}{dq}\frac{dq}{dt},$$

$$\ddot{\mathbf{r}} = \frac{d^2\mathbf{r}}{dq^2}\left(\frac{dq}{dt}\right)^2 + \frac{d\mathbf{r}}{dq}\frac{d^2q}{dt^2}.$$

For an equilibrium configuration $\dot{\mathbf{r}} = \ddot{\mathbf{r}} = 0$ which imply that $\dot{q} = \ddot{q} = 0$.

The kinetic energy $\mathscr{T}$ will depend on q and $\dot{q}$ since $\mathscr{T}$ is formed by summing or integrating terms involving the square of the velocity $\dot{\mathbf{r}}$. Thus the kinetic energy must take the form $\mathscr{T} = f(q)\dot{q}^2$. Let us suppose that the potential energy $\mathscr{V}$ depends only on the coordinate q. For a conservative system

$$\mathscr{T} + \mathscr{V} = \text{constant.}$$

Take the time derivative of this equation:

$$\frac{d(\mathscr{T} + \mathscr{V})}{dt} = 0,$$

or

$$\frac{\partial \mathscr{T}}{\partial q}\frac{dq}{dt} + \frac{\partial \mathscr{T}}{\partial \dot{q}}\frac{d\dot{q}}{dt} + \frac{d\mathscr{V}}{dq}\frac{dq}{dt} = 0,$$

or

$$f'(q)\dot{q}^2 + 2f(q)\ddot{q} + \frac{d\mathscr{V}}{dq} = 0.$$

In an equilibrium configuration $\dot{q} = \ddot{q} = 0$ and the last equation implies that $d\mathscr{V}/dq = 0$ in such a configuration. In order to find the equilibrium configuration we simply determine the turning points of the potential energy.

This theory assumes that the potential energy in a smooth function of q; the potential energy may have minima or maxima which are not revealed by considering the derivative of the potential energy. A ball placed in a cone is self-evidently in stable equilibrium but the potential energy does not have an analytic minimum, that is a minimum which can be found by setting the derivative equal to zero.

Suppose that the potential energy in an equilibrium state is $\mathscr{V}_0$ and that the system is given a small quantity of kinetic energy $\mathscr{T}_0$. The energy equation for this motion is

$$\mathscr{T} + \mathscr{V} = \mathscr{T}_0 + \mathscr{V}_0 \quad \text{or} \quad \mathscr{T} - \mathscr{T}_0 = \mathscr{V}_0 - \mathscr{V}.$$

For stable equilibrium $\mathscr{T} < \mathscr{T}_0$, according to our definition, which implies that $\mathscr{V}_0 < \mathscr{V}$ which in turn means that the potential must have a *minimum* value at the equilibrium position. If $\mathscr{V}$ does not have a minimum the configuration is unstable. The usual tests in calculus for a minimum apply if $\mathscr{V}$ is sufficiently smooth. There are three simple methods of testing for a minimum: $\mathscr{V}$ has a minimum at $q = q_0$ if $\mathscr{V}'(q_0) = 0$ and one of the following conditions holds:

  (i) $\mathscr{V}(q_0 + h) > \mathscr{V}(q_0)$, $\mathscr{V}(q_0 - h) > \mathscr{V}(q_0)$, $h > 0$ and sufficiently small,
  (ii) $\mathscr{V}'(q_0 + h) > 0$, $\mathscr{V}'(q_0 - h) < 0$, $h > 0$ and sufficiently small,
  (iii) $\mathscr{V}''(q_0) > 0$.

Example 8 Suppose in the system depicted in figure 73 the rod AB has mass m and length a, AC $= a$ and the spring CB has natural length $\frac{1}{2}a$ and modulus $\frac{1}{2}mg$. Find the equilibrium configurations.

Let θ be the inclination of the rod to the vertical. The potential energy has two terms, one for the rod and one for the stretched spring:

$$\mathscr{V} = \tfrac{1}{2}mga \cos \theta + \tfrac{1}{2} \cdot \frac{2\lambda}{a}(d - \tfrac{1}{2}a)^2,$$

where

$$d = \text{BC} = 2a \sin \tfrac{1}{2}\theta.$$

Putting $\lambda = \tfrac{1}{2}mg$, we have

$$\mathscr{V} = \tfrac{1}{2}mga \cos \theta + \tfrac{1}{2}mga(2 \sin \tfrac{1}{2}\theta - \tfrac{1}{2})^2.$$

In the equilibrium configurations

$$\frac{d\mathscr{V}}{d\theta} = 0 = -\tfrac{1}{2}mga \sin \theta + mga \cos \tfrac{1}{2}\theta(2 \sin \tfrac{1}{2}\theta - \tfrac{1}{2}).$$

Expressing $\sin \theta$ in terms of half-angles the condition reduces to

$$\cos \tfrac{1}{2}\theta \cdot (\sin \tfrac{1}{2}\theta - \tfrac{1}{2}) = 0,$$

or

$$\cos \tfrac{1}{2}\theta = 0 \quad \text{and} \quad \sin \tfrac{1}{2}\theta = \tfrac{1}{2}.$$

The equilibrium configurations are essentially $\theta = 180°$ and $\theta = 60°$.

To investigate the stability we obtain the second derivative of $\mathscr{V}$. It is easy to verify that

$$\mathscr{V}''(\theta) = \tfrac{1}{4}mga(2 \cos \theta \cdot + \sin \tfrac{1}{2}\theta),$$

whence

$$\mathscr{V}''(\pi) = \tfrac{1}{4}mga(-2 + 1) < 0, \qquad \mathscr{V}''(\tfrac{1}{3}\pi) = \tfrac{1}{4}mga(1 + \tfrac{1}{2}) > 0.$$

The configuration in which ABC is an equilateral triangle is in stable equilibrium, and the one with B vertically below A is unstable.

Example 9   A simple pendulum consists of a bob of mass m suspended by a light rod of length a from a free pivot. A spring of stiffness k and natural length b is attached to the bob and to a wheel which runs in a horizontal groove passing through the support (figure 74). The spring remains vertical.

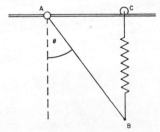

FIGURE 74

Let θ be the inclination of the pendulum to the downward vertical.

The potential energy of the bob $= - mga \cos \theta$.
  The potential of the spring $= \frac{1}{2}k(a \cos \theta - b)^2$.
  The total potential energy, $\mathscr{V} = - mga \cos \theta + \frac{1}{2}k(a \cos \theta - b)^2$.

The turning points of $\mathscr{V}$ are given by

$$\mathscr{V}'(\theta) = 0 = mga \sin \theta - ak \sin \theta(a \cos \theta - b),$$

which has solutions

$$\sin \theta = 0 \quad \text{and} \quad \cos \theta = (mg + bk)/ak.$$

The second solution is real if $mg + bk \leqslant ak$. There are two solutions $\theta = 0$, $\theta = \pi$ if $mg + bk \geqslant ak$ and essentially three solutions (taking account of symmetry about $\theta = 0$) if $mg + bk < ak$; the additional equilibrium position is $\cos^{-1}[(mg + bk)/ak]$.
  Now

$$\mathscr{V}''(\theta) = \cos \theta \cdot (mga - a^2k \cos \theta + akb) + a^2k \sin^2 \theta.$$

For the equilibrium position $\theta = 0$:

$$\mathscr{V}''(0) = a(mg + kb - ak) > 0 \quad \text{if} \quad mg + kb > ak$$
$$\leqslant 0 \quad \text{if} \quad mg + kb \leqslant ak.$$

The situation in which B is below A is stable if only two equilibrium positions exist, and unstable otherwise.
  For $\theta = \pi$:

$$\mathscr{V}''(\pi) = - a(mg + kb + ak) < 0,$$

and the position with B above A is always unstable.
  The third position exists only if $mg + bk < ak$ in which case (call the angle θ_1):

$$\mathscr{V}''(\theta_1) = a^2k \sin^2 \theta_1 > 0,$$

and this position is always stable.

We can summarize the method by looking at a graph of potential energy against the coordinate q shown in figure 75. Suppose (a), (b), (c) and (d) are positions of equilibrium. The behaviour of $\mathscr{V}$ at these points is as follows:

 (a) $\mathscr{V}$ has maximum; unstable equilibrium,
 (b) $\mathscr{V}$ has minimum; stable equilibrium,
 (c) $\mathscr{V}$ has point of inflexion; unstable equilibrium,
 (d) $\mathscr{V}$ has a maximum which is a cusp; unstable equilibrium.

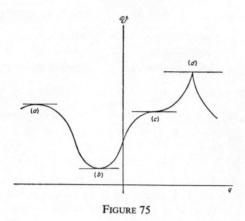

FIGURE 75

5.8 Non-conservative systems with one degree of freedom

The equation of motion for a non-conservative system will be generally an ordinary differential equation of the form

$$f(x, \dot{x}) = \ddot{x}, \tag{12}$$

where x is not necessarily displacement but may be an angle or an area, etc., depending on the particular coordinate chosen. However, the equation may be thought of as expressing force/unit mass = acceleration. Equilibrium positions will occur when $\ddot{x}$ and $\dot{x}$ simultaneously vanish and consequently we can find them by solving the equation $f(x, 0) = 0$ for x. Their stability will depend on the behaviour of the kinetic energy in the neighbourhood of the equilibrium positions and this will necessitate one integration of (12). We can do no more than outline the technique by two examples since no energy equation of the form $\mathscr{T} + \mathscr{V} = $ constant holds for non-conservative systems.

Example 10   A block of mass m is held on a rough inclined plane by a spring parallel to the plane as shown in figure 76. The natural length of the spring is a and its modulus is λ. The frictional force is in magnitude proportional to the speed of the block. Find the position of equilibrium.

Let x be the displacement of the block. The forces acting on the block are the tension of the spring, the frictional force, the weight of the block and the reaction due to the plane (not shown in figure 76 since it is not required). The equation of motion parallel to the inclined plane is

$$mg \sin \alpha - T - F = m\ddot{x},$$

or

$$mg \sin \alpha - \frac{\lambda(x - a)}{a} - k\dot{x} = m\ddot{x}, \qquad (13)$$

where k is a known constant. The equilibrium position occurs where $\ddot{x} = \dot{x} = 0$, that is, where

$$x = a + \frac{mga}{\lambda} \sin \alpha.$$

In fact this is the position in which the tension in the spring is balanced by the component of the weight of the block down the plane.

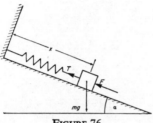

FIGURE 76

Example 11   A parabolic wire with equation $2y = x^2$ rotates with constant angular speed ω about the y-axis which points vertically upwards. The distance x of a bead, which slides on the wire, from the axis of rotation satisfies the differential equation

$$(1 + x^2)\ddot{x} + (g - \omega^2 + \dot{x}^2)x = 0. \qquad (14)$$

Find the positions of equilibrium and determine their stability.

An equilibrium position is such that $\ddot{x} = \dot{x} = 0$ which from the given equation must satisfy

$$(g - \omega^2)x = 0.$$

Thus $x = 0$ is an equilibrium position provided that $g \neq \omega^2$ and the bead is in equilibrium for any value of x if $g = \omega^2$.

In order to investigate the relative stability we examine firstly the kinetic energy *relative to the wire*. The bead has velocity components $\dot{x}$ outwards and $\dot{y}$ upwards relative to the wire. The kinetic energy is therefore

$$\mathcal{T} = \tfrac{1}{2}m(\dot{x}^2 + \dot{y}^2)$$
$$= \tfrac{1}{2}m(\dot{x}^2 + x^2\dot{x}^2),$$

where m is the mass of the bead. We now require $\dot{x}$ from equation (14). We can write the equation as

$$(1 + x^2)\dot{x}\frac{d\dot{x}}{dx} + (g - \omega^2 + \dot{x}^2)x = 0,$$

which is an equation of separable type. Consequently

$$\int \frac{\dot{x}\,d\dot{x}}{g - \omega^2 + \dot{x}^2} = - \int \frac{x\,dx}{1 + x^2} + C,$$

or

$$\tfrac{1}{2}\ln(g - \omega^2 + \dot{x}^2) = -\tfrac{1}{2}\ln(1 + x^2) + C,$$

or

$$(g - \omega^2 + \dot{x}^2)(1 + x^2) = A,$$

a further constant. Thus

$$\dot{x}^2 = \frac{A}{1 + x^2} + \omega^2 - g,$$

and finally

$$\mathscr{T} = \tfrac{1}{2}m[A + (\omega^2 - g)(1 + x^2)].$$

Suppose now that $\mathscr{T} = \mathscr{T}_0$ when $x = 0$ so that

$$\mathscr{T}_0 = \tfrac{1}{2}m(A + \omega^2 - g),$$

or

$$A = \frac{2\mathscr{T}_0}{m} - \omega^2 + g.$$

The kinetic energy difference

$$\mathscr{T} - \mathscr{T}_0 = \tfrac{1}{2}m(\omega^2 - g)x^2.$$

Now $\mathscr{T} < \mathscr{T}_0$ for $x \neq 0$ if $\omega^2 < g$, and the lowest point of the parabola is a position of stable equilibrium. If $\omega^2 \geqslant g$, $\mathscr{T} \geqslant \mathscr{T}_0$ and, according to the definition, the bead must then be in unstable equilibrium.

It should be noted that the stability illustrated in this problem is relative to the wire. The actual kinetic energy $\mathscr{T}'$ of the bead including the rotation is given by

$$\mathscr{T}' - \mathscr{T}_0 = \tfrac{1}{2}m(\omega^2 - g)x^2 + \tfrac{1}{2}m\omega^2 x^2 = \tfrac{1}{2}m(2\omega^2 - g)x^2.$$

The lowest point is now absolutely stable if $\omega^2 < \tfrac{1}{2}g$ even though any oscillation about this point is bounded for $\omega^2 < g$. The reason for this apparent contradiction is that the actual *speed* of the bead *increases* for $\omega^2 > \tfrac{1}{2}g$ whilst the speed relative to the wire decreases for $\omega^2 < g$.

Exercises

1. Find the work required to lift a satellite of mass 200 kg to a height of 1,000 km above the earth's surface. [Radius of earth = 6,400 km].

2. Calculate the work done in sliding a block of weight 22 kg up a plane inclined at 30° to the horizontal through a distance of 15 m against a frictional force of 30 N.

3. Water flows over a waterfall of height 100 m at a rate of 250 m³/s. Estimate the total power of the waterfall.

4. Determine the efficiency of a pump which is driven by a 1·6 kW motor if it takes 60 hours to raise 10^4 m³ of water to a height of 3 m. [The mechanical efficiency of a machine is the ratio of output work to input work and must always be less than unity since work is lost in overcoming internal resistance in the machine.]

5. With the steam shut off, a train of mass 3×10^5 kg descends an incline of 1 in 100 at a constant speed of 50 km/h. Find the resistance to motion. At the foot of the incline the steam is turned on and the train moves on a level track. If the engine develops 500 kW and the resistance to motion is unchanged, find the initial acceleration of the train, and its maximum speed on the level.

6. A train of mass 10^5 kg starts from rest along a level track. It reaches a speed of 50 km/h in 2 min and the resistance to motion is 4,000 N. Calculate the power at which the engine must be capable of working assuming it accelerates uniformly.

7. A sphere sliding along a horizontal plane with velocity v_1 collides with a second sphere moving in the same straight line with velocity v_2 in the same direction. If the coefficient of restitution is e and the spheres both have the same mass m, find the kinetic energy lost in the impact.

8. The power output of the engine of a car is given in kW by

$$P = An\, e^{-nk},$$

where n is the engine speed in r.p.m. and A and k are constants. The maximum output of 50 kW occurs at 4,000 r.p.m. In top gear 5,000 r.p.m. corresponds to 100 km/h. Obtain the shortest time for the car to accelerate from 50 km/h to 120 km/h in top gear if its weight is 1,000 kg.

9. Express the kinetic energy of a particle moving in a plane in terms of polar coordinates.

Two particles of masses M and m are connected by an inextensible string of negligible mass which passes through a small smooth ring on a smooth horizontal table. The particles are at rest with the string taut and straight and M at a distance a from the ring. M is now projected at right angles to the string. Prove that its path until m reaches the ring is

$$r = a \sec \{\theta[M/(M+m)]^{\frac{1}{2}}\}$$

in polar coordinates.

10. A light elastic string passing over a smooth peg has masses M and m attached to its ends. The system is released from rest with the string just slack. Show that after time t, the tension (assumed to be the same throughout the string) is $2mMg(1 - \cos nt)/(m + M)$ where $n^2 = \lambda(M + m)/aMm$, λ and a being the modulus of elasticity and natural length of the string respectively.

11. An elastic string of natural length 50 cm has an extension of 5 cm when a mass of 10 gm is suspended by it. The mass is pulled down a further 10 cm and released. Find the maximum height reached by the mass subsequently.

12. The overhead door shown in figure 77 weighs 100 kg and is released from rest in the position shown. The two springs each have an unstrained length of 0·4 m and are designed so that the door just comes to rest when closed, and is held in that position by a catch. Determine the elastic properties of the springs. Ignore friction and any energy losses occurring at the impact of the door and springs.

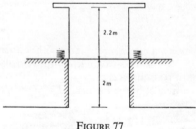

FIGURE 77

13. Figure 78 shows (schematically) a 'block and tackle'. What force F must be applied at the free end of the rope in order to lift a load of weight W? The weight of the lower block is w and friction is negligible.

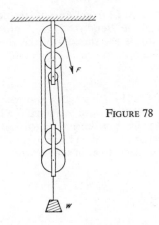

FIGURE 78

14. A heavy uniform rod AB of length $2a$ rests with A in contact with a smooth vertical wall and a point of it against a smooth peg distance b ($< a$) from the wall. Find the equilibrium position and examine its stability.

15. On the smooth surface of a fixed horizontal circular cylinder lie two masses m and M connected by a light cord, the cord subtending an angle ϕ at the centre of the circular cross-section in which it lies. Find the position of equilibrium and show that it is always unstable.

16. A uniform plank of thickness $2h$ can roll without slipping on a fixed horizontal circular cylinder of radius a. Show that the equilibrium position in which the plank lies perpendicular to the cylinder is stable or unstable according as $a \gtrless h$.

17. A heavy uniform rod AB of length $2a$ and mass $2M$ is hinged at a fixed point A. End B is tied to a light string which passes over a smooth peg fixed vertically above A and distance c above A. A particle of mass M is attached to the other end of the string. Find the positions of equilibrium and show that the position in which AB is vertical is stable if $a < c$.

18. A pulley of radius a, free to rotate in a vertical plane, has its centre fixed at a distance $2a$ from a vertical rod. A mass m hangs from a light cord which is attached to the circumference of the pulley at a point R on the upper semi-circle of the pulley. A spring of natural length $2a$ and modulus $8mg$ extends from R to a slide B which runs freely on the vertical rod such that RB always remains horizontal. Find the positions of equilibrum of the system and determine their stability.

19. A bead of mass m can slide freely on a vertical circular wire of radius a. A spring of natural length $3a/2$ and modulus λ joins the bead to the highest point of the wire. Investigate the stability of the equilibrium positions in the two cases $\lambda = 12mg, \lambda = mg$.

20. A crane boom of mass 600 kg and length 8 m supports a load of mass 5,000 kg at its end (see figure 79). A cable attached to a point 6 m from the hinged end of the boom passes over a fixed pulley 8 m above the hinge and carries a load of mass M. Neglecting friction, determine the relation between θ, the inclination of the boom to the vertical, and M for the system to be in equilibrium.

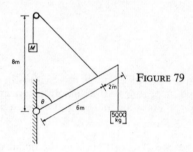

FIGURE 79

21. An inverted pendulum consists of a light rigid rod of length l which carries a mass m at its upper end and is smoothly pivoted at its lower end. At a distance d from the pivot, two springs each of modulus λ with the same natural length are attached to the rod and join the rod to two vertical walls on either side of the rod and equidistant from it when the rod is vertical. In this position the springs are horizontal. Find the condition that this position of equilibrium is stable in the vertical plane perpendicular to the walls.

22. A square frame, consisting of four equal uniform rods of length $2a$ joined rigidly together, hangs at rest in a vertical plane on two smooth pegs P and Q at the same level. If PQ $= c$ and the pegs are not both in contact with the same rod, show that there are three positions of equilibrium if $c < a < \sqrt{2}c$ and one otherwise. Investigate their stability.

23. A uniform heavy chain of mass M and length $2l$ hangs symmetrically over a rough roller of radius a which is free to turn on its axis. A mass M is attached to the lowest point of the roller. Find the condition for this position of equilibrium to be stable. If it is stable show that there are an odd number of positions of equilibrium on each side of the symmetrical position and that they are alternately unstable and stable.

24. A block lies on a rough horizontal plane. A spring of modulus W and natural length h is attached to the block and to a fixed point distance h above the block. The block, which has weight W, slips if the applied horizontal force exceeds μR where R is the normal reaction between block and plane. Find all positions of equilibrium if $\mu = \sqrt{3}$.

25. A block of mass m stands on a rough belt which moves with constant velocity v being driven by two rollers. The block is restrained by a horizontal spring attached to a fixed support as shown in figure 80. The modulus of elasticity

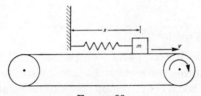

FIGURE 80

of the spring is λ and its natural length is a. The frictional resistance between the block and belt is k times the slip velocity (the velocity of the block relative to the belt). Find the equation of motion of the block in terms of its displacement x from the support. Where is the equilibrium position? In its equilibrium position the block is given a velocity w. Find the subsequent displacement and velocity of the block if $k = 3m$ and $\lambda = 5ma/4$.

6

Variable mass: rocket motion

6.1 The equation of motion

So far we have dealt exclusively with particles and bodies whose mass remains constant during the motion. In certain problems we cannot make this assumption. A rocket is propelled by ejecting burnt fuel which causes the total mass of the rocket to decrease substantially as the rocket accelerates. A raindrop falling through a damp atmosphere coalesces with smaller droplets which increase its mass. In both these illustrations the mass of a body is varying with time; the term 'variable mass' is slightly misleading since we do not mean that mass is being created or destroyed, but simply that it is being continuously removed from or added to the body.

Let a body of mass $m(t)$ moving with velocity **v** coalesce with a small mass δm moving with velocity **u** so that after a time interval δt we have a

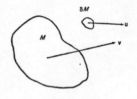

FIGURE 81

body with a combined mass of $m + \delta m$ (figure 81). We shall assume that the body is translating and that the acquisition of additional mass does not create a rotation of the body. Suppose the body is subject to an external force **F**; our fundamental postulate asserts that force will balance the rate of change of linear momentum for the system. However the force will include a term due to the continuous impulsive action on the body of the mass being acquired. During the time interval δt the body must acquire *additional* linear momentum $\mathbf{u}\delta m$ since δm *coalesces* with m. The rate of acquisition of this linear momentum must therefore be

$$\lim_{\delta t \to 0} \mathbf{u}\frac{\delta m}{\delta t} = \mathbf{u}\frac{dm}{dt}.$$

This additional *force* combines with the external force $\mathbf{F}$ to give the total *effective* force acting on the body. Thus

$$\mathbf{F} + \mathbf{u}\frac{dm}{dt} = \frac{d}{dt}(m\mathbf{v}) = \mathbf{v}\frac{dm}{dt} + m\frac{d\mathbf{v}}{dt},$$

since $m\mathbf{v}$ is the linear momentum of the body. Alternatively, we may write

$$\mathbf{F} = (\mathbf{v} - \mathbf{u})\frac{dm}{dt} + m\frac{d\mathbf{v}}{dt}. \tag{1}$$

Equation (1) is the fundamental equation for motion with variable mass and in this equation the rate of mass addition and its velocity will be required as functions of time. If mass is being removed, as in a rocket, dm/dt will be negative.

It should be emphasized that for variable mass problems the equation of motion becomes

force = rate of change of linear momentum

only if $\mathbf{u} = \mathbf{0}$, that is, if the mass being added or removed is at rest.

Example 1   A balloon of mass M contains a bag of sand of mass m_0, and the balloon is in equilibrium. The sand is released at a constant rate and is disposed of in a time t_0. Find the height of the balloon and its velocity when all the sand has been released. Assume that the balloon experiences a constant upthrust and neglect air resistance.

In equilibrium the upthrust F must balance the weight of the balloon and sand:

$$F = (M + m_0)g.$$

Let m be the mass of sand at time t where $0 \leqslant t \leqslant t_0$. Then

$$m = m_0\left(1 - \frac{t}{t_0}\right), \tag{2}$$

since the sand is released at a constant rate. The velocity of the sand relative to the balloon is zero on release with the result that $\mathbf{v} = \mathbf{u}$ in equation (1). Let x be the subsequent displacement of the balloon. Its equation of motion becomes

$$(M + m_0)g - (M + m)g = (M + m)\frac{dv}{dt}, \tag{3}$$

where $v = \dot{x}$. On substituting for m from (2) into (3):

$$\frac{dv}{dt} = \frac{m_0 g t}{(M + m_0)t_0 - m_0 t} = -g + \frac{(M + m_0)g t_0}{(M + m_0)t_0 - m_0 t}.$$

This is a variables separable equation with solution

$$v = -gt - \frac{(M + m_0)g t_0}{m_0} \ln\left[1 - \frac{m_0 t}{(M + m_0)t_0}\right], \tag{4}$$

where the initial condition $v = 0$ when $t = 0$ has been used.
   The differential equation for the displacement,

$$\frac{dx}{dt} = -gt - \frac{(M + m_0)g t_0}{m_0} \ln\left[1 - \frac{m_0 t}{(M + m_0)t_0}\right],$$

is again of separable type with solution

$$x = C - \int\left[gt + \frac{g}{k} \ln(1 - kt)\right] dt, \qquad k = m_0/t_0(M + m_0),$$

$$= C - \tfrac{1}{2}gt^2 - \frac{gt}{k} \ln(1 - kt) - g\int \frac{t\,dt}{1 - kt}, \text{ integrating by parts,}$$

$$= C - \tfrac{1}{2}gt^2 - \frac{gt}{k} \ln(1 - kt) - \frac{g}{k}\int\left(-1 + \frac{1}{1 - kt}\right) dt$$

$$= C - \tfrac{1}{2}gt^2 - \frac{gt}{k} \ln(1 - kt) + \frac{gt}{k} + \frac{g}{k^2} \ln(1 - kt)$$

$$= C - \tfrac{1}{2}gt^2 + \frac{g}{k^2}(1 - kt) \ln(1 - kt) + \frac{gt}{k}.$$

Taking the initial condition to be $x = 0$ when $t = 0$, we see that $C = 0$. Thus

$$x = \frac{gt}{k} - \tfrac{1}{2}gt^2 + \frac{g}{k^2}(1 - kt) \ln(1 - kt). \tag{5}$$

All equations and solutions hold only during the time interval $0 \leqslant t \leqslant t_0$.

At time $t = t_0$ the balloon has reached a height

$$x_0 = \frac{gt_0^2}{2m_0^2}\left[(2M + m_0)m_0 + 2M(M + m_0)\ln\left(\frac{M}{M + m_0}\right)\right],$$

and is moving with speed

$$v_0 = \frac{gt_0}{m_0}\left[(M + m_0)\ln\left(\frac{M + m_0}{M}\right) - m_0\right].$$

In practice the quantity of sand carried is small so that the ratio m_0/M is small: denote this ratio by ε. Then, for small ε,

$$x_0 = \frac{gt_0^2}{2\varepsilon^2}[(2 + \varepsilon)\varepsilon - 2(1 + \varepsilon)\ln(1 + \varepsilon)]$$

$$= \frac{gt_0^2}{2\varepsilon^2}\left[2\varepsilon + \varepsilon^2 - 2(1 + \varepsilon)\left(\varepsilon - \frac{\varepsilon^2}{2} + \frac{\varepsilon^3}{3} - \cdots\right)\right]$$

$$\simeq \frac{gt_0^2\varepsilon}{6},$$

by using the Maclaurin expansion for $\ln(1 + \varepsilon)$. Similarly

$$v_0 = \frac{gt_0}{\varepsilon}[(1 + \varepsilon)\ln(1 + \varepsilon) - \varepsilon]$$

$$= \frac{gt_0}{\varepsilon}\left[(1 + \varepsilon)\left(\varepsilon - \frac{\varepsilon^2}{2} + \cdots\right) - \varepsilon\right]$$

$$\simeq \tfrac{1}{2}gt_0\varepsilon.$$

A simple calculation shows that a balloon of mass 500 kg will rise through a height of about 330 m from equilibrium if 10 kg of sand is released over a period of 100 s.

6.2 Rocket motion

The rocket motor is an important application of the variable mass equation. It can be thought of in very simple terms as a cylinder closed at one end in which fuel is burnt and ejected through the open end. The analysis of rocket motion can be extremely complicated when such factors as gravitational effects and rocket orientation, and the construction of the rocket are taken into account. We shall look at some simple models which are capable of relatively simple analysis. Two parameters are assumed known—the rate at which the propellant is ejected and its exhaust velocity. The exhaust velocity **c** is the velocity of the burnt fuel relative to the rocket casing; that is, $c = u - v$. Thus the equation of motion of a rocket of mass m moving with velocity v subject to an external force F is

$$F = m\frac{dv}{dt} - c\frac{dm}{dt}.$$ (6)

Remember that dm/dt is negative in rocket problems.

Example 2   A rocket of total mass M contains fuel of mass εM $(0 < \varepsilon < 1)$. When ignited the fuel burns at a constant mass-rate k, ejecting exhaust gases with constant speed c. Ignoring gravity, find the speed imparted to the rocket by the complete burning of the fuel.

Let m be the mass of the rocket at time t whilst the fuel is burning, so that $m = M$ at $t = 0$ and $m = M(1 - \varepsilon)$ when the fuel is exhausted. We are given that

$$k = -\frac{dm}{dt},$$

from which we deduce that

$$m = M - kt.$$ (7)

Suppose the rocket starts from rest and achieves a final velocity Vi where i is a unit vector in the direction of motion. Since no external force acts on the rocket, $F = 0$. The exhaust velocity $c = -ci$. Equation (6) becomes

$$m\frac{dv}{dt} = ck,$$

or, with m given by (7),

$$\frac{dv}{dt} = \frac{ck}{M - kt}.$$ (8)

Also from (7), we note that the fuel is burnt in a time $T = \varepsilon M/k$. Integration of (8) through the burning time yields

$$\int_0^V dv = ck \int_0^T \frac{dt}{M - kt},$$

or

$$V = -c[\ln(M - kt)]_0^T$$
$$= -c\ln[(M - kT)/M] = -c\ln(1 - \varepsilon),$$

which is the final speed of the rocket.

A typical maximum value for ε is about $\frac{5}{6}$ (that is, $\frac{5}{6}$ of the total mass of the rocket is fuel; the remaining $\frac{1}{6}$ being the mass of the rocket casing, payload, etc.). Such a rocket could achieve a speed of $c \ln 6 \simeq 1 \cdot 8c$, that is $1 \cdot 8 \times$ exhaust velocity of the burning propellant.

Example 3   A rocket engine of mass 3×10^5 kg can eject exhaust gases at 3,000 m/s at a rate of 10^4 kg/s. The rocket is fired vertically from the earth's surface. Show that such a rocket would not be capable, in practice, of escaping from the earth's gravitational field. Assume that the gravitational force on the rocket is constant for the period during which the fuel burns.

Let $\mathbf{k}$ be the upward unit vector at the earth's surface. In the notation of equation (6), $\mathbf{F} = -mg\mathbf{k}$, $\mathbf{c} = -c\mathbf{k}$, $m = M - kt$, where $M = 3 \times 10^5$ kg, $c = 3,000$ m/s and $k = 10^4$ kg/s. The equation of motion becomes

$$- (M - kt)g = (M - kt)\frac{\mathrm{d}v}{\mathrm{d}t} - ck,$$

or

$$\frac{\mathrm{d}v}{\mathrm{d}t} = -g + \frac{ck}{M - kt}.$$

Integrating this equation, we find that

$$v = -gt - c \ln (M - kt) + c \ln M,$$

after putting $v = 0$ when $t = 0$. Writing $v = \mathrm{d}x/\mathrm{d}t$ in the preceding equation and integrating a second time, we obtain

$$x = -\tfrac{1}{2}gt^2 + ct + \frac{c}{k}(M - kt) \ln [(M - kt)/M],$$

using the condition $x = 0$ when $t = 0$.

The maximum ratio of fuel mass to total mass of a rocket is about $\frac{5}{6}$ which means that the maximum fuel capacity is $2 \cdot 5 \times 10^5$ kg. With the figures given above the fuel is exhausted at a height of 99,000 m which, by the way, justifies our uniform approximation for the gravitational force on the rocket. At this height the rocket is moving at about 5,000 m/s. The escape velocity from the surface of the earth is 11,000 m/s (Example 6, section 4.2), which differs little from the escape velocity at 99,000 m. A *single-stage* rocket with the characteristics given will therefore not escape the earth's gravitational field.

6.3 The multi-stage rocket

The overall performance of a rocket can be improved by designing the rocket in stages which in the two-stage rocket means that one rocket is placed on top of a second rocket. When the fuel in the first stage is exhausted its rocket casing is detached and the second stage ignited. The shedding of the surplus mass contained in the casing of the expended fuel considerably improves a rocket's performance.

Consider a rocket consisting of two equal stages each of mass M of which the proportion $\varepsilon M (0 < \varepsilon < 1)$ in each stage is propellant. The rocket carries a payload of mass m. Suppose we wish to find the final velocity given to the payload. The exhaust speed is c throughout. The problem has two parts. The total mass of the rocket is initially $2M + m$ and during the first stage εM mass of fuel is burnt. This is essentially the same problem as that solved in Example 2 above. Modifying the result slightly, we can deduce that the rocket's velocity at the end of the first stage is

$$- c \ln \left(1 - \frac{\varepsilon M}{2M + m} \right).$$

Mass $(1 - \varepsilon)M$ is now detached from the rocket, and we have exactly the same problem as in Example 2 again with fuel of mass εM and a rocket of mass $M + m$. The rocket receives an additional boost in velocity of

$$- c \ln \left(1 - \frac{\varepsilon M}{M + m} \right)$$

during the second stage. The total velocity imparted to the payload is therefore

$$- c \ln \left(1 - \frac{\varepsilon M}{2M + m} \right) - c \ln \left(1 - \frac{\varepsilon M}{M + m} \right).$$

If $\varepsilon = \frac{5}{6}$ and $M = 100m$, the total added velocity becomes

$$- c \ln \left(1 - \frac{500}{1206} \right) - c \ln \left(1 - \frac{500}{606} \right) = (0 \cdot 5 + 1 \cdot 8)c = 2 \cdot 3c,$$

compared with a single-stage rocket with $\varepsilon = \frac{5}{6}$ and $M = 200m$ (to keep the payload in the same proportion to the total mass) in which the added velocity is

$$- c \ln \left(1 - \frac{1000}{1206} \right) = 1 \cdot 8c.$$

The reader should verify that the formula for the final velocity of the two-stage rocket generalizes to a rocket of n equal stages each containing the same proportion ε of fuel. The final velocity of such a rocket is

$$- c \ln \prod_{r=1}^{n} \left(1 - \frac{\varepsilon M}{rM + m} \right).$$

In fact, the rocket of equal stages is not generally the optimum construction. We shall obtain now under rather simple conditions the best two-stage rocket of mass M in order that it should give the maximum velocity to a satellite of mass m. Suppose that a proportion ε of each stage is fuel. Let M_1 and M_2 be the masses of the two stages so that

$$M_1 + M_2 = M.$$

Using the technique above again, we see that the velocity achieved by the satellite is given by

$$v = -c \ln\left(1 - \frac{\varepsilon M_1}{M + m}\right) - c \ln\left(1 - \frac{\varepsilon M_2}{M_2 + m}\right)$$

$$= -c \ln\left[1 - \frac{\varepsilon(M - M_2)}{M + m}\right] - c \ln\left(1 - \frac{\varepsilon M_2}{M_2 + m}\right), \qquad (9)$$

expressed in terms of the unknown M_2. We wish to find M_2 such that v takes its maximum value. The turning points of v are given by the equation $dv/dM_2 = 0$, or

$$\frac{\varepsilon}{M + m - \varepsilon(M - M_2)} = \frac{\varepsilon m}{(M_2 + m - \varepsilon M_2)(M_2 + m)}.$$

Simplifying this equation, we have

$$M_2{}^2 + 2mM_2 - mM = 0.$$

Note that the relation is *independent* of ε. Obviously M_2 must be the *positive* root of this quadratic equation:

$$M_2 = -m + (m^2 + mM)^{\frac{1}{2}}.$$

In practice m/M will be a small number α, say. Thus

$$\frac{M_2}{M} = -\alpha + \alpha^{\frac{1}{2}}(1 + \alpha)^{\frac{1}{2}} \simeq \alpha^{\frac{1}{2}},$$

discarding α compared with $\alpha^{\frac{1}{2}}$. We find from (9) that

$$v_{max} \simeq -c \ln\left[1 - \frac{\varepsilon(1 - \alpha^{\frac{1}{2}})}{1 + \alpha}\right] - c \ln\left(1 - \frac{\varepsilon \alpha^{\frac{1}{2}}}{\alpha + \alpha^{\frac{1}{2}}}\right)$$

$$\simeq -c \ln\left[1 - \varepsilon(1 - \alpha^{\frac{1}{2}})\right] - c \ln\left[1 - \varepsilon(1 - \alpha^{\frac{1}{2}})\right]$$

$$= -2c \ln\left[1 - \varepsilon(1 - \alpha^{\frac{1}{2}})\right],$$

if we neglect powers of α of degree higher than $\alpha^{\frac{1}{2}}$.

If $\alpha = 1/100$, $M_2 = M/10$, and

$$v_{max} = 2c \ln 4 = 2 \cdot 8 c$$

by using $\varepsilon = \frac{5}{6}$ again. We conclude that the first stage should be made much larger than the second in order to obtain a high final speed for the satellite.

Exercises

1. A rocket of total mass M contains a proportion εM $(0 < \varepsilon < 1)$ as fuel. If the exhaust speed c is constant show that the final speed of the rocket is independent of the rate at which the fuel is burnt.

2. A rocket of mass M ejects fuel at a constant rate k with exhaust speed c. Show that the rocket will not rise initially from the earth's surface unless $k > Mg/c$.

3. A rocket of total mass $M + m_0$ contains fuel of mass εM $(\varepsilon < 1)$. The payload is of mass m_0 and $(1 - \varepsilon)M$ is the mass of the rocket casing. Suppose it is technically possible to discard the casing continuously at a constant rate whilst the fuel is burning so that no casing remains when the fuel is burnt. If the fuel is burnt at the constant rate k show that the casing must be discarded at the rate $(1 - \varepsilon)k/\varepsilon$. Verify that, if $\varepsilon = \frac{5}{6}$ and $m_0 = M/100$, the rocket's final speed will be approximately $3 \cdot 8c$.

4. A liquid oxygen rocket has an exhaust speed of 2,440 m/s. How far will a single-stage rocket burning liquid oxygen travel from the earth if its fuel/total mass ratio is $\frac{2}{3}$ and the fuel is burnt in 150 s? Assume g to be constant.

5. A balloon of mass 400 kg has suspended from it a rope of mass 100 kg and length 100 m. The buoyancy force of the balloon is sufficient to support a mass of 450 kg. Initially it is falling at its terminal speed of 10 m/s due to air resistance which is proportional to the square of its speed. Show that if m is the total mass of the balloon and rope t sec after the rope has first touched the ground, then the equation of motion can be written as

$$m\frac{\mathrm{d}^2 m}{\mathrm{d}t^2} + g(m - 450) = 0.$$

By writing $\dfrac{\mathrm{d}^2 m}{\mathrm{d}t^2}$ as $\dfrac{\mathrm{d}m}{\mathrm{d}t}\dfrac{\mathrm{d}}{\mathrm{d}m}\left(\dfrac{\mathrm{d}m}{\mathrm{d}t}\right)$, solve the differential equation and find the speed of the balloon:
   (i) when 50 m of rope lies on the ground,
   (ii) when the balloon hits the ground.
Give a physical explanation for the speeds you obtain.

6. A rocket consists of a payload of mass m propelled by two stages of masses M_1 (first stage) and M_2 (second stage). Each stage has the same exhaust speed c and contains the same proportion ε (< 1) of fuel. Show that the final speed of the rocket is given by

$$v = -c \ln\left(1 - \frac{\varepsilon M_1}{M_1 + M_2 + m}\right) - c \ln\left(1 - \frac{\varepsilon M_2}{M_2 + m}\right).$$

If $\varepsilon = \frac{5}{6}$ and $M_1 = 9M_2$, show that the maximum payload which can be given a final velocity of $2 \cdot 5c$ is $0 \cdot 019\,(M_1 + M_2)$.

$m = 0.019\ 10M_2$

$\dfrac{m}{m_2} = 0.19$

7. A rocket is fired from an aircraft flying horizontally with speed V. The fuel is burnt at a constant rate k and ejected at a constant speed c. The attitude control of the rocket always maintains it in a horizontal position. If the total mass of the rocket is M find the path of the rocket during its powered flight. Assume that g is constant.

8. A uniform layer of snow whose surface is a rectangle with two sides horizontal, rests on a mountain-side of inclination α to the horizontal. The adhesion is just sufficient to hold the snow while at rest. At a certain instant an avalanche starts by the uppermost line of snow moving downwards and collecting with it the snow it meets on the way down. Assuming that there is no friction between the snow and the slope, show that if v is its speed when a distance x of the slope has been uncovered, then

$$\frac{\mathrm{d}}{\mathrm{d}x}(x^2 v^2) = 2gx^2 \sin \alpha.$$

Deduce that the avalanche has a constant acceleration $\frac{1}{3}g \sin \alpha$.

9. Show that it is technically impossible with present rockets to use a single-stage rocket to put a payload on the moon. Use the following data:

$$\text{exhaust speed of the rocket} = 2{,}440 \text{ m/s}$$
$$\text{mass of the earth} = 6{\cdot}0 \times 10^{24} \text{ kg}$$
$$\text{mass of the moon} = 1/81 \text{ mass of the earth}$$
$$\text{radius of the moon's orbit} = 3{\cdot}9 \times 10^5 \text{ km}$$
$$\gamma = 6{\cdot}7 \times 10^{-11} \text{ m}^3/\text{kg s}^2$$

The fuel is burnt in 300 s.

[Hint: assume that the take-off mass of the rocket is M of which εM is fuel. Find the burn-out speed required for the rocket just to reach the equilibrium point between the moon and the earth so that the rocket will fall to the moon's surface under the action of the moon's gravity. Show that this speed leads to an unrealistic value for ε. Make any further assumptions which you feel are justifiable.]

10. A rocket of mass 10,000 kg contains a satellite of mass 100 kg and fuel of mass 7,500 kg. The rocket can be designed in two stages each containing the same proportion of fuel which in both cases can be burnt at a rate of 500 kg/s giving an exhaust speed of 2,500 m/s. Design the optimum two-stage rocket which will give the maximum final speed to the rocket, assuming that it is fired vertically under constant gravity. What is the maximum final speed?

7

Mechanical vibrations

7.1 Introduction

Most machinery contains rotating or reciprocating parts which cause *periodic* or continuously repeated forces to be applied to the structure of the machine. These forces cause the machinery to *oscillate* or *vibrate*. Excessive vibrations may damage the support on which the machine rests, may cause undue wear in the moving parts or may be responsible for the emission of noise.

Periodic motion occurs widely in nature ranging over such examples as the daily rotation of the earth, the annual change of the seasons, the tides, the vibration of an insect's wings and the heartbeat. The engineer's attitude to vibrations is determined by the purpose for which the mechanism under consideration is designed. In a clock the vibrations of the pendulum or the balance wheel need to be maintained in order to produce an oscillation of fixed period: the energy put into the system must be just sufficient to overcome the energy dissipated through friction. On the other hand the car spring is needed to protect the car and its occupants from sudden jolts, but the initial oscillation set up must be damped as quickly as possible by shock absorbers which dissipate the energy of the spring.

We shall examine in detail some simple models of systems with a single degree of freedom. The material on linear differential equations of the second order contained in section 4.5 is required.

7.2 Oscillations of conservative systems

In section 5.7 we derived the equation of motion for a conservative system with one degree of freedom in which the kinetic energy and potential energy are given respectively by $\mathcal{T} = f(q)\dot{q}^2$ and $\mathcal{V}(q)$:

$$f'(q)\dot{q}^2 + 2f(q)\ddot{q} + \mathcal{V}'(q) = 0, \tag{1}$$

where q specifies the single coordinate required. We showed further that $q = \alpha$ is a position of equilibrium if $\mathcal{V}'(\alpha) = 0$ and that the equilibrium

172

is stable if $\mathscr{V}''(\alpha) > 0$. Let us now consider the motion in the immediate neighbourhood of such a position of stable equilibrium.

Let $q = \alpha + x$ where x is a small quantity and let us assume that $\dot{q} = \dot{x}$ and $\ddot{q} = \ddot{x}$ are also small quantities. Employing Taylor expansions about $q = \alpha$ (assuming the functions to be sufficiently well-behaved), we may write

$$f(q) = f(\alpha + x) = f(\alpha) + xf'(\alpha) + \frac{x^2}{2!}f''(\alpha) + \dots,$$

$$f'(q) = f'(\alpha + x) = f'(\alpha) + xf''(\alpha) + \dots,$$

$$\mathscr{V}'(q) = xV''(\alpha) + \frac{x^2}{2!}\mathscr{V}'''(\alpha) + \dots,$$

where, in the last expansion, we have noted that $\mathscr{V}'(\alpha) = 0$. Substituting these series into (1), we obtain

$$\dot{x}^2[f'(\alpha) + \dots] + 2\ddot{x}[f(\alpha) + \dots] + [x\mathscr{V}''(\alpha) + \dots] = 0.$$

If all terms of the second degree and higher in x, $\dot{x}$ and $\ddot{x}$ are neglected, this equation reduces to the second-order linear equation

$$2\ddot{x}f(\alpha) + \mathscr{V}''(\alpha)x = 0,$$

or

$$\ddot{x} + \Omega^2 x = 0 \tag{2}$$

where $\Omega^2 = \mathscr{V}''(\alpha)/2f(\alpha)$. For stable equilibrium we already have $\mathscr{V}''(\alpha) > 0$ and the kinetic energy must be non-negative which implies $f(\alpha) > 0$. Thus Ω must be a real number for small *oscillations* about a position of stable equilibrium.

Differential equation (2) has been investigated previously in section 4.5 and its solution is (as may also be easily verified)

$$x = A \cos \Omega t + B \sin \Omega t,$$

or

$$x = K \sin (\Omega t + \varepsilon), \tag{3}$$

where A, B, K are ε are constants which are related through

$$K \cos \varepsilon = B, \qquad K \sin \varepsilon = A.$$

In the solution (3), $|K|$ is called the *amplitude* of the oscillation and ε is called the *phase angle* (it is usual to choose ε so that K is positive). The motion itself is *simple harmonic*. A graph of 'displacement' x against time is shown in figure 82. The motion is periodic with *period* $2\pi/\Omega$ since

$$\sin (\Omega t + \varepsilon) = \sin \left[\Omega\left(t + \frac{2\pi}{\Omega} \right) + \varepsilon \right]$$

Mechanics

for all t. The period is the time interval between successive maxima on
the graph. The reciprocal of the period, $\Omega/2\pi$, is called the *frequency* and
gives the number of oscillations occurring per second if time is measured
in seconds. The *angular frequency* is simply Ω and it is measured in radians
per second. The phase angle ε measures the shift of the sine curve relative
to the origin. Any system for which equation (2) holds is described as a
linear harmonic oscillator.

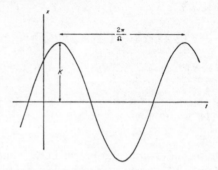

FIGURE 82 Displacement—time graph for simple harmonic
motion

Simple harmonic motion can be represented geometrically by a point B
describing a circle of radius K (supposed positive) at an angular rate Ω
(see figure 83). The projection of the radius OB on to a fixed line through

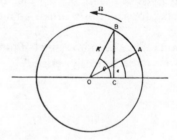

FIGURE 83 An interpretation of simple harmonic motion—as B
describes a circle at a constant angular rate Ω, the point C is a linear
harmonic oscillator

the centre of the circle is OC and OC $= K \cos \theta$, where θ is the angle
between OB and the fixed line. Suppose the point starts from A where ε
is the angle between OA and the line. Then $\theta = \Omega t + \varepsilon$ and

$$OC = K \cos (\Omega t + \varepsilon);$$

that is, the displacement of the point C is simple harmonic.

Example 1 A bead slides on a smooth parabolic wire with equation $y = 4x^2$ fixed in a vertical plane. Show that the bead makes small oscillations with period $\pi/\sqrt{(2g)}$ about the position of equilibrium.

The kinetic energy of the bead,

$$\mathcal{T} = \tfrac{1}{2}m(\dot{x}^2 + \dot{y}^2)$$
$$= \tfrac{1}{2}m\dot{x}^2(1 + 64x^2),$$

where m is the mass of the bead. The potential energy

$$\mathcal{V} = mgy = 4mgx^2.$$

Clearly $x = 0$ is the position of equilibrium. In the earlier notation $\mathcal{T} = f(x)\dot{x}^2$ where $f(x) = \tfrac{1}{2}m(1 + 64x^2)$.

For oscillations of small amplitude, the horizontal displacement x satisfies equation (2):

$$\ddot{x} + \Omega^2 x = 0,$$

with $\Omega^2 = \mathcal{V}''(0)/2f(0) = 8mg/m = 8g$. The period of the oscillations is therefore given by $2\pi/\Omega = \pi/\sqrt{(2g)}$.

Example 2 A bob of mass m is suspended by·a light spring of natural length a and stiffness k. Find the subsequent displacement of the body if initially

(a) the bob is pulled down a distance $\tfrac{1}{4}a$ from its position of equilibrium and released,

(b) the bob is given a downward speed v_0 from its position of equilibrium.

For an extension y of the spring the restoring force is $- ky$. When the bob is in equilibrium $y = mg/k$. For a further extension x, the equation of motion of the bob is (referring back to Example 7, section 5.5)

$$m\ddot{x} = mg - k\left(\frac{mg}{k} + x\right) = - kx.$$

Thus

$$\ddot{x} + \Omega^2 x = 0, \qquad \Omega^2 = k/m,$$

which has a general solution $x = K \sin (\Omega t + \varepsilon)$.

Case (a). At $t = 0$, $x = \tfrac{1}{4}a$ and $\dot{x} = 0$. Therefore

$$\tfrac{1}{4}a = K \sin \varepsilon, \qquad 0 = \Omega K \cos \varepsilon.$$

Since $\Omega \neq 0$, $K \neq 0$, the second condition implies that $\varepsilon = \tfrac{1}{2}\pi$ and the first that $K = \tfrac{1}{4}a$. The required solution is

$$x = \tfrac{1}{4}a \sin (\Omega t + \tfrac{1}{2}\pi) = \tfrac{1}{4}a \cos \Omega t.$$

Case (b). At $t = 0$, $x = 0$ and $\dot{x} = v_0$. Therefore

$$0 = K \sin \varepsilon, \qquad v_0 = \Omega K \cos \varepsilon,$$

which give $\varepsilon = 0$ and $K = v_0/\Omega$. The oscillation is given by

$$x = \frac{v_0}{\Omega} \sin \Omega t.$$

The body oscillates about the equilibrium position with amplitude v_0/Ω. Note that, whatever the initial conditions, the period of the oscillations is the same; only the amplitude and phase vary.

Both problems could have been approached using energy considerations rather than the equation of motion. The motion is truly simple harmonic for the linear spring, no approximation being necessary.

Example 3   Transverse oscillations. A particle of mass m is attached by two elastic strings of the same modulus of elasticity λ and natural lengths a_1 and a_2 to two fixed points on a smooth horizontal plane. The points are distance $k(a_1 + a_2)$ $(k > 1)$ apart. The particle is displaced slightly from its equilibrium position in a direction perpendicular to the strings. Discuss the motion.

In equilibrium, let b_1 and b_2 be lengths of the elastic strings. The tensions in the two strings must balance and it is a simple matter to verify that $b_1 = ka_1$ and $b_2 = ka_2$.

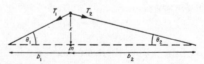

FIGURE 84   Transverse oscillations of a particle on a stretched elastic string

Consider now the situation when the particle has a transverse displacement x. Let T_1 and T_2 be the tensions in the strings and θ_1 and θ_2 the inclinations of the strings as shown in figure 84. The transverse equation of motion becomes

$$T_1 \sin \theta_1 + T_2 \sin \theta_2 = -m\ddot{x}.$$

For oscillations of small amplitude

$$\sin \theta_1 \simeq \theta_1 \simeq x/b_1 = x/ka_1, \qquad \sin \theta_2 \simeq \theta_2 \simeq x/b_2 = x/ka_2,$$

so that x satisfies

$$\frac{T_1 x}{ka_1} + \frac{T_2 x}{ka_2} = -m\ddot{x}.$$

We are retaining only terms not greater than the first degree in x, which implies that we may use the equilibrium tension as a sufficiently good approximation to T_1 and T_2. Hence

$$T_1 = T_2 \simeq \lambda(k - 1).$$

The equation of motion becomes

$$\frac{\lambda(k - 1)(a_1 + a_2)x}{ka_1a_2} = -m\ddot{x},$$

which is simple harmonic motion of period

$$2\pi\left[\frac{mka_1a_2}{\lambda(k - 1)(a_1 + a_2)}\right]^{\frac{1}{2}}.$$

7.3 Damped and forced oscillations

In the last section we examined the motion of a conservative system about an equilibrium configuration, this motion taking place only under the action of forces contained within the system. In any real situation two additional factors must be taken into account. The first of these is *friction.* Friction introduced into an otherwise conservative system will oppose the motion and we should expect the amplitude of the oscillations to be progressively reduced or *damped* since energy is being steadily dissipated. In the case of the simple pendulum friction will be present in the air drag on the bob of the pendulum and in the resistance at the point of suspension. Both these effects are usually very small but they do ultimately produce a significant reduction in the amplitude of the pendulum.

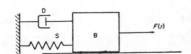

FIGURE 85   Schematic diagram for a block B attached by a spring S
and dashpot D to a fixed wall

The application of an external disturbing force to a system is the second factor which we must include. For example, the motion of an engine on a spring mounting is affected by the periodic motion of the rotating internal machinery of the engine and this leads to a *self-maintained* or *self-excited* oscillation of the engine. However, the general effects of disturbing forces are not easily predictable.

The general system with one degree of freedom may be represented by figure 85. The block B in the figure slides on a smooth table subject to a time-dependent disturbing force $F(t)$ and attached to a fixed wall by a spring

S and *dashpot* D, set in parallel. A dashpot may be thought of as a piston sliding in a pot of oil. It provides resistance to the motion of the block and, in its simplest form, this resistance is proportional to the velocity of the piston *relative* to that of the pot. For a linear spring S, a further force is applied to the block which is proportional to the extension of the spring. Measuring x to the right in figure 85, and letting zero displacement of the block occur where the spring is unstrained, we can write the equation of motion of the block as

$$F(t) - kx - c\dot{x} = m\ddot{x},$$

or

$$m\ddot{x} + c\dot{x} + kx = F(t), \tag{4}$$

where m is the mass of the block, k is the stiffness of the spring and c is a constant determined by the damping action of the dashpot.

Equation (4) is a second-order linear differential equation with constant coefficients. The method of solving such an equation was described in section 4.5. The solution is the sum of two terms, one being the complementary function which is the solution of the homogeneous equation

$$m\ddot{x} + c\dot{x} + kx = 0 \tag{5}$$

and represents the unforced motion of the system, and the other being the particular integral or forcing term giving the effect of the disturbing force $F(t)$ on the system.

Let us first consider the unforced system since it is relevant to the forced system also. The auxiliary equation corresponding to (5) is

$$mp^2 + cp + k = 0,$$

with roots

$$p_1 = [- b + \sqrt{(b^2 - 1)}]\Omega, \qquad p_2 = [- b - \sqrt{(b^2 - 1)}]\Omega, \tag{6}$$

where $\Omega^2 = k/m$ and $b = c/2\sqrt{(mk)}$; Ω is the angular frequency of the corresponding *undamped* system (that is, the equation with $c = 0$). The required solution is therefore

$$x = A \exp\{[- b + \sqrt{(b^2 - 1)}]\Omega t\} + B \exp\{[- b - \sqrt{(b^2 - 1)}]\Omega t\}. \tag{7}$$

The precise effect of the dashpot will depend on the relative magnitudes of m, c and k. We shall now look at the motion of the system in the three cases $b > 1$, $b < 1$ and $b = 1$.

Strong damping ($b > 1$ or $c^2 > 4mk$). The roots in (6) are both real and negative with the result that the displacement will be the sum of two exponentially decreasing terms:

$$x = A e^{-\alpha_1 t} + B e^{-\alpha_2 t}, \tag{8}$$

where α_1 and α_2 are positive. For given initial conditions the system can pass at most once through its equilibrium position ($x = 0$) before approaching rest exponentially with time. Figure 86 shows two typical solutions.

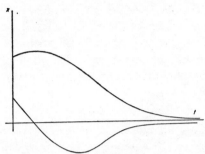

FIGURE 86   Typical solutions for strongly damped oscillations.

Example 4   A block is suspended by a spring and a dashpot with a strong damping action. Show that if the block is displaced downwards and given a downward velocity, it never passes through its equilibrium position again.

With x measured downwards from the equilibrium position,
$$m\ddot{x} + c\dot{x} + kx = 0$$
in the notation used above. The initial conditions are $x = x_0$ and $\dot{x} = v_0$ with both x_0 and v_0 positive. For strong damping the required solution takes the form (8) and without loss of generality we may take $\alpha_2 > \alpha_1$. The constants A and B satisfy
$$x_0 = A + B,$$
$$v_0 = -\alpha_1 A - \alpha_2 B,$$
so that
$$A = (\alpha_2 x_0 + v_0)/(\alpha_2 - \alpha_1), \qquad B = -(\alpha_1 x_0 + v_0)/(\alpha_2 - \alpha_1).$$
The displacement
$$x = \frac{1}{\alpha_2 - \alpha_1}[(\alpha_2 x_0 + v_0)\,e^{-\alpha_1 t} - (\alpha_1 x_0 + v_0)\,e^{-\alpha_2 t}]$$
$$= \frac{1}{\alpha_2 - \alpha_1}[(\alpha_2\,e^{-\alpha_1 t} - \alpha_1\,e^{-\alpha_2 t})x_0 + (e^{-\alpha_1 t} - e^{-\alpha_2 t})v_0].$$
With $\alpha_2 > \alpha_1$, we must have $e^{-\alpha_1 t} > e^{-\alpha_2 t}$ and $\alpha_2\,e^{-\alpha_1 t} > \alpha_1\,e^{-\alpha_2 t}$ for $t > 0$ and consequently $x > 0$ for $t > 0$, which means that the block does not pass through the equilibrium position again.

Weak damping ($b < 1$ or $c^2 < 4mk$). In this case the damping action of the dashpot is relatively small. The roots given by (6) are now complex.

Put $\beta = \Omega\sqrt{(1 - b^2)}$ in equation (7) so that

$$x = e^{-b\Omega t}(A\,e^{i\beta t} + B\,e^{-i\beta t})$$
$$= e^{-b\Omega t}(A'\cos\beta t + B'\sin\beta t),$$

for new constants A' and B'. Let $A' = K\sin\varepsilon$ and $B' = K\cos\varepsilon\,(K > 0)$ so that

$$x = K\,e^{-bt\Omega}\sin(\beta t + \varepsilon). \qquad (9)$$

The motion can be considered as a distortion of simple harmonic motion in which the amplitude decreases exponentially. Figure 87 shows a

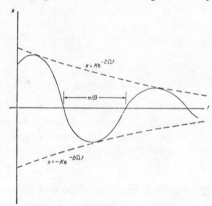

FIGURE 87   An oscillation with weak damping

typical graph of displacement plotted against time. Unlike strong damping, oscillations persist in a weakly damped system. The displacement x vanishes every π/β units of time and we may speak of $2\pi/\beta$ as the period of the oscillation even though the motion never repeats itself as in simple harmonic motion.

Example 5   The angular frequency of a harmonic oscillator is 16 rad/sec. With weak damping imposed it is found that the amplitude of two consecutive oscillations are 5 cm and $\frac{1}{4}$ cm. Find the new period of the system.

Since weak damping is present the displacement of the system will be given by (9) above. The amplitude of successive oscillations decreases by a factor $e^{-2b\Omega\pi/\beta}$. Thus

$$e^{-2b\Omega\pi/\beta} = \frac{1}{4} \times \frac{1}{5} = \frac{1}{20},$$

or

$$2b\Omega\pi = \beta\log_e 20 = 3{\cdot}0 \times \Omega\sqrt{(1 - b^2)},$$

whence
$$4b^2\pi^2 = 9.0 \times (1 - b^2).$$
From this equation we obtain
$$b^2 = 9/(9 + 4\pi^2).$$
Finally $\beta = \Omega\sqrt{(1 - b^2)} = 16 \times 2\pi/\sqrt{(9 + 4\pi^2)}$ and the new period
$$\frac{2\pi}{\beta} = \frac{\sqrt{(9 + 4\pi^2)}}{16} = 0.44 \text{ sec.}$$

Critical damping ($b = 1$ or $c^2 = 4mk$). The roots (6) are now equal:
$$p_1 = p_2 = -\Omega$$
and the corresponding solution is
$$x = e^{-\Omega t} (A + Bt).$$
The behaviour of the system is very similar to that portrayed in figure 86 for strong damping.

The general linear system for forced oscillations is represented by equation (4) which we repeat:
$$m\ddot{x} + c\dot{x} + kx = F(t).$$

Following discussion in section 4.5 on second-order differential equations, the solution of this equation is the sum of a complementary function (the general solution of the equation with $F(t)$ replaced by 0) and a particular integral. The complementary function gives the *free* or *natural* damped motion of the system and is covered by the cases of strong, weak and critical damping described above. However this motion will diminish with time leaving only the particular integral or *forced oscillation*. For this reason the complementary function is known as a *transient* in the theory of oscillations.

The precise effect of a forcing term will naturally depend upon its form. We shall look in detail at the sinusoidal applied force represented by
$$F(t) = F_0 \cos (\omega t + \beta).$$
We proceed to find constants A and B such that
$$A \cos (\omega t + \beta) + B \sin (\omega t + \beta)$$
satisfies the equation
$$m\ddot{x} + c\dot{x} + kx = F_0 \cos (\omega t + \beta).$$

Substituting the expression into the equation and equating the coefficients of $\cos (\omega t + \beta)$ and $\sin (\omega t + \beta)$ to zero, we find that
$$- m\omega^2 A + c\omega B + kA = F_0,$$
$$- m\omega^2 B - c\omega A + kB = 0.$$

These equations have the solution

$$A = F_0(\Omega^2 - \omega^2)/m[(\Omega^2 - \omega^2)^2 + 4b^2\Omega^2\omega^2],$$
$$B = 2F_0b\Omega\omega/m[(\Omega^2 - \omega^2)^2 + 4b^2\Omega^2\omega^2],$$

wherein the relations $\Omega^2 = k/m$ and $b = c/2\sqrt{(mk)}$ have been used. It is more convenient to put

$$A = \sqrt{(A^2 + B^2)}\cos\phi, \qquad B = \sqrt{(A^2 + B^2)}\sin\phi,$$

where

$$\sqrt{(A^2 + B^2)} = F_0/m[(\Omega^2 - \omega^2)^2 + 4b^2\Omega^2\omega^2]^{\frac{1}{2}}$$

and $\tan\phi = 2b\Omega\omega/(\Omega^2 - \omega^2)$. By using a simple trigonometric identity, the general solution can be expressed as

$$x = \text{transient} + \frac{F_0\cos(\omega t + \beta - \phi)}{m[(\Omega^2 - \omega^2)^2 + 4b^2\Omega^2\omega^2]^{\frac{1}{2}}}.$$

Usually we are interested in the behaviour of the system after a considerable time has elapsed, in which case the transient becomes negligible and only the forced oscillation persists. The forced oscillation contains certain important general characteristics. Its frequency is the same as that of the applied force but it has suffered a phase shift ϕ. The amplitude K_0 of the oscillation is independent of the initial conditions:

$$K_0 = F_0/m\Omega^2\left[\left(1 - \frac{\omega^2}{\Omega^2}\right)^2 + \frac{4b^2\omega^2}{\Omega^2}\right]^{\frac{1}{2}}. \tag{10}$$

For any given system the amplitude of the forced oscillation depends on Ω, the undamped natural angular frequency, with b as an additional parameter. The characteristic shape of K_0 is determined by the behaviour of the denominator in (10). Putting $\xi^2 = \omega^2/\Omega^2$, we see that the turning values of

$$u = (1 - \xi^2)^2 + 4b^2\xi^2$$

occur where $du/d\xi = 0$, that is where

$$-4\xi(1 - \xi^2) + 8b^2\xi = 0,$$

which has solutions $\xi = 0$ and $\xi^2 = 1 - 2b^2$. The second derivative is given by

$$\frac{d^2u}{d\xi^2} = -4 + 12\xi^2 + 8b^2,$$

and at $\xi = 0$, $d^2u/d\xi^2 = 4(2b^2 - 1)$ and at $\xi^2 = 1 - 2b^2$, $d^2u/d\xi^2 = 8(1 - 2b^2)$.

The sign of the second derivative depends on the sign of $1 - 2b^2$: $b = 1/\sqrt{2}$ is a critical value. If $2b^2 > 1$, u has one extreme value—a minimum—at $\xi = 0$. There are two extreme values if $2b^2 < 1$, a maximum at $\xi = 0$ and a minimum at $\xi = \sqrt{(1 - 2b^2)}$.

In terms of the amplitude, K_0 has a maximum at $\omega = 0$ if $2b^2 > 1$, and a maximum at $\omega = \Omega\sqrt{(1 - 2b^2)}$ and a minimum at $\omega = 0$ if $2b^2 < 1$. The amplitude variation for several values of b is plotted in figure 88 in

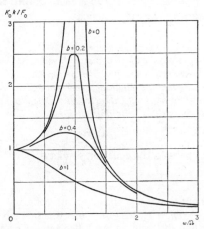

FIGURE 88   Amplitude versus frequency ratio of a forced oscillation
for selected values of b

terms of the angular frequency of the forcing term. The pronounced peak which occurs in the neighbourhood of $\omega = \Omega$ for small values of b displays the phenomenon of *resonance*—large amplitude oscillations which occur when the frequency of the applied force is near the undamped natural frequency of the system. It is these resonant oscillations which can be destructive in mechanisms. This resonant behaviour can always be eliminated by adding a larger damping term, which is obtained by increasing the value of b. For example with $b = 1$ the *response curve* in figure 88 shows no magnification of the amplitude. At the other extreme the amplitude becomes infinite at $\omega = \Omega$ if no damping is present.

Associated with this damped forced system there are three important frequencies:

(i) the undamped natural frequency $\Omega/2\pi$;
(ii) the damped frequency $\Omega(1 - b^2)^{\frac{1}{2}}/2\pi$;
(iii) the resonant frequency $\Omega(1 - 2b^2)^{\frac{1}{2}}/2\pi$.

The second and third of these frequencies approach the first as $b \to 0$.

The phase difference ϕ between the applied force and the forced oscillation depends principally on the closeness or otherwise of ω and Ω. In the formula

$$\tan \phi = 2b\Omega\omega/(\Omega^2 - \omega^2),$$

as $\omega \to \Omega$, $\tan \phi \to \pm \infty$ and $\phi \to \pi/2$. For a slow forcing term ($\omega \ll \Omega$), $\tan \phi$ is small and the displacement is approximately in phase with the applied force. On the other hand if $\omega \gg \Omega$, $\tan \phi$ is negative and $\tan \phi \to 0$ as $\omega \to \infty$. Thus ϕ approaches π for a fast forcing term which is then exactly out of phase with the displacement.

Example 6   The mounting of an electric motor of mass 500 kg consists of a spring of stiffness $1\cdot2 \times 10^5$ N/m and a dashpot. The motor may take speeds ranging from 0 to 5,000 r.p.m. Assuming that the mounting experiences a sinusoidal force having the same frequency as the rotation, what characteristics should the dashpot have in order that the motor should not oscillate with large amplitude?

With x measured upwards, the equation of motion for the system is given by equation (4),

$$m\ddot{x} + c\dot{x} + kx = F(t),$$

where m is the mass of the motor, c the damping coefficient, k the stiffness of the spring and $F(t) = - mg + F_0 \cos (\omega t + \beta)$, the first term representing the weight of the motor and the second the applied force. The weight merely causes the spring to be depressed and we need not consider it, nor need we consider the transient effects. Let $x = x' - mg/k$ so that x' satisfies

$$m\ddot{x}' + c\dot{x}' + kx' = F_0 \cos (\omega t + \beta).$$

The natural undamped angular frequency

$$\Omega = (k/m)^{\frac{1}{2}} = (120,000/500)^{\frac{1}{2}} = 4\sqrt{15} \text{ rad/s}.$$

The angular frequency of the applied force ω has a maximum value of

$$5,000/60 = 250/3 \text{ rad/s}.$$

Clearly the maximum ω exceeds Ω and consequently resonance could occur if the damping is sufficiently weak. Reference to figure 88 indicates that resonance effects do not appear if we choose $b > 1$ (say). The relative amplitude of the forced oscillations then decreases with increasing ω. Since $b = c/2\sqrt{(mk)}$ we conclude that c should exceed $2(500 \times 120,000)^{\frac{1}{2}} = 15,500$ kg/s.

7.4 Forces transmitted by rotating machinery

The reduction of vibrations transmitted by rotating machinery is important in engineering. For example, the motor-car engine is usually supported in the frame of a car by rubber mountings which may be thought of as a spring and dashpot system. Their purpose is to insulate the car from uncomfortable vibrations caused by the engine. The system is essentially that shown in figure 85, but with the system turned on its side. The equation of motion is therefore equation (4) essentially:

$$m\ddot{x} + c\dot{x} + kx = - mg + F(t), \qquad (11)$$

the weight of the engine now entering the equation on the right-hand side since the motion is taking place vertically. However we can eliminate the weight by the substitution $x = x' - mg/k$ so that x' satisfies

$$m\ddot{x}' + c\dot{x}' + kx' = F(t).$$

We have shown in the previous section that an applied force

$$F(t) = F_0 \cos (\omega t + \beta)$$

leads to a displacement $x' = K_0 \cos (\omega t + \beta - \phi)$ where K_0 is given by equation (10). The force on the car or support of the system is (apart from the weight which produces a constant force) ultimately

$$c\dot{x}' + kx' = K_0[k \cos (\omega t + \beta - \phi) - c\omega \sin (\omega t + \beta - \phi)].$$

The amplitude or maximum value of this force is

$$K_0\sqrt{(k^2 + c^2\omega^2)} = K_0 k \sqrt{(1 + 4b^2\omega^2/\Omega^2)}$$

since $c = 2\sqrt{(km)}$, $b = 2kb/\Omega$. In practice we want to make this quantity small compared with the amplitude of the applied force. It is convenient to overturn the ratio transmitted-force/applied-force so that

$$\frac{F_0}{K_0 k \sqrt{(1 + 4b^2\omega^2/\Omega^2)}} = \left[1 + \frac{\omega^2(\omega^2 - 2\Omega^2)}{\Omega^2(\Omega^2 + 4b^2\omega^2)} \right]^{\frac{1}{2}}$$

must be made as large as possible. If $\omega^2 < 2\Omega^2$ the ratio is less than 1 and the transmitted force is greater than the applied force irrespective of the damping. A softer spring will reduce Ω but the critical value $\omega = \sqrt{2}\Omega$ must always occur. If $\omega^2 > 2\Omega^2$, the ratio is always greater than 1 and takes its maximum value for any fixed ω and Ω when $b = 0$, in which case no damping is present. However we must remember that serious resonance of the engine may occur if the damping is too weak and ω is near Ω. The two factors must be balanced in designing the system. A soft spring with modest damping is usually the best combination.

For the motor-car engine ω would be the same as the angular speed of the rotating parts of the engine. The slowest speed of the engine is usually its idling speed (ω_i say) and we would choose $\omega_i^2 > 2\Omega^2$. This explains in part why an engine which is misfiring causes vibrations of large amplitude in the car.

The applied force due to rotating machinery may be periodic but not simple harmonic in form. If the angular speed is ω the period of the applied force can be taken as $2\pi/\omega$ in which case for a periodic force

$$F(t) = F(t + 2\pi/\omega).$$

The equation for x is still given by equation (11). Introducing the relative displacement $x = x' - mg/k$ again, we have

$$m\ddot{x}' + c\dot{x}' + kx' = F(t).$$

We now write the periodic force $F(t)$ as the sum of cosines and sines:

$$F(t) = \tfrac{1}{2}a_0 + \sum_{n=1}^{\infty} (a_n \cos n\omega t + b_n \sin n\omega t) \qquad (12)$$

and determine the coefficients by multiplying both sides successively by 1, $\cos n\omega t$, $\sin n\omega t$ and integrating over the interval $(0, 2\pi/\omega)$. Since (as the reader may easily verify)

$$\int_0^{2\pi/\omega} \cos n\omega t \; dt = \int_0^{2\pi/\omega} \sin \omega t \; dt = 0,$$

$$\int_0^{2\pi/\omega} \cos n\omega t \cos r\omega t \; dt = \int_0^{2\pi/\omega} \sin n\omega t \sin r\omega t \; dt = 0 \quad (r \neq n),$$

$$\int_0^{2\pi/\omega} \cos n\omega t \sin r\omega t \; dt = 0,$$

$$\int_0^{2\pi/\omega} \cos^2 n\omega t \; dt = \int_0^{2\pi/\omega} \sin^2 n\omega t \; dt = \frac{\pi}{\omega},$$

it follows that

$$a_0 = \frac{\omega}{\pi} \int_0^{2\pi/\omega} F(t) \; dt, \qquad a_n = \frac{\omega}{\pi} \int_0^{2\pi/\omega} F(t) \cos n\omega t \; dt,$$

$$b_n = \frac{\omega}{\pi} \int_0^{2\pi/\omega} F(t) \sin n\omega t \; dt. \qquad (13)$$

The right-hand side of equation (12) is known as the *Fourier series* of $F(t)$ and a_n and b_n are called the *Fourier coefficients*.

The significance of this expansion is that it expresses the applied force as an infinite series of harmonic terms each of which we have already discussed separately. The constant term $\tfrac{1}{2}a_0$ leads to a further constant displacement of x' and is of little interest. We have to solve essentially the differential equations

$$m\ddot{x}' + c\dot{x}' + kx' = a_n \cos n\omega t,$$
$$m\ddot{x}' + c\dot{x}' + kx' = b_n \sin n\omega t = b_n \cos (n\omega t - \tfrac{1}{2}\pi).$$

We leave it as an exercise for the reader to show that the relative displacement

$$x' = \frac{a_0}{2k} + \sum_{n=1}^{\infty} Q_n[a_n \cos(n\omega t - \phi_n) + b_n(\sin n\omega t - \phi_n)], \quad (14)$$

where

$$Q_n = 1/m\Omega^2\left[\left(1 - \frac{n^2\omega^2}{\Omega^2}\right)^2 + \frac{4b^2n^2\omega^2}{\Omega^2}\right]^{\frac{1}{2}}, \quad (15)$$

and

$$\tan \phi_n = 2b\Omega n\omega/(\Omega^2 - n^2\omega^2). \quad (16)$$

We can see that resonance will occur for weak damping ($b \ll 1$) if ω is in the neighbourhood of Ω/n for $n = 1, 2,...$, since the corresponding amplitude Q_n will become relatively large. However this is usually only significant for the first few frequencies Ω/n because the second term in the denominator of Q_n becomes rapidly large as n increases.

Example 7 A linear damped system is subject to the applied force

$$F(t) = \begin{cases} \dfrac{F_0\omega t}{\pi}, & 0 \leqslant t < \dfrac{\pi}{\omega}, \\ -\dfrac{F_0\omega}{\pi}\left(t - \dfrac{2\pi}{\omega}\right), & \dfrac{\pi}{\omega} \leqslant t < \dfrac{2\pi}{\omega}, \end{cases}$$

with $F(t) = F(t + 2\pi/\omega)$. Obtain the sustained response of the system.

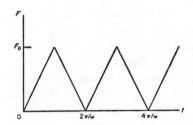

FIGURE 89 A triangular wave function

The applied force is the triangular wave shown in figure 89. The equation of motion is

$$m\ddot{x} + c\dot{x} + kx = F(t).$$

We express $F(t)$ as a Fourier series whose coefficients are given by equations (13):

$$a_0 = \frac{2\omega}{\pi} \int_0^{\pi/\omega} \frac{F_0 \omega t}{\pi} \, dt = F_0,$$

$$a_n = \frac{2\omega}{\pi} \int_0^{\pi/\omega} \frac{F_0 \omega}{\pi} t \cos n\omega t \, dt$$

$$= \frac{2F_0 \omega^2}{\pi^2} \left[\left(\frac{1}{n\omega} t \sin n\omega t \right)_0^{\pi/\omega} - \frac{1}{n\omega} \int_0^{\pi/\omega} \sin n\omega t \, dt \right]$$

$$= \frac{2F_0}{n^2 \pi^2} (\cos n\omega t)_0^{\pi/\omega} = \frac{2F_0}{n^2 \pi^2} (\cos n\pi - 1),$$

$$b_n = 0,$$

where we have used the symmetry properties of the triangular wave, the sine and the cosine functions. Now $\cos n\pi = (-1)^n$, so that $a_n = 2F_0[(-1)^n - 1]/n^2 \pi^2$ which implies that $a_{2n} = 0$ and that $a_{2n-1} = -4F_0/(2n-1)^2 \pi^2$ for $n = 1, 2, \ldots$. Thus

$$F(t) = \tfrac{1}{2} F_0 - \frac{4F_0}{\pi^2} \sum_{n=1}^{\infty} \frac{\cos(2n-1)\omega t}{(2n-1)^2}.$$

By equation (14), the response of the system, apart from the transient, is

$$x' = \frac{F_0}{2k} - \frac{4F_0}{\pi^2} \sum_{n=1}^{\infty} \frac{Q_{2n-1}}{(2n-1)^2} \cos\left[(2n-1)\omega t - \phi_{2n-1}\right],$$

where Q_{2n-1} and ϕ_{2n-1} are given by equations (15) and (16).

7.5 The seismograph

Disturbances within the earth such as those created by an earthquake are measured and recorded by an instrument known as a *seismograph*. The simple seismograph may be thought of as a mass suspended by a spring and dashpot from a platform fixed to the earth. Oscillations are transmitted from the platform to the mass. A pointer attached to the mass records its displacement on a scale attached to the platform. Note that the *relative* displacement of the mass is observed (see figure 90).

Let the displacement of the platform be y and let x be the displacement of the mass relative to the platform. The plunger in the dashpot is moving with speed $\dot{y}$ and the pot is descending with speed $(\dot{x} + \dot{y})$. The descent of the mass is therefore resisted by a force $c\dot{x}$. If a is the natural length of the spring, the equation of motion becomes

$$mg - c\dot{x} - k(x - a) = m(\ddot{x} + \ddot{y}),$$

or

$$m\ddot{x} + c\dot{x} + kx = mg + ka - m\ddot{y}.$$

Putting $x = x' + mg/k + a$, where x' is the displacement of the mass from its equilibrium position, we find that

$$m\ddot{x}' + c\dot{x}' + kx' = -m\ddot{y}. \qquad (17)$$

Essentially x' is the recorded displacement.

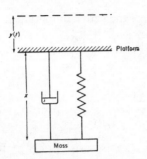

FIGURE 90   Diagram of a seismograph

Let us suppose that the platform oscillates with simple harmonic motion of amplitude A and angular frequency ω. If we write $y = A \cos(\omega t + \beta)$, equation (17) reads

$$m\ddot{x}' + c\dot{x}' + kx' = mA\omega^2 \cos(\omega t + \beta),$$

an equation which has already been considered in section 7.3. The forced oscillation induced in the mass is

$$x' = K_0 \cos(\omega t + \beta - \phi),$$

where

$$K_0 = A\left(\frac{\omega^2}{\Omega^2}\right)\left[\left(1 - \frac{\omega^2}{\Omega^2}\right)^2 + \frac{4b^2\omega^2}{\Omega^2}\right]^{-\frac{1}{2}}, \qquad \tan\phi = \frac{2b\Omega\omega}{\Omega^2 - \omega^2}.$$

The known characteristics of the spring and dashpot enable the observer, in principle, to obtain the frequency and amplitude A of the oscillations of the platform in terms of the recorded value of K_0 and ϕ.

As $\omega/\Omega \to \infty$, $K_0 \to A$, that is K_0 approaches the amplitude of the oscillation of the platform. Consequently for high frequency oscillations the mass remains fixed in space since the phase difference between the oscillations of the platform and the mass approaches π. Let us see how we can achieve the best approximation for modest values of Ω/ω. We can write the amplitude

$$K_0 = A\left[\left(1 - \frac{\Omega^2}{\omega^2}\right)^2 + \frac{4b^2\Omega^2}{\omega^2}\right]^{-\frac{1}{2}} = A\left[1 + 2(2b^2 - 1)\frac{\Omega^2}{\omega^2} + \frac{\Omega^4}{\omega^4}\right]^{-\frac{1}{2}}, \quad (18)$$

which suggests the error between K_0 and A will be small for modest Ω/ω if we choose $b^2 = \frac{1}{2}$ or $b \approx 0\cdot7$. For this value of b, the middle term on the right-hand side of (18) disappears which implies that $K_0 - A$ is of the order of the fourth power in Ω/ω. Thus

$$0 < A - K_0 = A\left[1 - \left(1 + \frac{\Omega^4}{\omega^4}\right)^{-\frac{1}{2}}\right],$$

and K_0 is within, say, 5% of the actual amplitude if

$$1 - \left(1 + \frac{\Omega^4}{\omega^4}\right)^{-\frac{1}{2}} < 1/20$$

or

$$\Omega < \frac{(39)^{\frac{1}{4}}}{(19)^{\frac{1}{4}}}\omega \approx 0\cdot57\omega.$$

In designing the seismograph we wish firstly to make ω/Ω large enough to ensure that the approximation above is appropriate. We thus make $\Omega\,(= \sqrt{(k/m)})$ as small as possible by supporting a large block of concrete (m large) on soft springs (k small). We then adjust the damping so that $b(= c/\sqrt{(2mk)}) \approx 0\cdot7$.

If we had designed an instrument so that ω/Ω is small, by using a small mass on a stiff spring, the amplitude of the forced oscillation is approximately $A\omega^2/\Omega^2$. Now Ω^2 is known and $A\omega^2$ is the amplitude of $\ddot{y}$, the acceleration of the platform. Thus such an instrument, called an accelerometer for obvious reasons, can be used in an aircraft to measure the accelerations induced by up and down currents in the atmosphere.

Exercises

1. A body of mass $10\,\text{kg}$ is supported by a spring of stiffness $200\,\text{N/m}$. The mass is pulled down a distance of $0\cdot5\,\text{m}$ from its equilibrium position and released from rest. Find the period, frequency and angular frequency of the oscillations of the body.

2. A particle is held by two springs each of modulus mg and natural length a. The free ends of the springs are attached to a horizontal beam at two points distance $2a\sqrt{3}$ apart. Write down the potential energy of the system when the particle is at a depth x below the mid-point of the spring attachments. Find the equilibrium position of the particle when it is below the beam and the period of small vertical oscillations of the particle about its equilibrium position.

3. A body of mass m is suspended by two springs with stiffness k_1 and k_2. Show that if the springs are in parallel the period of vertical oscillations of the body is $2\pi\sqrt{[m/(k_1 + k_2)]}$, and if the springs are in series the period is

$$2\pi\sqrt{[m(k_1 + k_2)/k_1k_2]}.$$

Which arrangement gives the longer period?

4. A bob of mass 5 gm suspended by a spring is found to oscillate vertically with period 2 s. Find the stiffness of the spring.

5. Find the frequency of oscillations of the mass in the system shown in figure 91. The pulley has negligible mass and the spring has stiffness k.

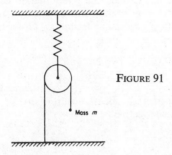

FIGURE 91

Mass m

6. A particle of mass m moves in the plane $z = 0$ under the attractive force $2m\pi^2 r$ towards the origin, r being the distance from the origin. In addition there is a force of magnitude $m\pi v$ in the direction of $\mathbf{v} \times \mathbf{k}$ where $\mathbf{v}$ is the velocity of the particle and $\mathbf{k}$ is a unit vector perpendicular to $z = 0$. Show that

$$\pi\dot{y} - 2\pi^2 x = \ddot{x}, \qquad -\pi\dot{x} - 2\pi^2 y = \ddot{y}.$$

Solve the equations for x and y and show that the motion in the x and y directions is the sum of two simple harmonic oscillations of periods 1 and 2.

7. The displacement x of a spring-mounted mass under the action of Coulomb dry friction satisfies

$$m\ddot{x} + kx = \begin{cases} -F, & \dot{x} > 0, \\ F, & \dot{x} < 0, \end{cases}$$

where m, k and F are positive constants. The mass is in equilibrium if $\dot{x} = \ddot{x} = 0$ and $|x| < F/k$. If $x = x_0$, $\dot{x} = 0$ at $t = 0$ where $x_0 > 3F/k$, show that at time $t = 2\pi(m/k)^{\frac{1}{2}}$ the displacement of the mass is $x_0 - 4F/k$.

8. A particle of mass m lying on a smooth horizontal table is attached by two springs of moduli λ_1, λ_2 and natural lengths a_1 and a_2 to two points on the table distance $a_1 + a_2$ apart. In its equilibrium position the mass is subject to a horizontal force $F_0 \cos \omega t$ along the springs. At what angular frequency does the system resonate?

9. Show that the solution of

$$\ddot{x} + \Omega^2 x = F_0 \cos [(\Omega + \varepsilon)t],$$

with $x = \dot{x} = 0$ when $t = 0$ can be written

$$x = - \frac{2F_0}{\Omega^2 - (\Omega + \varepsilon)^2} \sin \tfrac{1}{2}\varepsilon t \sin (\Omega + \tfrac{1}{2}\varepsilon)t.$$

If $0 < |\varepsilon| \ll \Omega$ this solution reveals the phenomenon of *beats*. The frequency of the second sine is much higher than that of the first and the motion may be thought of as an oscillation of angular frequency $\Omega + \tfrac{1}{2}\varepsilon$ with a slowly varying amplitude of

$$\frac{2F_0|\sin \tfrac{1}{2}\varepsilon t|}{|\Omega^2 - (\Omega + \varepsilon)^2|}.$$

The period of the beats is $4\pi/\varepsilon$. Beats occur when the natural frequency and forcing frequency are close together.

10. Solve the equation

$$\ddot{x} + \Omega^2 x = F_0 \cos \Omega t,$$

with $x = \dot{x} = 0$ when $t = 0$. This is the equation of a forced harmonic oscillator in the critical resonating case. Show that the oscillation with period $2\pi/\Omega$ builds up with amplitude increasing linearly with time.

11. The equation of motion of a simple pendulum is given by

$$\ddot{\theta} + \Omega^2 \sin \theta = 0, \qquad \Omega^2 = g/\ell,$$

where ℓ is the length of the pendulum and θ is its angular displacement from the downward vertical. By retaining the first *two* terms in the expansion of $\sin \theta$, show that θ satisfies, for small θ, the *non-linear* equation

$$\ddot{\theta} + \Omega^2(\theta - \tfrac{1}{6}\theta^3) = 0.$$

We should expect this equation to give a better approximation to the motion. Substitute $\theta = \theta_0 \sin \omega t$ into the differential equation, and use the identity $4 \sin^3 x = 3 \sin x - \sin 3x$. Rejecting the consequent third harmonic, show that the equation is approximately satisfied if

$$\omega^2 = \Omega^2(1 - \tfrac{1}{8}\theta_0^2).$$

The angular frequency to the second order depends on the amplitude of the oscillations. The method also suggests that the next term in a series expansion for θ will be of the form $\theta_1 \sin 3\omega t$.

12. The spring system shown in figure 92 hits the plane with speed v_0. Before impact the spring is unstrained, has natural length a and modulus λ. If the impact between the lower plate and the plane is inelastic show that this plate will subsequently remain in contact with the plane if

$$v_0 \leqslant g(3am/\lambda)^{\frac{1}{2}}.$$

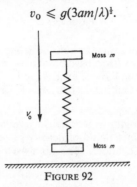

FIGURE 92

13. A machine of mass 1,000 kg contains rotating parts which produce a force on the base of the machine of amplitude F and frequency equal to the frequency of the machine. Its normal running speed is 5,000 r.p.m. What stiffness should a spring-mounting have if the transmitted force is to be less than 20% of the applied force?

14. A clock pendulum should have a period of 1 sec, but the clock is found to lose 36 seconds per day. Assuming that the pendulum can be treated as simple, find by how much its length should be altered.

15. An elastic string of modulus λ and natural length a is attached to a fixed point on a smooth horizontal table. The other end of the string is attached to a particle of mass m. The particle is placed on the table with the string of length $\frac{3}{2}a$ and released. Find the period of the oscillations which follow.

16. A spring of stiffness 908 N/m is attached to a fixed support and carries at its free end a block of mass 9 kg. When suspended in equilibrium the block is subject to a downward periodic force $F_0 \sin \omega t$ where $F_0 = 69$ N. The spring yields if its extension exceeds 1 m. For what frequencies can the periodic force be safely applied?

17. Two masses are linked by a spring as shown in figure 93. The spring which has modulus λ and natural length a is compressed to $\frac{3}{4}$ of its natural length and released from rest. Determine completely the subsequent displacements of both masses. (This system has *two* degrees of freedom—the displacements, with respect to a fixed point, of both masses. There are therefore two equations of motion to be solved simultaneously.)

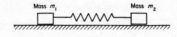

FIGURE 93

18. A block of mass m stands on a smooth horizontal plane and is attached by a horizontal spring of stiffness k to a fixed point of the plane. When in equilibrium the block receives a horizontal blow of magnitude I in the direction of the spring. Find the amplitude of the resulting oscillations of the block.

19. A circular cylinder of radius a and height h, and composed of material of uniform density ρ_1, floats in a liquid of density ρ_2 ($> \rho_1$). Find the period of vertical oscillations of the cylinder. (The upthrust on the cylinder equals the weight of liquid displaced.)

20. Classify the system represented by

$$m\ddot{x} + c\dot{x} + kx = 0$$

as strongly or weakly damped in the following cases:

(i) $m = 12$ kg; $c = 10$ kg/s; $k = 2$ N/m,
(ii) $m = 10$ kg; $c = 8$ kg/s; $k = 2$ N/m,
(iii) $m = 5$ kg; $c = 4$ kg/s; $k = 3$ N/m,
(iv) $m = 2$ kg; $c = 5$ kg/s; $k = 3$ N/m.

21. Write down the equations of motion for the spring-dashpot systems shown in figure 94.

22. The displacement of a linear damped oscillator is given, for weak damping, by

$$x = Ke^{-b\Omega t} \sin (\beta t + \varepsilon)$$

(see section 7·3). Show that x has a maximum at times given by $\beta t = 2n\pi + d$ where n is an integer and d gives the position of the first maximum. Show also that the ratio of successive maxima is $\exp (2b\Omega\pi/\beta)$. The quantity $2b\Omega\pi/\beta$ is called the *logarithmic decrement* and is a measure of the rate of decay of the oscillation. Note that it is independent of n and K.

Such an oscillator is found to have successive maxima of 2·1 cm and 1·3 cm. If the damping coefficient is 10 gm/s, find the stiffness of the spring given that the oscillator supports a mass of 5 gm.

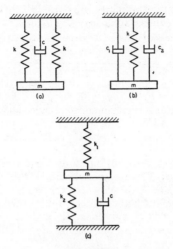

FIGURE 94

23. The displacement x of a linear damped oscillator satisfies

$$m\ddot{x} + c\dot{x} + kx = 0.$$

Multiplying this equation by $\dot{x}$ and integrating from $t = 0$ to $t = \tau$ show that the energy dissipated by the system is

$$c \int_0^\tau \dot{x}^2 \, dt$$

in time τ. In mechanical systems this energy is transformed into heat by the friction of the dashpot.

24. A body of mass 10 gm is suspended by a spring of stiffness 0·25 N/m and subject to damping which is 1% of critical. After approximately how many oscillations will the amplitude of the system be halved?

25. The frictional resistance acting on the block in figure 95 is assumed to be proportional to its speed. The block has mass 5 kg and is set oscillating. It is found that successive maximum displacements of the block from the wall diminish in the ratio 0·85 and that the period of oscillations is 0·8 s. Find the resistance to motion and the stiffness of the spring.

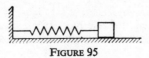

FIGURE 95

26. Show that for damping which is less than 10% of critical, the undamped natural frequency, the damped frequency and the resonant frequency for forced oscillations agree to within 1%.

27. A linear damped system with $m = 10$ kg, $k = 200$ N/m and $c = 25$ kg/s is subject to a periodic force $F_0 \cos(\omega t + \beta)$ where $F_0 = 1.83$ N. For what value of ω are the sustained oscillations of maximum amplitude and what is their phase shift?

28. A jet of water issues vertically upwards from a nozzle with speed v and strikes a ball of mass M. If the vertical velocity of the water relative to the ball is destroyed on striking the ball, show that the equilibrium height of the ball is $(k^2v^2 - g^2)/2gk^2$ where kM is the mass of water issued per unit time.

Show that a small vertical motion of the ball is a critically damped free oscillation. (Neglect the square of the velocity of the ball.)

29. A particle of mass m moves along the straight line OX. It is attracted to O by a force $17mk^2x/2$ and its motion is retarded by a force $3mk\dot{x}$, x being the distance from O. A force $mA \cos \omega t$ is applied to the particle along OX. Show that the greatest amplitude of the forced oscillations occurs for $\omega = 2k$ and is $2A/15k^2$.

30. The mounting of an electric motor is equivalent to a single spring of stiffness 1.1×10^5 N/m and a dashpot with a damping coefficient 20% of the value required for critical damping. The motor is subject to an alternating force which has the same frequency as that of its rotation. The mass of the motor is 454 kg. Show that, if the speed of rotation is less than 210 r.p.m. the amplitude of the force transmitted to the foundation is greater than the amplitude of the exciting force. Find the range of values of the speed of rotation for which the transmitted force is less than 50% of the exciting force.

31. Find the displacement x of the damped oscillator

$$m\ddot{x} + c\dot{x} + kx = 0, \qquad \beta^2 = 4km - c^2 > 0,$$

given that $x = 0$, $\dot{x} = v$ at $t = 0$. After the first and subsequent cycles the kinetic energy of the system is increased instantaneously by T_0. Show that periodic motion takes place if

$$T_0 = \tfrac{1}{2}mv^2[1 - \exp(2c\pi/m\beta)].$$

This system represents a possible model for a clock mechanism. Each cycle the system is impulsively excited by giving it extra speed which maintains the periodic oscillations.

32. Obtain the Fourier expansion of the function

$$
F(t) = \begin{cases} 0 & 0 \leqslant t < \dfrac{\pi}{2\omega} \\[2mm] F_0 & \dfrac{\pi}{2\omega} < t < \dfrac{3\pi}{2\omega} \\[2mm] 0 & \dfrac{3\pi}{2\omega} < t \leqslant \dfrac{2\pi}{\omega} \end{cases}
$$

with $F(t) = F[t + (2\pi/\omega)]$. Find the sustained response of the linear system

$$m\ddot{x} + c\dot{x} + kx = F(t)$$

to this input.

33. Consider a microphone as a movable vertical plate of mass m separated by an air gap from a fixed vertical plate. The effect of the mounting of the movable plate may be modelled by two forces acting on the centre of mass:

(i) a force $5mk^2 \times$ (deflection) restoring the plate to its equilibrium position,
(ii) a force $2mk \times$ (velocity) resisting the motion.

Output from the microphone is undistorted provided the separation between the plates is greater than ra ($0 < r < 1$), where a is the equilibrium separation. Suppose that the sound waves exert a horizontal force $P \cos \omega t$ on the centre of mass and show that the output due to these forced oscillations is undistorted for all ω provided

$$2k \geqslant \{P/[ma(1 - r)]\}^{\frac{1}{2}}.$$

Find the work done per cycle by the sound waves.

8

Rotating frames of reference

8.1 The earth as a rotating frame

As we described in section 3.1, a frame of reference fixed in the earth is not an inertial frame but a rotating one with period equal to one day. The axis of rotation is the line joining the poles. Taking the earth to be a sphere, we can imagine the origin to be at the centre of the earth with $OXYZ$ as the fixed or inertial frame (we assume that the axes are parallel to those of a sidereal frame) and $Oxyz$ as the rotating frame, these axes being specified directions in the earth as indicated in figure 96. Strictly

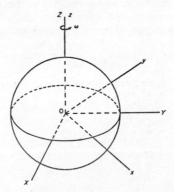

FIGURE 96   Inertial and rotating frames in the earth; OZ is the polar axis

speaking $OXYZ$ is not an inertial frame since the earth orbits the sun and the motion of the origin O along this path induces further accelerations in $OXYZ$. However, as we saw in section 3.1, this acceleration is smaller than that due to the spin of the earth.

Before we derive the equations for motion relative to a rotating frame, it is interesting to look at the effect of the earth's spin on a simple pendulum suspended at the earth's surface. Suppose the pendulum is suspended from the point S with its bob at P in the Oxz plane as shown in exaggerated form in figure 97. We should expect correctly that the bob would be thrown outwards due to the spin of the earth and to appear as in figure 97.

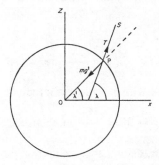

FIGURE 97

Let T be the tension in the string, λ' the angle which the radius to the pendulum makes with Ox and λ the angle which the string makes to Ox. The bob experiences a force mg' which is the gravitational attraction of the earth, that is

$$mg' = \frac{\gamma m M_{\mathrm{E}}}{a^2},$$

where m is the mass of the bob, M_{E} the mass of the earth, a the radius of the earth and γ the gravitational constant. The quantity mg' is not the 'weight' which we measure since we measure weight, in practice, on the rotating earth.

With the pendulum in equilibrium the forces acting on it must balance the accelerations. The earth is spinning with angular speed ω, say, about the z-axis and the bob must therefore be subject to an acceleration $\omega^2 a \cos \lambda'$ towards the z-axis. Resolving parallel to the x- and z-axes, we conclude that

$$mg' \cos \lambda' - T \cos \lambda = m\omega^2 a \cos \lambda', \tag{1}$$

$$T \sin \lambda = mg' \sin \lambda'. \tag{2}$$

The tension in the string is what we usually understand as the weight of the bob, mg, where g is the acceleration due to gravity—the acceleration which we measure at the earth's surface. Putting $T = mg$ in equations (1) and (2), we obtain

$$g' \cos \lambda' - g \cos \lambda = \omega^2 a \cos \lambda', \tag{3}$$

$$g \sin \lambda = g' \sin \lambda'. \tag{4}$$

The quantities g and λ can be measured and these equations give g' and λ' provided a (or $a \cos \lambda'$ if the oblateness of the earth is taken into account) is known.

Eliminating g' between (3) and (4) we have

$$g(\sin \lambda \cos \lambda' - \sin \lambda' \cos \lambda) = \omega^2 a \sin \lambda' \cos \lambda',$$

or

$$\sin (\lambda - \lambda') = \frac{\omega^2 a}{g} \sin \lambda' \cos \lambda'.$$

The ratio $\omega^2 a/g$ is small with the result that $\sin (\lambda - \lambda') \approx \lambda - \lambda'$. Thus

$$\lambda - \lambda' \approx \frac{\omega^2 a}{g} \sin \lambda' \cos \lambda'.$$

The angle λ which measures the inclination of the pendulum is the *astronomical* or *geographic latitude* and is what is generally understood by the term latitude. The angle λ' is the *geocentric latitude* and indicates the direction of the true vertical at a point on the earth. The maximum deviation between λ and λ' occurs where $\sin \lambda' \cos \lambda' = \frac{1}{2} \sin 2\lambda'$ takes its greatest value, namely at $\lambda' = 45°$. Taking $a = 6{,}370$ km (the mean radius of the earth) and $g = 981$ cm/sec^2, and computing $\omega = 7{\cdot}29 \times 10^{-5}$ rad/s, we find that $a\omega^2/g = 3{\cdot}450 \times 10^{-3}$. The maximum deviation at latitude $45°$ is therefore

$$\frac{1}{2} \frac{a\omega^2}{g} = 1{\cdot}725 \times 10^{-3} \text{ rad},$$

which is about 6 min of arc. However, it must be emphasized that the oblateness of the earth is a factor which should be taken into account although the estimate of the angular difference between the true vertical and apparent vertical (indicated by a plumb-line) is fairly good. A more accurate treatment requires consideration of the gravitational field associated with an oblate spheroid which is the surface obtained by spinning an ellipse about its minor axis. For the earth the polar radius is about 6,357 km and the equatorial radius 6,378 km.

8.2 Frame rotating about a fixed axis

As before let OXY represent the fixed frame and Oxy the rotating frame as shown in figure 98 with the common z-axis and Z-axis both pointing out from the paper. The Z-axis is the fixed axis about which Oxy is rotating. The angle θ is the angular displacement of the rotating frame and will be a function of time. Let **I** and **J** be fixed unit vectors in the directions OX

and OY and let **i** and **j** be unit vectors in the directions Ox and Oy. We can see from the diagram that, by the triangle law for addition of vectors,

$$\mathbf{i} = \mathbf{I}\cos\theta + \mathbf{J}\sin\theta, \qquad \mathbf{j} = -\mathbf{I}\sin\theta + \mathbf{J}\cos\theta. \tag{5}$$

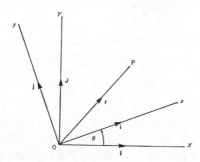

FIGURE 98   Unit vectors in the fixed and rotating frames

Note that the vectors **i** and **j** will be time-dependent, so that

$$\frac{d\mathbf{i}}{dt} = (-\mathbf{I}\sin\theta + \mathbf{J}\cos\theta)\dot{\theta} = \mathbf{j}\dot{\theta},$$

$$\frac{d\mathbf{j}}{dt} = (-\mathbf{I}\cos\theta - \mathbf{J}\sin\theta)\dot{\theta} = -\mathbf{i}\dot{\theta}.$$

If **r** is the position vector of a point P in the plane, then we can write both

$$\mathbf{r} = X\mathbf{I} + Y\mathbf{J} \quad \text{and} \quad \mathbf{r} = x\mathbf{i} + y\mathbf{j}.$$

The velocity of P as it appears to an observer in the fixed frame of reference will be

$$\frac{d\mathbf{r}}{dt} = \dot{\mathbf{r}} = \dot{X}\mathbf{I} + \dot{Y}\mathbf{J}.$$

But to an observer moving with the rotating frame, P has velocity

$$\frac{\delta\mathbf{r}}{\delta t} = \dot{x}\mathbf{i} + \dot{y}\mathbf{j}.$$

We adopt the notation $\delta/\delta t$ for time-derivatives within a rotating frame relative to an observer moving with that frame, for it is certainly not true, in general, that $d\mathbf{r}/dt$ and $\delta\mathbf{r}/\delta t$ represent the same function of time. However we can easily find the relation between the two derivatives.

Clearly,

$$\frac{d\mathbf{r}}{dt} = \dot{x}\mathbf{i} + \dot{y}\mathbf{j} + x\frac{d\mathbf{i}}{dt} + y\frac{d\mathbf{j}}{dt}$$

$$= \frac{\delta\mathbf{r}}{\delta t} + x\omega\mathbf{j} - y\omega\mathbf{i},$$

where $\dot{\theta}$ has been replaced by ω—the angular rate of rotation of the rotating frame. By the definition of a vector product (section 1.4), we can verify that

$$\frac{d\mathbf{r}}{dt} = \frac{\delta\mathbf{r}}{\delta t} + \boldsymbol{\omega} \times \mathbf{r}, \tag{6}$$

where $\boldsymbol{\omega} = \omega\mathbf{k}$ is the *angular velocity* of the rotating frame.

Whilst this formula has been obtained specifically for the position vector, it is true for any vector. Thus, if $\mathbf{a}$ is a function of time then

$$\frac{d\mathbf{a}}{dt} = \frac{\delta\mathbf{a}}{\delta t} + \boldsymbol{\omega} \times \mathbf{a}.$$

The result we have really shown is the identity of the two operators d/dt and $(\delta/\delta t + \boldsymbol{\omega} \times)$ operating on a vector function of time.

If $\mathbf{r}$ is fixed in the rotating frame $\delta\mathbf{r}/\delta t$ must vanish and

$$\frac{d\mathbf{r}}{dt} = \boldsymbol{\omega} \times \mathbf{r},$$

Example 1 A bead slides so that its displacement along a straight wire is given by $A \cos \Omega t$. The wire rotates with constant angular velocity ω about an axis which is perpendicular to the wire and passes through the mean position O of the bead. Find the actual velocity and acceleration of the bead.

Let Ox and Oy be axes along and perpendicular to the wire and let OX and OY be fixed axes, the two sets of axes coinciding at, say, time $t = 0$ (figure 98 should be consulted again). The bead moves with simple harmonic motion along the wire so that

$$\mathbf{r} = \mathbf{i}A \cos \Omega t.$$

The velocity relative to the rotating frame is given by

$$\frac{\delta\mathbf{r}}{\delta t} = -\mathbf{i}A\Omega \sin \Omega t.$$

Using equation (6) with $\boldsymbol{\omega} = \omega\mathbf{k}$, the velocity $\mathbf{v}$ relative to the fixed frame is given by

$$\mathbf{v} = \frac{d\mathbf{r}}{dt} = -\,iA\Omega \sin \Omega t + \omega\mathbf{k} \times iA \cos \Omega t$$

$$= -\,iA\Omega \sin \Omega t + jA\omega \cos \Omega t,$$

in components parallel to the moving axes. To obtain the velocity components referred to the fixed axes, we use the transformation (equations 5) relating the pairs of unit vectors with $\theta = \omega t$. Thus

$$\mathbf{v} = -\,A\Omega \sin \Omega t(\mathbf{I} \cos \omega t + \mathbf{J} \sin \omega t) +$$
$$A\omega \cos \Omega t(-\,\mathbf{I} \sin \omega t + \mathbf{J} \cos \omega t)$$
$$= -\,\mathbf{I}A(\Omega \sin \Omega t \cos \omega t + \omega \cos \Omega t \sin \omega t) +$$
$$\mathbf{J}A(\omega \cos \Omega t \cos \omega t - \Omega \sin \Omega t \sin \omega t).$$

The acceleration $\mathbf{f}$ is found by repeating the operator for moving axes on the velocity:

$$\mathbf{f} = \frac{d\mathbf{v}}{dt} = \frac{\delta\mathbf{v}}{\delta t} + \boldsymbol{\omega} \times \mathbf{v},$$

or by straightforward differentiation of the velocity in terms of its components in the fixed coordinate system. Adopting the first approach, we have

$$\mathbf{f} = -\,iA\Omega^2 \cos \Omega t - jA\omega\Omega \sin \Omega t + \omega\mathbf{k} \times (-\,iA\Omega \sin \Omega t + jA\omega \cos \Omega t)$$
$$= -\,iA(\Omega^2 + \omega^2) \cos \Omega t - 2jA\Omega\omega \sin \Omega t,$$

in components parallel to the rotating axes. Consider now a particle of mass m placed on the point P and subject to a plane force $\mathbf{F}$. In the fixed or inertial frame, we must have

$$\mathbf{F} = m\ddot{\mathbf{r}}$$

$$= m\left(\frac{\delta}{\delta t} + \boldsymbol{\omega} \times \right)\left(\frac{\delta}{\delta t} + \boldsymbol{\omega} \times \right)\mathbf{r}$$

$$= m\left(\frac{\delta}{\delta t} + \boldsymbol{\omega} \times \right)\left(\frac{\delta\mathbf{r}}{\delta t} + \boldsymbol{\omega} \times \mathbf{r}\right)$$

$$= m\left[\frac{\delta^2\mathbf{r}}{\delta t^2} + \boldsymbol{\omega} \times \frac{\delta\mathbf{r}}{\delta t} + \frac{\delta}{\delta t}(\boldsymbol{\omega} \times \mathbf{r}) + \boldsymbol{\omega} \times (\boldsymbol{\omega} \times \mathbf{r})\right]$$

$$= m\left[\frac{\delta^2\mathbf{r}}{\delta t^2} + 2\boldsymbol{\omega} \times \frac{\delta\mathbf{r}}{\delta t} + \frac{\delta\boldsymbol{\omega}}{\delta t} \times \mathbf{r} + \boldsymbol{\omega} \times (\boldsymbol{\omega} \times \mathbf{r})\right].$$

Since the rate of change of angular velocity

$$\dot{\boldsymbol{\omega}} = \frac{\delta\boldsymbol{\omega}}{\delta t} + \boldsymbol{\omega} \times \boldsymbol{\omega} = \frac{\delta\boldsymbol{\omega}}{\delta t},$$

it follows that

$$\mathbf{F} = m\left[\frac{\delta^2 \mathbf{r}}{\delta t^2} + 2\boldsymbol{\omega} \times \frac{\delta \mathbf{r}}{\delta t} + \dot{\boldsymbol{\omega}} \times \mathbf{r} + \boldsymbol{\omega} \times (\boldsymbol{\omega} \times \mathbf{r})\right]. \tag{7}$$

This is the equation for motion in a rotating frame of reference. Note that the force $\mathbf{F}$ is not proportional to the relative accleration $\delta^2\mathbf{r}/\delta t^2$ in such a frame. Remember also that $\mathbf{F}$ and $\mathbf{r}$ are plane vectors; however the vector equation for a frame rotating about a fixed axis suggests its generalization to a frame rotating in an unrestricted manner. We shall look at the general case in section 8.6.

Equation (7) can be rearranged into

$$\mathbf{F} - 2m\boldsymbol{\omega} \times \frac{\delta \mathbf{r}}{\delta t} - m\dot{\boldsymbol{\omega}} \times \mathbf{r} - m\boldsymbol{\omega} \times (\boldsymbol{\omega} \times \mathbf{r}) = m\frac{\delta^2 \mathbf{r}}{\delta t^2} \tag{8}$$

and may be thought of as a statement that force balances the product of mass and acceleration in the rotating frame if 'force' is interpreted to include the apparent forces which arise from the rotation. Of the terms on the left-hand side of (8), $- 2m\boldsymbol{\omega} \times (\delta\mathbf{r}/\delta t)$ is called the *Coriolis* force and $- m\boldsymbol{\omega} \times (\boldsymbol{\omega} \times \mathbf{r})$ the *centrifugal* force. Since the Coriolis force is the vector product of $- 2m\boldsymbol{\omega}$ and $\delta\mathbf{r}/\delta t$, it must appear, to an observer moving with the rotating frame, to act in a direction perpendicular to the particle's path at any instant. The centrifugal force is a triple vector product and by the expansion given at the end of section 1.6 :

$$- m\boldsymbol{\omega} \times (\boldsymbol{\omega} \times \mathbf{r}) = - m(\boldsymbol{\omega} \cdot \mathbf{r})\boldsymbol{\omega} + m\omega^2\mathbf{r} = m\omega^2\mathbf{r},$$

remembering that $\boldsymbol{\omega} = \omega\mathbf{k}$ and therefore that $\boldsymbol{\omega} \cdot \mathbf{r} = 0$ in the special case we are considering. The direction of this force coincides with that of the position vector and acts outwards.

If the moving frame rotates with constant angular velocity then $\dot{\boldsymbol{\omega}} = \mathbf{0}$, and

$$\mathbf{F} - 2m\boldsymbol{\omega} \times \frac{\delta \mathbf{r}}{\delta t} - m\boldsymbol{\omega} \times (\boldsymbol{\omega} \times \mathbf{r}) = m\frac{\delta^2 \mathbf{r}}{\delta t^2}. \tag{9}$$

Example 2   A straight wire of length a rotates with constant angular velocity ω about a fixed perpendicular axis through one end of the wire. A bead of mass m is placed on the wire at its mid-point and released. If friction is negligible and the wire rotates in a horizontal plane, describe the motion of the bead.

Take rotating axes Ox along and Oy perpendicular to the wire, and let Ox coincide with the fixed axis OX when the bead is in its initial position. The scheme of axes is shown in figure 99. The only horizontal force acting on the bead is the reaction due to the wire and this acts in a direction perpendicular to the wire since no friction is present. Thus the reaction is given by $R\mathbf{j}$, say. The position vector of the bead in the *rotating frame* is given by $\mathbf{r} = x\mathbf{i}$ where x is the distance of the bead from O at time t. Since the angular velocity is a constant $\omega\mathbf{k}$, we apply equation (9):

$$R\mathbf{j} - 2m\omega\mathbf{k} \times \dot{x}\mathbf{i} - m\omega\mathbf{k} \times (\omega\mathbf{k} \times x\mathbf{i}) = m\ddot{x}\mathbf{i},$$

which simplifies to

$$R\mathbf{j} - 2m\omega\dot{x}\mathbf{j} + m\omega^2 x\mathbf{i} = m\ddot{x}\mathbf{i}.$$

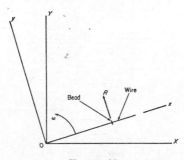

FIGURE 99

This vector equation is equivalent to the two scalar equations

$$R = 2m\omega\dot{x}, \qquad \omega^2 x = \ddot{x}.$$

The second of these gives the displacement of the bead and is a standard second-order equation with solution

$$x = A\,e^{\omega t} + B\,e^{-\omega t}.$$

Initially, we are given that $x = \tfrac{1}{2}a$ and $\dot{x} = 0$. Hence the constants A and B are given by

$$\tfrac{1}{2}a = A + B, \qquad 0 = A - B,$$

from which we find that $A = B = \tfrac{1}{4}a$. The displacement of the bead is given by

$$x = \tfrac{1}{4}a(e^{\omega t} + e^{-\omega t}) = \tfrac{1}{2}a \cosh \omega t.$$

The bead leaves the wire at time $t = T$ where $2 = \cosh \omega T$ with velocity

$$\frac{\delta x}{\delta t} = \tfrac{1}{2}a\omega \sinh \omega T = \tfrac{1}{2}a\omega\sqrt{(\cosh^2 \omega T - 1)} = \frac{\sqrt{3}}{2}a\omega,$$

relative to the wire.

8

8.3 Rotation of a rigid body about a fixed axis

Consider now a rigid body constrained to rotate about a fixed axis in the body. Suppose that the origin O is a point on this axis and that OZ is the axis of rotation. The axes Ox and Oy are taken to be axes fixed in the rigid body, which means that there is no relative rotation between these axes and the body. As before OX and OY specify the inertial frame (see figure 100). We showed in section 3.9 that the moment **M** of the external

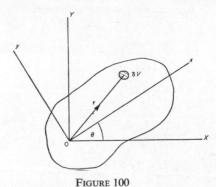

FIGURE 100

forces about a fixed point balances the rate of change of angular momentum **h**:

$$\mathbf{M} = \dot{\mathbf{h}}$$

where the angular momentum

$$\mathbf{h} = \int_V \mathbf{r} \times \dot{\mathbf{r}}\rho \, dV,$$

r being the position vector of a typical volume element δV, and ρ being the density of the rigid body. The moment **M** may also include *couples* which, although they add nothing to the resultant force on the system, do affect the moment. For example, the frictional resistance between an axle and wheel will be a couple. A couple may be thought of as a pair of equal and opposite forces which do not act in the same straight line.

We shall now examine the angular momentum in relation to a body rotating about a fixed axis. Choose the element of volume to be a cylinder parallel to the axis OZ. In figure 100, δV is really a cylinder erected on the shaded element. Obviously we take moments about the axis of rotation. Consider now a point in the plane OXY with the *plane* position vector **r**. By equation (6) the velocity of this point

$$\dot{\mathbf{r}} = \frac{\delta \mathbf{r}}{\delta t} + \boldsymbol{\omega} \times \mathbf{r},$$

where ω is the angular velocity of the rotating frame which, since this frame is embedded in the rigid body, we describe as the angular velocity of the body. But $\mathbf{r}$ is the position vector of a *fixed* point in the rotating frame so that $\delta\mathbf{r}/\delta t = 0$, and

$$\dot{\mathbf{r}} = \omega \times \mathbf{r}.$$

Consequently the angular momentum

$$\mathbf{h} = \int_V \mathbf{r} \times (\omega \times \mathbf{r})\rho \, dV$$

$$= \int_V [r^2\omega - (\omega \cdot \mathbf{r})\mathbf{r}]\rho \, dV \quad \text{(expanding the triple vector product)}$$

$$= \omega \int_V r^2\rho \, dV,$$

since $\omega \cdot \mathbf{r} = 0$ and ω does not depend on the positions of individual parts of the body. We write

$$\mathbf{h} = I\omega,$$

where I, called the *moment of inertia*, is the integral $\int_V r^2\rho \, dV$, a fixed number for any selected rigid body and axis of rotation. It cannot depend on time or position since r, the distance of the element δV from the origin is a constant. The moment of inertia distinguishes the rotational behaviour of two bodies in much the same way as differences in mass distinguish the behaviour of the translational motion of particles and bodies.

The equation of motion for the body can be written

$$\mathbf{M} = I\dot{\omega}.$$

Since $\mathbf{h}$, ω and consequently $\mathbf{M}$ can have only one component—in the direction of $\mathbf{k}$—we can replace this equation by the single scalar equation

$$M = I\dot{\omega} = I\ddot{\theta},$$

where $\omega = \omega\mathbf{k} = \dot{\theta}\mathbf{k}$. Having obtained the equation of motion, we can forget the rotating frame since θ is essentially the angle between a line fixed in the body and one fixed in space.

Consider a rigid body of mass m rotating freely about a fixed horizontal axis which passes through the point O of the body, the only external force being a uniform gravitational field. The total effect of this force is equivalent to a single force mg acting at the mass-centre G of the body (figure 101). If $OG = b$, the moment of the weight about O is $mgb \sin \theta$ (there will be reactions on the body at the axis but these forces must have zero moment about the axis) and the equation of motion is therefore

$$- mgb \sin \theta = I\ddot{\theta}. \tag{10}$$

The angle θ is the angle between OG and the downward vertical. This equation should be compared with the equation of motion for a simple pendulum of length a:

$$- g \sin \theta = a\ddot{\theta}.$$

The equations of motion are similar and the rigid body behaves as a simple pendulum of length I/mb.

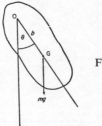

FIGURE 101

8.4 Moments of inertia

The moment of inertia I of a body about a fixed axis of itself is defined by

$$I = \int_V r^2 \rho \, dV,$$

which is a volume integral. However, it may reduce to a surface integral for a lamina or a line integral for a wire, the density being then interpreted as mass per unit area or mass per unit length as the case may be. We shall derive some moments of inertia for simple bodies.

(i) *Rod about an axis through its mid-point.* Suppose that the axis is perpendicular to the rod and that the density per unit length ρ is constant. An element of length δx at a distance x from the mid-point of the rod will have mass $\rho \delta x$ and its moment of inertia is $x^2 \rho \delta x$ about O. The total moment of inertia is the sum of such quantities throughout the length of the rod. Thus, for a rod of length $2a$,

$$I = \int_{-a}^{a} x^2 \rho \, dx = \rho(\tfrac{1}{3}x^3)_{-a}^{a} = \tfrac{2}{3}\rho a^3 = \tfrac{1}{3}ma^2,$$

where m, the mass of the rod, is $2\rho a$.

(ii) *Circular disc about its axis.* The axis is through the centre of the disc perpendicular to its plane. We use the obvious symmetry of the disc and take a circular element of width δr and radius r as shown in figure 102.

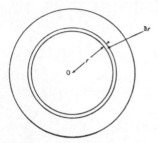

FIGURE 102

Every part of the element is, to the first order, at the same distance r from the axis and consequently $2\rho\pi r^3 \delta r$ is, to the same order, the moment of inertia of this element about the axis. If a is the radius of the disc, the total moment of inertia is given by

$$I = 2\pi\rho \int_0^a r^3 \, \mathrm{d}r = 2\pi\rho(\tfrac{1}{4}r^4)_0^a = \tfrac{1}{2}\pi\rho a^4 = \tfrac{1}{2}ma^2,$$

where $m = \pi\rho a^2$ is the mass of the disc. The circular cylinder has the same moment of inertia about its axis.

(iii) *Uniform block about a central axis parallel to two forces.* Let the edges of the block have lengths $2a$, $2b$, $2c$ parallel to the axes Ox, Oy, Oz where O is the centre of the block (figure 103). Take a small rectangular

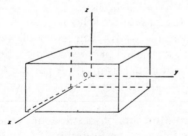

FIGURE 103

block with edges δx, δy, δz as the element of volume. The square of the distance of this element from the axis (say the x-axis) is $y^2 + z^2$, and the moment of inertia of the element is $\rho(y^2 + z^2)\delta x\delta y\delta z$. The total moment is therefore given by

$$I = \int_{-c}^{c} \int_{-b}^{b} \int_{-a}^{a} \rho(y^2 + z^2)\, dx\, dy\, dz$$

$$= \rho \int_{-c}^{c} \int_{-b}^{b} [(y^2 + z^2)x]_{x=-a}^{x=a}\, dy\, dz$$

$$= 2\rho a \int_{-c}^{c} (\tfrac{1}{3}y^3 + z^2 y)_{y=-b}^{y=b}\, dz$$

$$= 4\rho a b \int_{-c}^{c} (\tfrac{1}{3}b^2 + z^2)\, dz$$

$$= 4\rho a b(\tfrac{1}{3}b^2 z + \tfrac{1}{3}z^3)_{z=-c}^{z=c}$$

$$= \tfrac{8}{3}\rho abc(b^2 + c^2) = \tfrac{1}{3}m(b^2 + c^2),$$

where $m = 8abc\rho$ is the mass of the block.

(iv) *Uniform sphere about a diameter.* Let a be the radius of the sphere. Slice a disc of thickness δx and distance x from the centre of the sphere perpendicular to the chosen axis. By (ii) the moment of inertia of this disc is, to the first order, $\tfrac{1}{2}\pi\rho(a^2 - x^2)^2 \delta x$. Summing this expression throughout the sphere, we find that the moment of inertia is

$$I = \tfrac{1}{2}\pi\rho \int_{-a}^{a} (a^2 - x^2)^2\, dx$$

$$= \tfrac{1}{2}\pi\rho(a^4 x - \tfrac{2}{3}a^2 x^3 + \tfrac{1}{5}x^5)_{-a}^{a}$$

$$= \pi\rho a^5(1 - \tfrac{2}{3} + \tfrac{1}{5}) = \tfrac{8}{15}\pi\rho a^5$$

$$= \tfrac{2}{5}ma^2,$$

where $m = \tfrac{4}{3}\pi a^3 \rho$ is the mass of the sphere.

The moment of inertia is always the product of mass and (length)^2 and if it is written as mk^2, k is called the *radius of gyration*. Thus the radius of gyration of a disc about its axis is $a/\sqrt{2}$. A particle of mass m situated at a distance k from the axis will have the same moment of inertia as the body.

Parallel axis theorem. Moments of inertia about other axes can often be found quickly by the following useful result. If I_G is the moment of inertia of a body of mass m about an axis through its mass-centre and I is the moment of inertia about a parallel axis which is at a distance d from the first, then

$$I = I_G + md^2.$$

In figure 104, GA is the axis through the mass-centre G and BC is the parallel axis. Consider an element δV of volume which is at a distance r from GA and r' from BC. By definition

$$I_G = \int_V \rho r^2 \, dV.$$

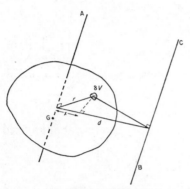

FIGURE 104

In the triangle shown we observe that $r^2 = r'^2 - d^2 + 2xd$ so that

$$I_G = \int_V \rho(r'^2 - d^2 + 2xd) \, dV$$

$$= I - d^2 \int_V \rho \, dV + 2d \int_V x\rho \, dV$$

$$= I - md^2,$$

the last integral vanishing since x is the distance of δV from a fixed plane passing through the mass-centre.

Example 3   Investigate the difference between the periods of a simple pendulum and a similar pendulum in which the bob is replaced by a small sphere of the same mass for small oscillations.

If the simple pendulum has length a and a bob (idealized as a particle) of mass m, its equation for small displacements θ from the downward vertical is

$$a\ddot{\theta} = -g\theta.$$

The period of the oscillations is $2\pi\sqrt{(a/g)}$.

Let the sphere have radius ε. By the parallel axis theorem the moment of inertia of the sphere about the point of suspension will be $\frac{2}{5}m\varepsilon^2 + ma^2$. The equation of motion is

$$(\tfrac{2}{5}\varepsilon^2 + a^2)\ddot{\theta} = -ga\theta$$

from equation (10) for small θ. The period of the oscillations is therefore

$$2\pi[(\tfrac{2}{5}\varepsilon^2 + a^2)/ga]^{\frac{1}{2}} = 2\pi\left[\frac{a}{g}\left(1 + \frac{2\varepsilon^2}{5a^2}\right)\right]^{\frac{1}{2}}$$

$$\approx 2\pi\left[\left(\frac{a}{g}\right)\cdot\left(1 + \frac{\varepsilon^2}{5a^2}\right)\right]^{\frac{1}{2}}$$

using the binomial expansion for $\varepsilon \ll a$. The period is *increased* by a factor $\varepsilon^2/5a^2$ approximately.

The kinetic energy of a body rotating about a fixed axis is given by

$$\mathscr{T} = \tfrac{1}{2}\int_V \rho\dot{\mathbf{r}}\cdot\dot{\mathbf{r}}\,dV$$

(section 5.4), where the velocity $\dot{\mathbf{r}} = \boldsymbol{\omega} \times \mathbf{r} = -\omega y\mathbf{i} + \omega x\mathbf{j}$ and $\boldsymbol{\omega} = \omega\mathbf{k}$ is the angular velocity of the body. Thus

$$\mathscr{T} = \tfrac{1}{2}\int_V \rho\omega^2(x^2 + y^2)\,dV = \tfrac{1}{2}\omega^2\int_V \rho r^2\,dV$$

$$= \tfrac{1}{2}I\omega^2,$$

and, as before, I is the moment of inertia about the axis.

For a rigid body rotating freely about a fixed axis, the energy of the body will be conserved (section 5.4). Referring back to figure 101, we see that the potential energy of the body is given by

$$\mathscr{V} = -mga\cos\theta,$$

which is negative because $a\cos\theta$ is the *depth* of the mass-centre below O. Energy conservation implies that

$$\tfrac{1}{2}I\dot{\theta}^2 - mga\cos\theta = \text{constant},$$

an equation which can also be obtained by integrating the equation of motion.

Example 4 *One end of a uniform heavy chain is attached to a drum of radius a, and the chain is wrapped round the drum. It makes n complete turns with a small piece of chain hanging free from the horizontal diameter. The drum is mounted on a smooth horizontal axis, and the chain is allowed to unwrap. If the moment of inertia of the drum about the axis is I, find the angular speed of the drum when the chain has just unwrapped itself.*

Figure 105 shows the drum and chain at the instant when the chain has unwrapped itself. Let the drum then have an angular speed ω. Since there is no frictional resistance in the system, energy will be conserved. Initially the mass-centre of the chain lies on the axis and finally G will be at a depth πna below the axis since the chain has length $2\pi na$. This loss of potential energy of $Mg\pi na$ is compensated by a gain in kinetic energy of $\frac{1}{2}I\omega^2$ for the drum and $\frac{1}{2}M\omega^2a^2$ for the chain (the chain will at this instant be falling vertically with speed ωa).

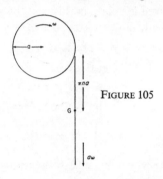

FIGURE 105

Hence

$$\tfrac{1}{2}I\omega^2 + \tfrac{1}{2}M\omega^2a^2 = Mg\pi na,$$

whence

$$\omega = [2Mg\pi na/(I + Ma^2)]^{\frac{1}{2}}.$$

8.5 General plane motion of a rigid body

By the term plane motion of a system, we mean that every point of the system moves parallel to a fixed plane. Suppose that OXY represents, in figure 106, this fixed plane. Let G be the mass-centre of a rigid body and

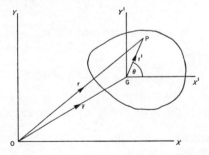

FIGURE 106 Coordinate scheme for the plane motion of a rigid body

let GX' and GY' be axes which remain parallel to OX and OY respectively. Without loss of generality we can let the planes OXY and $GX'Y'$ coincide, since the velocity of every point of the body on a line parallel to the Z-axis (drawn out of the paper) will be the same by the definition of plane motion. Suppose that P is a point of the body with (plane) position vectors **r** relative to O and **r′** relative to G.

The motion may be considered as the combination of a translation of the mass-centre and a rotation about the mass-centre. The angular velocity of the body is **ω**, where $\boldsymbol{\omega} = \dot{\theta}\mathbf{k}$ and θ is an angle between a direction fixed in the body and one fixed in space, in this case the angle PGX'. By analogy with the motion of a body about a fixed axis the velocity of P *relative to* G is

$$\dot{\mathbf{r}}' = \boldsymbol{\omega} \times \mathbf{r}'.$$

The actual velocity of P will therefore be

$$\dot{\mathbf{r}} = \dot{\bar{\mathbf{r}}} + \boldsymbol{\omega} \times \mathbf{r}'. \tag{11}$$

The angular momentum of the body about O is defined by

$$\mathbf{h} = \int_V \rho \mathbf{r} \times \dot{\mathbf{r}} \, dV. \tag{12}$$

By the triangle law $\mathbf{r} = \bar{\mathbf{r}} + \mathbf{r}'$, and substituting for the velocity from (11) into (12), we find that

$$\mathbf{h} = \int_V \rho(\bar{\mathbf{r}} + \mathbf{r}') \times (\dot{\bar{\mathbf{r}}} + \boldsymbol{\omega} \times \mathbf{r}') \, dV$$

$$= \int_V \rho[\bar{\mathbf{r}} \times \dot{\bar{\mathbf{r}}} + \mathbf{r}' \times \dot{\bar{\mathbf{r}}} + \bar{\mathbf{r}} \times (\boldsymbol{\omega} \times \mathbf{r}') + \mathbf{r}' \times (\boldsymbol{\omega} \times \mathbf{r}')] \, dV$$

$$= \bar{\mathbf{r}} \times \dot{\bar{\mathbf{r}}} \int_V \rho \, dV + \int_V \rho \mathbf{r}' \, dV \times \dot{\bar{\mathbf{r}}} + \bar{\mathbf{r}} \times \left(\boldsymbol{\omega} \times \int_V \rho \mathbf{r}' \, dV\right) +$$

$$\int_V \rho \mathbf{r}' \times (\boldsymbol{\omega} \times \mathbf{r}') \, dV.$$

Since **r′** is the position vector relative to the mass-centre, $\int_V \rho \mathbf{r}' \, dV = \mathbf{0}$ by definition. Therefore

$$\mathbf{h} = m\bar{\mathbf{r}} \times \dot{\bar{\mathbf{r}}} + \int_V \rho \boldsymbol{\omega} r'^2 \, dV,$$

where $m = \int_V \rho \, dV$ is the mass of the body. The expansion for the triple vector product has been used in the integrand of the last integral. Finally, since **ω** depends on time only,

$$\mathbf{h} = m\bar{\mathbf{r}} \times \dot{\bar{\mathbf{r}}} + I_G \boldsymbol{\omega} \tag{13}$$

where $I_G = \int_V \rho r'^2 \, dV$ is the moment of inertia of the body about an axis through its mass-centre.

The laws of motion for a rigid body are described in section 3.9 and are equivalent to

(i) the total force equals the product of the mass and the acceleration of the mass-centre,

(ii) the moment of the forces about a *fixed* point equals the rate of change of angular momentum about that point.

For the plane motion considered above,

$$\mathbf{F} = m\ddot{\mathbf{r}}, \qquad \mathbf{M} = \dot{\mathbf{h}},$$

where $\mathbf{F}$ is the total force and $\mathbf{M}$ is the moment of the forces about O. The second of these equations can be expressed in a more convenient form if we substitute for $\mathbf{h}$ from (13):

$$\mathbf{M} = m\frac{\mathrm{d}}{\mathrm{d}t}(\bar{\mathbf{r}} \times \dot{\bar{\mathbf{r}}}) + I_G\dot{\omega}$$

$$= m\bar{\mathbf{r}} \times \ddot{\bar{\mathbf{r}}} + I_G\dot{\omega}$$

$$= \bar{\mathbf{r}} \times \mathbf{F} + I_G\dot{\omega}.$$

However $\mathbf{M} - \bar{\mathbf{r}} \times \mathbf{F}$ is $\mathbf{M}_G$, the moment of the forces about G, the mass-centre. The equations of motion can therefore be represented concisely by

$$\mathbf{F} = m\ddot{\bar{\mathbf{r}}}, \qquad \mathbf{M}_G = I_G\dot{\omega}.$$

These vector equations contain the three scalar equations

$$F_x = m\ddot{\bar{x}}, \qquad F_y = m\ddot{\bar{y}}, \qquad M_G = I_G\ddot{\theta},$$

(where we have let $\mathbf{F} = F_x\mathbf{i} + F_y\mathbf{j}$ and $\mathbf{M}_G = M_G\mathbf{k}$) to determine $\bar{x}$, $\bar{y}$ and θ; that is the position of the mass-centre and the orientation of the body about the mass-centre at any time.

As before, the kinetic energy is defined by

$$\mathscr{T} = \tfrac{1}{2}\int_V \rho\dot{\mathbf{r}} \cdot \dot{\mathbf{r}}\, \mathrm{d}V.$$

The velocity of any point of the body can be expressed as

$$\dot{\mathbf{r}} = \dot{\bar{\mathbf{r}}} + \boldsymbol{\omega} \times \mathbf{r}' = (\dot{\bar{x}} - \omega y')\mathbf{i} + (\dot{\bar{y}} + \omega x')\mathbf{j}$$

with the result that

$$\mathscr{T} = \tfrac{1}{2}\int_V [(\dot{\bar{x}} - \omega y')^2 + (\dot{\bar{y}} + \omega x')^2]\rho\, \mathrm{d}V$$

$$= \tfrac{1}{2}\int_V (\dot{\bar{x}}^2 + \dot{\bar{y}}^2)\rho\, \mathrm{d}V + \tfrac{1}{2}\int_V \omega^2(x'^2 + y'^2)\rho\, \mathrm{d}V -$$

$$\omega \int \rho y'\, \mathrm{d}V + \omega \int \rho x'\, \mathrm{d}V$$

$$= \tfrac{1}{2}m\bar{v}^2 + \tfrac{1}{2}I_G\omega^2, \tag{14}$$

the last two integrals on the right-hand side vanishing by the definition of the mass-centre. The kinetic energy may be considered as the sum of two terms, one giving the translational energy and the other the rotational energy of the body. If non-conservative forces acting on the body do no work, then the energy principle will hold.

Example 5　A uniform sphere of mass m is released from rest on a rough plane inclined at an angle α to the horizontal. If no slipping occurs between the sphere and the plane, discuss the motion of the sphere.

By the phrase 'no slipping occurs' we mean that the sphere rolls on the plane, the point of contact P on the sphere in figure 107 being instantaneously at rest.

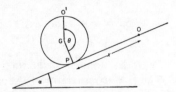

FIGURE 107　Sphere rolling down an inclined plane

Suppose that O is the initial point of contact with O′ the corresponding contact point on the sphere. Let $P\hat{G}O = \theta$ and $OP = x$. If a is the radius of the sphere, $a\theta = x$ for rolling contact. Since the reaction and frictional force between the sphere and the plane both act through P, which is instantaneously at rest, they do no work throughout the motion and the energy equation holds. By equation (14)

$$\mathcal{T} = \tfrac{1}{2}m\dot{x}^2 + \tfrac{1}{2} \cdot \tfrac{2}{5}ma^2 \cdot \theta^2,$$

since θ is the angular velocity of the sphere. Note also that $\tfrac{2}{5}ma^2$ is the moment of inertia of a sphere about its diameter. Since $a\theta = x$, we can write

$$\mathcal{T} = \tfrac{1}{2}m\dot{x}^2 + \tfrac{1}{5}m\dot{x}^2 = \tfrac{7}{10}m\dot{x}^2.$$

The kinetic energy must balance the potential energy lost. In this case the centre of the sphere falls a distance $x \sin α$, with a corresponding potential energy loss of $mgx \sin α$. Hence

$$\tfrac{7}{10}m\dot{x}^2 = mgx \sin α.$$

Taking the derivative of this equation with respect to the time, we find that

$$\ddot{x} = 5g \sin α/7,$$

from which we infer that the centre of the sphere moves with constant acceleration. Since $\dot{x} = x = 0$ at $t = 0$ (say) the position of the sphere at time t is given by $x = 5gt^2 \sin α/14$.

Example 6   In figure 108 the planetary gear B *is enmeshed between a fixed outer gear* C *and a free inner gear* A. *There is no resistance to motion. Initially the system is at rest and a constant couple* G *is applied to* A *for a time* t_0 *and then removed. Find the final angular speeds of the gears. (Assume that the motion takes place in a horizontal plane.)*

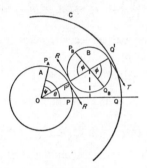

FIGURE 108

Let the radii of A and B be a and b and let their moments of inertia be I_A and I_B respectively. In figure 108, OPQ is the initial position of the gears when P_A, P_B and P, and Q_B and Q coincide. Let the angles θ, ϕ and ψ be as shown in the figure. It is clear from the geometry of the figure that the angular velocity of A is $\dot{\theta}$ and that of B is $\dot{\phi} - \dot{\theta} + \dot{\psi}$ (remember that in two dimensions angular velocity is the rate of change of an angle between a direction in the body and one fixed in space). However, there exist relations between the angles θ, ϕ and ψ. For rolling contact, the arc lengths $P'P_A$ and $P'P_B$ must be equal and Q_BQ' must equal QQ'. Thus

$$a\psi = b\phi = (a + 2b)(\theta - \psi),$$

so that

$$\psi = (a + 2b)\theta/2(a + b), \qquad \phi = a(a + 2b)\theta/2b(a + b).$$

After some simplification it follows that the angular velocity of B,

$$\dot{\phi} - \dot{\theta} + \dot{\psi} = a\dot{\theta}/2b.$$

For A we take moments about O, and for B we take moments about the centre of that gear and resolve transversely. With R and T the tangential reactions between the gear teeth (normal reactions are not required), the following equations result when the couple G is acting:

$$G - Ra = I_A\ddot{\theta}, \tag{15}$$

$$- Rb - Tb = - I_B(\ddot{\phi} - \ddot{\theta} + \ddot{\psi}) = - I_B a\ddot{\theta}/2b, \tag{16}$$

$$R - T = m_B(a + b)(\ddot{\theta} - \ddot{\psi}) = \tfrac{1}{2}m_B a\ddot{\theta}, \tag{17}$$

where in the last equation m_B is the mass of gear B and $\frac{1}{2}a\ddot{\theta}$ is the transverse acceleration of its centre.

The behaviour of θ supplies the information we require. Eliminate R and T between equations (15), (16) and (17) to give

$$G = \frac{\ddot{\theta}}{4b^2}(4b^2 I_A + m_B a^2 b^2 + a^2 I_B).$$

Integration of this equation with respect to t yields

$$Gt = \frac{\dot{\theta}}{4b^2}(4b^2 I_A + m_B a^2 b^2 + a^2 I_B).$$

Putting $\dot{\theta} = \omega$ when $t = t_0$, we find that the inner gear A ultimately rotates with angular speed

$$\omega = 4b^2 Gt_0 / (4b^2 I_A + m_B a^2 b^2 + a^2 I_B).$$

The reader should calculate the corresponding angular speed of B.

Example 7 A uniform circular cylinder of radius a and mass m rolls without slipping on the inner surface of a fixed circular cylinder of radius 4a. Find the period of small oscillations of the rolling cylinder.

Let O' coincide with O when the rolling cylinder is in equilibrium in figure 109. Let θ and ϕ be the angles shown in figure 109. The conditions for rolling contact implies that $a\phi = 4a\theta$. We shall apply the energy principle to the rolling cylinder; this is justifiable since both the normal reaction and the frictional force acting at the point of contact P between the cylinders do no work.

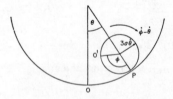

FIGURE 109

The centre of the rolling cylinder must move in a circle with speed $3a\dot{\theta}$ and its angular speed is given by $a(\dot{\phi} - \dot{\theta})$, the sense of both being shown in the figure. By equation (14),

$$\mathcal{T} = \tfrac{1}{2}m(9a^2\dot{\theta}^2) + \tfrac{1}{2} \cdot \tfrac{1}{2}ma^2(\dot{\phi} - \dot{\theta})^2.$$

Relative to the centre of the fixed cylinder,

$$\mathcal{V} = - 3mga \cos \theta.$$

The energy principle asserts that

$$\tfrac{9}{2}ma^2\dot{\theta}^2 + \tfrac{1}{4}ma^2(\dot{\phi} - \dot{\theta})^2 - 3mga\cos\theta = \text{constant},$$

or, by writing ϕ in terms of θ, that

$$\tfrac{9}{2}ma^2\dot{\theta}^2 + \tfrac{9}{4}ma^2\dot{\theta}^2 - 3mga\cos\theta = \text{constant},$$

that is

$$\tfrac{27}{4}ma^2\dot{\theta}^2 - 3mga\cos\theta = \text{constant}.$$

Differentiating this equation with respect to t, we deduce that

$$\tfrac{27}{2}ma^2\ddot{\theta} + 3mga\sin\theta = 0,$$

which for small values of θ can be approximated by

$$\ddot{\theta} + \frac{2g}{9a}\theta = 0.$$

Thus to the first order the cylinder rocks with simple harmonic motion of period $3\pi\sqrt{(2a/g)}$. Note that the methods of section 7.2 could have been applied to this problem.

8.6 General rotating frame of reference

Figure 110 shows a fixed frame of reference specified by the unit vectors **I**, **J**, **K** and a rotating frame whose axes are in the directions of the unit vectors **i**, **j**, **k**, the frames having a coincident origin O. The rotating frame

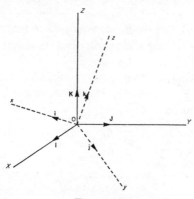

FIGURE 110

may be imagined fixed in a rigid body which is pivoted at the point O. The unit vectors **i**, **j**, **k**, which will be time dependent, must satisfy the relations

$$\mathbf{i}\cdot\mathbf{i} = \mathbf{j}\cdot\mathbf{j} = \mathbf{k}\cdot\mathbf{k} = 1, \qquad \mathbf{i}\cdot\mathbf{j} = \mathbf{j}\cdot\mathbf{k} = \mathbf{k}\cdot\mathbf{i} = 0.$$

Taking derivatives of these relations with respect to the time, we must have

$$\mathbf{i} \cdot \frac{d\mathbf{i}}{dt} = 0, \qquad \mathbf{j} \cdot \frac{d\mathbf{j}}{dt} = 0, \qquad \mathbf{k} \cdot \frac{d\mathbf{k}}{dt} = 0; \tag{18}$$

$$\frac{d\mathbf{i}}{dt} \cdot \mathbf{j} + \mathbf{i} \cdot \frac{d\mathbf{j}}{dt} = 0, \qquad \frac{d\mathbf{j}}{dt} \cdot \mathbf{k} + \mathbf{j} \cdot \frac{d\mathbf{k}}{dt} = 0, \qquad \frac{d\mathbf{k}}{dt} \cdot \mathbf{i} + \mathbf{k} \cdot \frac{d\mathbf{i}}{dt} = 0. \tag{19}$$

The three relations (18) imply that the derivative of the unit vector is perpendicular to that unit vector in each case. Therefore there exist functions $\alpha_2(t)$, $\alpha_3(t)$, $\beta_3(t)$, $\beta_1(t)$, $\gamma_1(t)$, $\gamma_2(t)$ such that

$$\frac{d\mathbf{i}}{dt} = \beta_1 \mathbf{j} + \gamma_1 \mathbf{k}, \qquad \frac{d\mathbf{j}}{dt} = \gamma_2 \mathbf{k} + \alpha_2 \mathbf{i}, \qquad \frac{d\mathbf{k}}{dt} = \alpha_3 \mathbf{i} + \beta_3 \mathbf{j},$$

but conditions (19) must also be satisfied, and they imply that

$$\beta_1 = -\alpha_2 = \omega_3 \text{ (say)}, \qquad \gamma_2 = -\beta_3 = \omega_1 \text{ (say)}, \qquad \alpha_3 = -\gamma_1 = \omega_2 \text{ (say)}.$$

Thus

$$\frac{d\mathbf{i}}{dt} = \omega_3 \mathbf{j} - \omega_2 \mathbf{k}, \qquad \frac{d\mathbf{j}}{dt} = \omega_1 \mathbf{k} - \omega_3 \mathbf{i}, \qquad \frac{d\mathbf{k}}{dt} = \omega_2 \mathbf{i} - \omega_1 \mathbf{j}.$$

We now introduce the vector $\boldsymbol{\omega} = \omega_1 \mathbf{i} + \omega_2 \mathbf{j} + \omega_3 \mathbf{k}$ and observe by the definition of a vector product that

$$\frac{d\mathbf{i}}{dt} = \boldsymbol{\omega} \times \mathbf{i}, \qquad \frac{d\mathbf{j}}{dt} = \boldsymbol{\omega} \times \mathbf{j}, \qquad \frac{d\mathbf{k}}{dt} = \boldsymbol{\omega} \times \mathbf{k}. \tag{20}$$

One immediate conclusion from this equation is that each of the points with position vectors $\mathbf{i}$, $\mathbf{j}$ and $\mathbf{k}$ is moving in a direction perpendicular to a certain direction indicated by the vector $\boldsymbol{\omega}$.

Consider now a point which is rigidly embedded in the rotating frame with position vector $\mathbf{r} = a\mathbf{i} + b\mathbf{j} + c\mathbf{k}$, where, of course, a, b and c must be constants. The velocity of this point is

$$\frac{d\mathbf{r}}{dt} = a\frac{d\mathbf{i}}{dt} + b\frac{d\mathbf{j}}{dt} + c\frac{d\mathbf{k}}{dt}$$

$$= a\boldsymbol{\omega} \times \mathbf{i} + b\boldsymbol{\omega} \times \mathbf{j} + c\boldsymbol{\omega} \times \mathbf{k}$$

$$= \boldsymbol{\omega} \times \mathbf{r},$$

using the relations above. With the frame considered attached to a rigid body we deduce that

$$\boldsymbol{\omega} \cdot \frac{d\mathbf{r}}{dt} = \boldsymbol{\omega} \cdot (\boldsymbol{\omega} \times \mathbf{r}) = 0,$$

which means that at any instant every point of the body is moving in a direction perpendicular to ω. Furthermore if the point $\mathbf{r}$ lies on the line through O in the direction of ω, so that $\mathbf{r} = \omega k / |\omega|$, where k is a constant, then

$$\frac{d\mathbf{r}}{dt} = \omega \times \frac{\omega k}{|\omega|} = \mathbf{0}.$$

At any instant there exists a straight line which is momentarily at rest and such that every point of the body is turning about that line. In other words at any instant the body is spinning about an *instantaneous axis of rotation*. This axis will, in general, be fixed neither in space nor in the body.

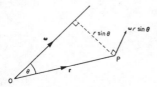

FIGURE 111

That the magnitude of ω represents an angular rate of rotation can be seen from figure 111. If θ is the angle between ω and $\mathbf{r}$, then the magnitude of the velocity of the body-fixed point P is given by

$$|\dot{\mathbf{r}}| = |\omega \times \mathbf{r}| = \omega r \sin \theta,$$

and clearly $r \sin \theta$ is the perpendicular distance from P on to ω. Thus P is moving instantaneously in a circle of radius $r \sin \theta$ at an angular rate ω. Note that the direction of $\dot{\mathbf{r}}$ is such that ω, $\mathbf{r}$ and $\dot{\mathbf{r}}$ form a right-handed set of vectors.

Let us consider now a point with position vector

$$\mathbf{r} = X\mathbf{I} + Y\mathbf{J} + Z\mathbf{K} = x\mathbf{i} + y\mathbf{j} + z\mathbf{k},$$

being not necessarily stationary in either frame. The velocity of the point is

$$\dot{\mathbf{r}} = \dot{X}\mathbf{I} + \dot{Y}\mathbf{J} + \dot{Z}\mathbf{K}$$

$$= \dot{x}\mathbf{i} + \dot{y}\mathbf{j} + \dot{z}\mathbf{k} + x\frac{d\mathbf{i}}{dt} + y\frac{d\mathbf{j}}{dt} + z\frac{d\mathbf{k}}{dt}.$$

If the frame $Oxyz$ is spinning with angular velocity ω, equations (20) hold and the velocity becomes

$$\dot{\mathbf{r}} = \frac{\delta\mathbf{r}}{\delta t} + \omega \times x\mathbf{i} + \omega \times y\mathbf{j} + \omega \times z\mathbf{k}$$

$$= \frac{\delta\mathbf{r}}{\delta t} + \omega \times \mathbf{r}, \tag{21}$$

the generalization of the previous two-dimensional formula in section 8.2.

8.7 Coriolis force

Consider now a particle of mass m with position vector $\mathbf{r}$ subject to a force $\mathbf{F}$. Suppose we wish to find the equation of motion relative to a frame rotating with angular velocity $\boldsymbol{\omega}$. The equation of motion of the particle will be $\mathbf{F} = m\ddot{\mathbf{r}}$ and we can express $\ddot{\mathbf{r}}$ in terms of the relative acceleration by using the result (21) twice. Thus

$$\mathbf{F} = m\ddot{\mathbf{r}} = m\left(\frac{\delta}{\delta t} + \boldsymbol{\omega} \times \right)\left(\frac{\delta \mathbf{r}}{\delta t} + \boldsymbol{\omega} \times \mathbf{r}\right)$$

$$= m\left[\frac{\delta^2 \mathbf{r}}{\delta t^2} + 2\boldsymbol{\omega} \times \frac{\delta \mathbf{r}}{\delta t} + \frac{\delta \boldsymbol{\omega}}{\delta t} \times \mathbf{r} + \boldsymbol{\omega} \times (\boldsymbol{\omega} \times \mathbf{r})\right]$$

$$= m\left[\frac{\delta^2 \mathbf{r}}{\delta t^2} + 2\boldsymbol{\omega} \times \frac{\delta \mathbf{r}}{\delta t} + \dot{\boldsymbol{\omega}} \times \mathbf{r} + \boldsymbol{\omega} \times (\boldsymbol{\omega} \times \mathbf{r})\right], \qquad (22)$$

since by replacing $\mathbf{r}$ by $\boldsymbol{\omega}$ in (21), $\dot{\boldsymbol{\omega}} = \delta\boldsymbol{\omega}/\delta t$. Equation (22) should be compared with equation (7). As before, equation (22) can be written as a balance between actual and apparent forces and the product of mass and relative acceleration:

$$\mathbf{F} - 2m\boldsymbol{\omega} \times \frac{\delta \mathbf{r}}{\delta t} - m\dot{\boldsymbol{\omega}} \times \mathbf{r} - m\boldsymbol{\omega} \times (\boldsymbol{\omega} \times \mathbf{r}) = m\frac{\delta^2 \mathbf{r}}{\delta t^2}.$$

The *centrifugal* force, $-m\boldsymbol{\omega} \times (\boldsymbol{\omega} \times \mathbf{r})$, acts towards the instantaneous axis of rotation and the *Coriolis* force, $-2m\boldsymbol{\omega} \times (\delta \mathbf{r}/\delta t)$, acts in a direction perpendicular to the particle's path as seen by an observer moving with the rotating frame.

We shall illustrate the Coriolis effect by investigating the motion of a particle on the rotating earth. Let $OXYZ$ in figure 112 be the inertial frame with its Z-axis along the polar axis of the earth. The earth is assumed to be a sphere. The rotating frame $Oxyz$ is embedded in the earth with the z-axis inclined at an angle θ to the axis of rotation and with the x-axis in the earth's equatorial plane. The earth's spin can be resolved into components in the rotating frame:

$$\boldsymbol{\omega} = -\omega \sin \theta \mathbf{j} + \omega \cos \theta \mathbf{k},$$

where ω is the angular speed in a sidereal frame. Let us restrict our attention to motion in the neighbourhood of the earth's surface so that the gravitational force experienced by a particle of mass m is mg in magnitude and directed towards the centre of the earth. In the vicinity of the point P, we can approximate this gravitational force by $-mg\mathbf{k}$.

The equation of motion (22) will become

$$- mg\mathbf{k} = m\left[\frac{\delta^2\mathbf{r}}{\delta t^2} + 2\boldsymbol{\omega} \times \frac{\delta\mathbf{r}}{\delta t} + \boldsymbol{\omega} \times (\boldsymbol{\omega} \times \mathbf{r})\right],$$

noting that $\dot{\boldsymbol{\omega}} = \mathbf{0}$.

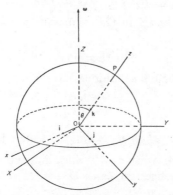

FIGURE 112

We could now write the vector equation of motion in its three components, but before we do this we will consider some approximations which can be made.

(i) We have

$$\mathbf{r} = x\mathbf{i} + y\mathbf{j} + (a + z)\mathbf{k},$$

where a is the mean radius of the earth. For z of the order of a few hundred metres, $a + z \approx a$, since $a = 6{,}370$ km.

(ii) In the term $\boldsymbol{\omega} \times (\boldsymbol{\omega} \times \mathbf{r})$ all the terms apart from $- a\omega^2 \sin\theta \cos\theta\mathbf{j}$ are of magnitude $x\omega^2$ or $y\omega^2$. From the second term on the right-hand side of the equation of motion, we obtain terms of magnitude $\dot{x}\omega$ and $\dot{y}\omega$. Now to fall a distance of a few hundred metres a particle will take a few seconds. Therefore $\dot{x} \approx x/(\text{few seconds})$ whereas $x\omega = 2\pi x/(1 \text{ day})$ since ω is the angular velocity of the earth. Thus $\dot{x}\omega \gg x\omega^2$ and $\dot{y}\omega \gg y\omega^2$.

(iii) For the earth $g \gg a\omega^2 \sin^2\theta$.

(iv) Provided θ is not small, $2\dot{x}\omega \cos\theta \ll a\omega^2 \sin\theta \cos\theta$.

With these approximations the equation of motion resolved into its components becomes

$$\ddot{x} - 2\omega(\dot{z}\sin\theta + \dot{y}\cos\theta) = 0, \tag{23}$$

$$\ddot{y} - a\omega^2 \sin\theta \cos\theta = 0, \tag{24}$$

$$\ddot{z} + 2\dot{x}\omega \sin\theta = -g. \tag{25}$$

Suppose a body at rest relative to the earth is dropped from a height h above the earth's surface. The initial conditions become $\dot{x} = \dot{y} = \dot{z} = 0$, $x = y = 0$, $z = h$ at $t = 0$. Equations (24) and (25) can be integrated immediately to give

$$\dot{y} = a\omega^2 t \sin\theta \cos\theta, \qquad \dot{z} + 2x\omega \sin\theta = -gt.$$

Substituting for $\dot{y}$ and $\dot{z}$ in (23) and using the approximations again we find that x satisfies

$$\ddot{x} + 2\omega gt \sin\theta = 0,$$

which, subject to the initial conditions, has the solution

$$x = -\tfrac{1}{3}\omega gt^3 \sin\theta.$$

Similarly

$$y = \tfrac{1}{2}a\omega^2 t^2 \sin\theta \cos\theta, \qquad z = h - \tfrac{1}{2}gt^2.$$

The body hits the earth when $z = 0$ which must occur in a time $\sqrt{(2h/g)}$. The body therefore reaches the earth at a point *east* of the vertical at an approximate distance

$$\tfrac{1}{3}\omega g \left(\frac{2h}{g}\right)^{\frac{3}{2}} \sin\theta,$$

and *south* of the true vertical at an approximate distance

$$ah\omega^2 \sin\theta \cos\theta/g$$

from the point where it would have fallen in the absence of rotation. Note that the curvature of the earth has been ignored. Since

$$\omega = 7{\cdot}29 \times 10^{-5} \text{ rad/s},$$

the deflection of a particle dropped at $\theta = 45°$ from a height of 100 m is about 1·6 cm to the east and 16 cm to the south.

The Coriolis force is of importance in atmospheric motions. It is found that for a particle of air the term $2\boldsymbol{\omega} \times \delta\mathbf{r}/\delta t$, or $2\boldsymbol{\omega} \times \mathbf{v}_w$ where $\mathbf{v}_w$ is the horizontal velocity of the wind, is the most dominant term on the right-hand side of equation (22). The horizontal component of the force $\mathbf{F}$ is the pressure force $\mathbf{F}_P$ directed from high to low pressure. We get therefore

$$\mathbf{F}_P \approx 2\boldsymbol{\omega} \times \mathbf{v}_w.$$

We see from the definition of the vector product that $\mathbf{v}_w$ will be perpendicular to the pressure force. This implies that the wind will blow *between* high and low pressure centres to the first approximation rather than *from* high to low pressure; that is along the lines of constant pressure, or *isobars*, as is indicated in figure 113. By further considering the direction of ω the reader will be able to deduce that in the northern hemisphere the winds blow anti-clockwise around centres of low pressure, whilst in the southern hemisphere they blow in the opposite sense.

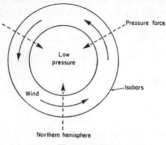

FIGURE 113

Exercises

1. A pendulum consists of a bob suspended by a wire of length 30 m. The pendulum is set up at a point on the earth's surface with geographic latitude of 30°. Assuming the earth to be a sphere, estimate the displacement of the bob from the true vertical. (Use the following data: radius of the earth = 6,370 km; g = 9·81 m/s^2; ω = 7·29 × 10^{-5} rad/s.)

2. A point has a position vector

$$\mathbf{r} = (a + b \cos \Omega t)\mathbf{I} + b \sin \Omega t \mathbf{J}$$

in an inertial frame (a, b and Ω are constants). Verify that the point describes a circle with constant speed. Show that the coordinates (x, y) of the point referred to a frame rotating with constant angular velocity $\omega \mathbf{k}$ satisfy

$$\dot{x} - \omega y = -b\Omega \sin \Omega t, \qquad \dot{y} + \omega x = b\Omega \cos \Omega t.$$

Show further that these equations can be combined into the single equation

$$\dot{z} + i\omega z = ib\Omega \, e^{i\Omega t}.$$

where $z = x + iy$. Assuming that the axes of the two frames coincide at time $t = 0$, obtain the solution of this equation in the case $\Omega + \omega \neq 0$:

$$z = \left(a + \frac{b\omega}{\Omega + \omega}\right)e^{-i\omega t} + \frac{b\Omega}{\Omega + \omega} e^{i\Omega t}.$$

3. A circular wire of radius a rotates with angular speed ω in its own plane about an axis which passes through a point of the wire. A bead slides on the wire with constant speed V relative to the wire. Find the actual velocity and acceleration of the bead in suitable rotating and fixed axes.

4. A satellite moves round the earth in a circular orbit of radius a. The angular speed ω of the radius to the satellite is given by $a^3\omega^2 = \gamma m$ where γ is the gravitational constant and m is the mass of the earth. An origin is taken in the satellite with the axis Ox along the radius from the earth and the axis Oy perpendicular to it in the direction in which the satellite is moving. Show that the equations of motion of an object in the vicinity of the satellite are given approximately by

$$\ddot{x} - 2\omega\dot{y} - 3\omega^2 x = 0,$$

$$\ddot{y} + 2\omega\dot{x} = 0,$$

with respect to the rotating frame. [Ignore the gravitational effect of the satellite.]

5. A smooth elliptic tube of eccentricity e rotates with constant angular velocity ω about a vertical axis through its centre and perpendicular to its plane. Show that a particle can remain at rest at an end of the major axis. If slightly disturbed show that it oscillates with period $2\pi\sqrt{(1 - e^2)}/e\omega$.

6. A horizontal turntable rotates with constant angular velocity ω about a vertical axis which intersects a smooth circular groove of radius a in the turntable. A particle of mass m in the groove moving in the same sense as that of the rotation just makes complete revolutions. Show that the force exerted by the groove on the particle at its greatest distance from the axis of rotation is of magnitude $10ma\omega^2$.

7. A rocking cylinder is pivoted at O and drives, through a linkage, a crankshaft B. The appropriate lengths are given in figure 114. If the rod BA rotates about B

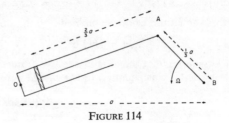

FIGURE 114

with a constant angular velocity Ω show that the magnitude of the reaction of the piston on the wall of the cylinder when BA is perpendicular to OA, i.e. when angle $A\hat{O}B$ has a maximum value, is $ma\Omega^2(2 - \sqrt{2})/6$ where m is the mass of the piston.

8. A turntable is rotating with angular velocity ω. A bullet of mass m is fired from a rifle barrel of length ℓ, fixed relative to the turntable, with a constant acceleration a. The bullet starts from the centre of the turntable. Show that, if $\omega^2 \ll a/\ell$, the reaction of the bullet on the barrel as it leaves the end is approximately

$$2m\omega(2a\ell)^{\frac{1}{2}}.$$

9. A smooth straight tube rotates in a plane with constant angular velocity ω about a perpendicular axis through a point O of it. Inside the tube is a particle of mass m joined to O by spring of stiffness $5m\omega^2$ and natural length a. The particle is released from its position of relative rest with the spring at its natural length. Show that the particle describes a simple harmonic motion of period π/ω and amplitude $\frac{1}{4}a$ relative to the tube. What is the largest reaction on the tube?

10. OA, OB are two perpendicular lines fixed in a smooth horizontal plane which rotates with constant angular velocity ω about a vertical axis OC (OA, OB, OC form a right-handed system). There is a smooth groove in the plane parallel to OB and meeting OA at L, where OL $= a$. A particle of mass m is projected from L along the groove at time $t = 0$ with speed $a\omega$ relative to the plane. Find the force, due to the constraint of the groove, on the particle at time t.

11. Find the moments of inertia of the following bodies:

(i) a spherical shell of radius a about a diameter,

(ii) a uniform disc of radius a about a diameter,

(iii) a composite body consisting of a circular cylinder of radius a and length h with two hemispheres of the same radius a attached to the plane faces of the cylinder about the axis of symmetry, the density of the body being uniform,

(iv) about the axis of a circular cylinder of radius a in which the density varies as distance from the axis,

(v) a uniform circular cylinder of radius a and length h about an axis through its centre perpendicular to its axis of symmetry,

(vi) a uniform square plate of side a about a diagonal.

12. Show that the moment of inertia of a plane lamina about a perpendicular axis is equal to the sum of its moments of inertia about two perpendicular axes in the plane which intersect the perpendicular axis.

13. Find the kinetic energy of a uniform circular cylinder of mass m and radius a which is rolling without slipping on a horizontal plane with speed V.

The cylinder is released from rest on a plane inclined at an angle α to the horizontal with its axis horizontal. Obtain the angular speed of the cylinder when it has rolled a distance x down the plane.

14. A flywheel has a mass of 900 kg and a radius of gyration of 85 cm and is rotating at 150 r.p.m. Calculate its kinetic energy. What is the maximum weight which the flywheel could lift through 1 m if 14% of the transmitted energy is lost through friction?

15. Find the period of small oscillations of a uniform sphere about a horizontal axis which is a tangent to the sphere.

16. A rigid body is moving in general plane motion with angular velocity $\omega\mathbf{k}$ and such that its mass-centre has velocity $\bar{\mathbf{v}} = \bar{u}\mathbf{i} + \bar{v}\mathbf{j}$. Show that the point with position vector (see figure 106)

$$\mathbf{r} = \bar{\mathbf{r}} - (\bar{v}\mathbf{i} - \bar{u}\mathbf{j})/\omega,$$

is instantaneously at rest (this point is known as the *instantaneous centre of rotation* and at any instant the body is rotating about this point; note that, in general, it is fixed neither in the body nor in space). Show that the kinetic energy of the body can be written as $\frac{1}{2}I'\omega^2$ where I' is the moment of inertia about the instantaneous centre of rotation.

Find the instantaneous centres in the following cases:

(i) a circular cylinder rolling on a plane;

(ii) a rod moving with its ends sliding on two straight intersecting perpendicular wires.

17. A uniform rod is smoothly pivoted at one end to a fixed point. The rod is released from rest in a horizontal position. Find the reaction at the pivot when the rod is inclined at an angle θ to the vertical.

18. A uniform rod of length $2a$ stands on a smooth horizontal table and is slightly displaced. Verify that the rod hits the plane with angular speed $\sqrt{(3g/2a)}$.

19. A uniform solid circular cylinder C of mass m and diameter a is placed between, and in contact with, two coaxial circular cylindrical surfaces of radii a and $2a$. The inner and outer surfaces rotate with angular velocities ω_1 and ω_2, respectively, about their common axis. If C rolls in contact with the two surfaces and no slipping occurs, show that the centre C describes a circle at an angular rate $\frac{1}{3}(2\omega_2 + \omega_1)$, and find the kinetic energy of C.

20. A particle of mass m is fixed to a point P of the rim of a uniform circular disc, centre O, mass m and radius a. The vertical disc is released from rest in contact with a rough horizontal table with OP inclined at $60°$ to the upward vertical.

If no slipping occurs, show that the angle θ between OP and the upward vertical satisfies

$$a(7 + 4 \cos \theta)\left(\frac{d\theta}{dt}\right)^2 = 2g(1 - 2 \cos \theta).$$

21. Kinetic energy can be represented by

$$\mathcal{T} = \tfrac{1}{2} \int_V \rho \dot{\mathbf{r}} \cdot \dot{\mathbf{r}} \, dV$$

in the usual notation. A rigid body rotates about a fixed point with angular velocity $\boldsymbol{\omega}$. Show that

$$\mathcal{T} = \tfrac{1}{2}\omega_x^2 I_{xx} + \tfrac{1}{2}\omega_y^2 I_{yy} + \tfrac{1}{2}\omega_z^2 I_{zz} + \omega_y\omega_z I_{yz} + \omega_z\omega_x I_{zx} + \omega_x\omega_y I_{xy},$$

where

$$I_{xx} = \int_V \rho(y^2 + z^2) \, dV, \text{ etc.,}$$

$$I_{yz} = -\int_V \rho yz \, dV, \text{ etc.}$$

The quantities I_{yz}, I_{zx}, I_{xy} are called the products of inertia of the body about the chosen set of rotating axes.

22. Show that the angular momentum $\mathbf{h}$ of a rigid body turning about a fixed point is given by

$$\mathbf{h} = \int_V \rho[r^2\boldsymbol{\omega} - (\mathbf{r} \cdot \boldsymbol{\omega})\mathbf{r}] \, dV$$

in the usual notation. Deduce that

$$\mathcal{T} = \tfrac{1}{2}\mathbf{h} \cdot \boldsymbol{\omega}.$$

23. Calculate the position of the point of impact of a body dropped from a height of 200 m above the earth's surface at the equator.

24. A particle is projected with a small speed V at an angle α to the horizontal from a point on the earth's surface whose angular displacement from the north pole is θ. With origin at the centre of the earth, take the z-axis through the point of projection and the x-axis in the equatorial plane of the earth as shown in

figure 112. Using equations (23), (24) and (25), show that the projectile's path is given by

$$x = -\tfrac{1}{3}\omega g t^3 \sin\theta + V\omega t^2(\sin\alpha\sin\theta + \cos\alpha\sin\beta\cos\theta) +$$
$$Vt\cos\alpha\cos\beta,$$

$$y = Vt\cos\alpha(\sin\beta - \omega t\cos\beta\cos\theta),$$

$$z = a - \tfrac{1}{2}gt^2 + Vt\sin\alpha - V\omega t^2\cos\alpha\cos\beta\sin\theta,$$

where β is the angle between the vertical plane through the initial velocity vector and the x-axis (ignore terms in ω^2, where ω is the angular speed of the earth, and variations in g).

25. A spacecraft, considered to be a solid cylinder of uniform density with mass 1,000 kg and radius 1 m, is rotating about its axis of symmetry once every 12 s. A compressed air jet, with muzzle velocity 150 m/s and cross-sectional area $\tfrac{1}{3}$ cm^2, is used tangentially at the extremity of a radius to arrest the rotation. For how many seconds should such a jet be activated if the density of the air in the jet is taken as 1 kg/m^3?

9

Orbits

9.1 Central forces

In the solar system the planets and asteroids have a combined mass which is less than 0·2% of the mass of the sun, with the result that the perturbative effects of the planets on the sun are very small. As defined in section 3.6, the gravitational force exerted by the sun on a planet is proportional to the product of the masses of the sun and the planet and inversely proportional to the square of the distance between the two. Since the dimensions of any planet are small compared with its distance from the sun, we can reasonably suppose that the planet occupies a point in space. The gravitational force is directed towards the sun which we have agreed is fixed. Such a force directed towards a fixed point is called a *central force*. The path described by the planet is called its *orbit*. Central forces occur in other contexts, for example in the case of a bob attached by an elastic string to a fixed point, the tension in the string always being directed towards that point.

We shall consider the general case first, in which a particle is subject to a central force alone, the force being a function of the radial distance only. It is clear that if, in such circumstances, the particle is fired with velocity $\mathbf{v}_A$ from a point A with position vector $\mathbf{r}_A$ then the motion will take place in the plane formed by the vectors $\mathbf{r}_A$ and $\mathbf{v}_A$. This follows since no linear momentum is created in the direction perpendicular to this plane. In other words, any orbit under the action of a central force must be a plane orbit.

Let the central *attractive* force be $F(r)$ and suppose that the particle occupies the point with position vector $\mathbf{r}$ at time t. From the remarks in the previous paragraph we can choose $\mathbf{r}$ to be a plane vector by adopting a suitable coordinate frame. In vector form, the force is given by $- F(r)\mathbf{r}/r$ and the equation of motion becomes

$$- F(r)\frac{\mathbf{r}}{r} = m\ddot{\mathbf{r}},$$

231

where m is the mass of the particle. Usually the most convenient coordinate system to choose is the polar one (r, θ) where θ is the angle between the position vector and some fixed direction (figure 115). The velocity and acceleration in polar coordinates were derived in section 1.10 and we repeat them here:

$$\dot{\mathbf{r}} = \dot{r}\mathbf{e}_r + r\dot{\theta}\mathbf{e}_\theta, \quad \ddot{\mathbf{r}} = (\ddot{r} - r\dot{\theta}^2)\mathbf{e}_r + \frac{1}{r}\frac{d}{dt}(r^2\dot{\theta})\mathbf{e}_\theta.$$

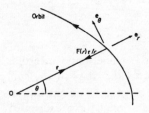

FIGURE 115

The equation of motion becomes

$$- F(r)\mathbf{e}_r = m(\ddot{r} - r\dot{\theta}^2)\mathbf{e}_r + \frac{m}{r}\frac{d}{dt}(r^2\dot{\theta})\mathbf{e}_\theta,$$

or, in terms of its components,

$$m(\ddot{r} - r\dot{\theta}^2) = - F(r), \tag{1}$$

$$\frac{d}{dt}(r^2\dot{\theta}) = 0. \tag{}$$

The second of these equations implies that

$$r^2\dot{\theta} = \text{constant} = h, \text{ say.} \tag{2}$$

Note that this condition could have been obtained directly since it simply represents conservation of angular momentum, the central force having no moment about the origin. The elimination of $\dot{\theta}$ between (1) and (2) yields the following equation relating r and t:

$$m\ddot{r} - \frac{mh^2}{r^3} = - F(r). \tag{3}$$

With the identity $\ddot{r} = \dot{r}\, d\dot{r}/dr$, the equation becomes

$$m\dot{r}\frac{d\dot{r}}{dr} - \frac{mh^2}{r^3} = - F(r),$$

which can be integrated once to give

$$\tfrac{1}{2}m\dot{r}^2 + \frac{mh^2}{2r^2} = -\int F(r)\,dr + \text{constant.}$$

The reader should note that this equation expresses conservation of energy since the indefinite integral $\int F(r)\,dr$ is the potential of the force $F(r)$ and the two terms on the left-hand side of the equation represent the kinetic energy of the particle.

Alternatively equation (3) can be cast into an equation relating $u = 1/r$ and θ. By using techniques of elementary calculus, as on p. 115,

$$\dot{r} = \frac{d\theta}{dt}\frac{dr}{d\theta} = \frac{h}{r^2}\frac{dr}{d\theta} = -h\frac{d(1/r)}{d\theta} = -h\frac{du}{d\theta},$$

where equation (2) has been employed. Similarly

$$\ddot{r} = \frac{d}{dt}(\dot{r}) = \frac{d\theta}{dt}\frac{d}{d\theta}\left(-h\frac{du}{d\theta}\right) = -h^2u^2\frac{d^2u}{d\theta^2}.$$

Substituting for $\ddot{r}$ in equation (3), we find that u satisfies

$$\frac{d^2u}{d\theta^2} + u = \frac{F(1/u)}{mh^2u^2}, \tag{4}$$

and the solution of this equation subject to the appropriate initial conditions will give the *orbit* of the particle in polar coordinates.

Example 1   A particle of mass m lies on a smooth horizontal table and is attached by a linear spring to a fixed point on the table. The particle is fired with speed V perpendicular to the unstrained spring along the table. If the spring has modulus of elasticity $3mV^2/4a$, where a is the natural length of the spring, show that subsequently the particle always lies within a circle of radius 2a.

The only horizontal force acting on the particle is that due to the tension in the spring which is directed towards a fixed point on the table. This represents a central force

$$F(r) = 3mV^2(r - a)/4a^2 \tag{5}$$

in the notation above. The path described by the particle satisfies equation (4) with $F(r)$ given by (5) and $h = aV$, the initial angular momentum per unit mass. Thus

$$\frac{d^2u}{d\theta^2} + u = \frac{3}{4a^4u^2}\left(\frac{1}{u} - a\right),$$

which is transformed into

$$\frac{du}{d\theta} \frac{d}{du}\left(\frac{du}{d\theta}\right) = -u + \frac{3}{4a^4 u^3} - \frac{3}{4a^3 u^2},$$

by the identity

$$\frac{d^2 u}{d\theta^2} = \frac{du}{d\theta} \frac{d}{du}\left(\frac{du}{d\theta}\right).$$

Separating the variables and integrating, we find that

$$\frac{1}{2}\left(\frac{du}{d\theta}\right)^2 = -\tfrac{1}{2}u^2 - \frac{3}{8a^4 u^2} + \frac{3}{4a^3 u} + C, \tag{6}$$

where the constant C is determined by the initial condition $du/d\theta = 0$ when $u = 1/a$. Therefore

$$C = \frac{1}{2a^2} + \frac{3}{8a^2} - \frac{3}{4a^2} = \frac{1}{8a^2}.$$

When the particle reaches its greatest distance from the centre, u will have a minimum value for which the necessary condition $du/d\theta = 0$ must hold. From equation (6) this must occur where

$$4a^4 u^4 - a^2 u^2 - 6au + 3 = 0,$$

or where, after replacing u by $1/r$,

$$3r^4 - 6ar^3 - a^2 r^2 + 4a^4 = 0.$$

The reader should verify that this quartic can be factorized into

$$(r - a)(r - 2a)(3r^2 + 3ar + 2a^2) = 0,$$

and its only real roots are $r = a$ and $r = 2a$. Equation (6) can be recast as

$$\left(\frac{du}{d\theta}\right)^2 = -\frac{1}{4a^4 r^2}(r - a)(r - 2a)(3r^2 + 3ar + 2a^2).$$

For the actual motion $(du/d\theta)^2 \geqslant 0$ and this will be the case if and only if $a \leqslant r \leqslant 2a$ for positive r since the term in the last bracket is always positive. The particle therefore oscillates within this region in the plane.

9.2 Gravitational central force

It is assumed that the satellite body does not significantly affect the position of the central body owing to the large difference in mass as, for example, in the cases of a planet moving round the sun and an artificial satellite circling the earth. To fix ideas we will consider a satellite of mass

m moving round the sun. By Newton's law of gravitation the satellite will experience a central attractive force

$$F(r) = \frac{\gamma m_s m}{r^2},$$

where γ is the gravitational constant, m_s the mass of the sun and r the distance of the satellite from the sun. The satellite's path must satisfy equation (4) with suitable polar coordinates (r, θ):

$$\frac{d^2 u}{d\theta^2} + u = \frac{\gamma m_s}{h^2}.$$

This is a second-order differential equation with constant coefficients of the type discussed in section 4.5, the solution being the sum of a complementary function and a particular integral. The corresponding homogeneous equation

$$\frac{d^2 u}{d\theta^2} + u = 0$$

has a solution $A \cos(\theta - \theta_0)$ where A and θ_0 are constants whilst it is easy to verify that the constant $\gamma m_s / h^2$ is a particular integral.

The full solution reads

$$u = \frac{1}{r} = A \cos(\theta - \theta_0) + \frac{\gamma m_s}{h^2}. \tag{7}$$

One particular orbit corresponds to the condition $A = 0$, in which case $r = h^2 / \gamma m_s$, a constant. This orbit is a circle with its centre coinciding with the centre of force. If a is the radius of the orbit and the orbit is described with speed V, then $h = aV$ and $a = a^2 V^2 / \gamma m_s$ implying $a = \gamma m_s / V^2$. Since $r^2 \dot{\theta} = h$ for any orbit and $r = a$, $\dot{\theta}$ must be constant which implies that the orbit can only be described with constant speed V. If a and V are known quantities from observation and if the satellite takes time T to complete one orbit of the sun in a sidereal frame,

$$\gamma m_s = aV^2 = 4\pi^2 a^3 / T^2, \tag{8}$$

since $VT = 2\pi a$. For the earth, whose orbit is almost circular, $a = 1 \cdot 5 \times 10^{11}$ m and $T = 3 \cdot 15 \times 10^7$ s, so that $\gamma m_s = 1 \cdot 3 \times 10^{20}$ m^3/s^2.

The quantity γm_s is called the *gravitational mass* of the sun and it is relatively easy to calculate it from a knowledge of the orbital radius and period of a planet. Once the gravitational constant has been found the *mass* of the sun can be found. Every body has associated with it a gravitational mass. For example, the gravitational mass of the earth can be computed from the behaviour of the moon, or, with greater accuracy, from the orbit of an artificial satellite. The mass of a planet with no satellites is more difficult to obtain and can usually only be discovered by analysing its effect on the orbits of neighbouring planets. The mass of Pluto, the most distant of the planets, is still not accurately known.

Let us express the orbit given by (7) in the alternative form

$$\frac{\ell}{r} = e \cos (\theta - \theta_0) + 1, \tag{9}$$

where $\ell = h^2/\gamma m_s$ and $e = Ah^2/\gamma m_s$ (without loss of generality we can assume that $A > 0$). Three cases need to be distinguished: $e < 1$, $e = 1$ and $e > 1$.

Elliptic orbit, $e < 1$. Since $|\cos (\theta - \theta_0)| \leqslant 1$, it follows that the right-hand side of (9) must always be positive so that to each value of θ in $0 \leqslant \theta < 2\pi$ there exists a corresponding positive value for r. Further ℓ/r is a periodic function of θ with period 2π so that the orbit is a closed curve called an *ellipse*.

The line $\theta = \theta_0$ is called the *major axis* and it cuts the ellipse at the points with polar coordinates $[\ell/(1 + e),\ \theta_0]$ and $[\ell/(1 - e),\ \theta_0 + \pi]$. The length of the semi-major axis, denoted by a, is given by

$$a = \tfrac{1}{2}\left(\frac{\ell}{1 + e} + \frac{\ell}{1 - e}\right) = \frac{\ell}{1 - e^2}.$$

The centre of the ellipse is located at the mid-point of the major axis; it has polar coordinates $[e\ell(1 - e^2),\ \theta_0 + \pi]$. The *minor axis* is perpendicular to the major axis and passes through the centre of the ellipse. The co-ordinates of the points common to the minor axis and the ellipse are $[\sqrt{(b^2 + a^2e^2)},\ \theta_0 \pm (\pi - \alpha)]$ where $\cos \alpha = ae/\sqrt{(b^2 + a^2e^2)}$ and b is the length of the semi-minor axis. Since this point lies on the ellipse

$$\frac{\ell}{\sqrt{(b^2 + a^2e^2)}} = -\frac{ae^2}{\sqrt{(b^2 + a^2e^2)}} + 1,$$

or

$$(\ell + ae^2)^2 = b^2 + a^2e^2,$$

and, since $\ell = a(1 - e^2)$,

$$a^2 = b^2 + a^2e^2, \quad \text{or} \quad b = a\sqrt{(1 - e^2)}.$$

The number e is called the *eccentricity* of the ellipse; if $e = 0$ the ellipse becomes a circle. The main dimensions of the ellipse are shown in figure 116. The point O to which the force is directed is called a *focus* of the ellipse and ℓ is the length of the *semi-latus rectum*. Note that the angle θ_0 merely indicates the orientation of the ellipse to the fixed axis.

The closest approach A of a planet or satellite to the sun at O is called the *perihelion* and the furthest point B is called the *aphelion*. The corresponding points for elliptic orbits of the earth are called the *perigee* and *apogee*. In general, a point where the velocity is perpendicular to its position vector is called an *apse*.

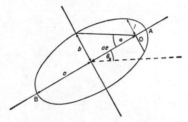

FIGURE 116 The elliptic orbit

Hyperbolic orbit, e > 1. The right-hand side of equation (9) will vanish when $\cos(\theta - \theta_0) = -1/e$. Let β be such that $\cos \beta = 1/e$ with $0 < \beta < \frac{1}{2}\pi$. As $\theta \to \pm(\pi - \beta)$, $r \to \infty$; the graph of the orbit is shown in figure 117. The curve, which is one branch of a hyperbola, is symmetric about the line $\theta = \theta_0$ and cuts this line where $r = \ell/(1 + e)$.

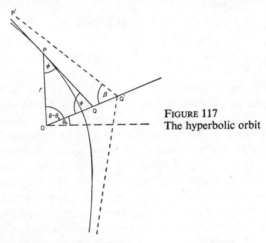

FIGURE 117
The hyperbolic orbit

Consider a point P on the curve and let the tangent to the curve there be the line PQ. Let $O\hat{P}Q = \phi$ and $O\hat{Q}P = \psi$. The cotangent of the angle ϕ must be the ratio of the radial and transverse components of velocity at P:

$$\cot \phi = \frac{\dot{r}}{r\dot{\theta}} = \frac{1}{r}\frac{dr}{d\theta} = \frac{re}{\ell}\sin(\theta - \theta_0),$$

9

using equation (9). By the sine rule in triangle OPQ,

$$\frac{OQ}{\sin \phi} = \frac{r}{\sin \psi} = \frac{r}{\sin (\theta - \theta_0 + \phi)}.$$

Therefore

$$OQ = \frac{r \sin \phi}{\sin (\theta - \theta_0) \cos \phi + \cos (\theta - \theta_0) \sin \phi}$$

$$= \frac{r}{\sin (\theta - \theta_0) \cot \phi + \cos (\theta - \theta_0)}$$

$$= \frac{r\ell}{re \sin^2 (\theta - \theta_0) + \ell \cos (\theta - \theta_0)}.$$

With P on the section of the hyperbola shown in figure 117, $\theta - \theta_0 \to \pi - \beta$ as $r \to \infty$, with the result that

$$OQ \to \frac{\ell}{e \sin^2 \beta} = \frac{\ell e}{e^2 - 1} = OQ', \text{ say,}$$

in figure 117. The tangent QP approaches the line Q'P' which is called an *asymptote* of the hyperbola. There is a second asymptote which is the image of the first in the line OQ.

Parabolic orbit, $e = 1$. The equation of the orbit becomes

$$\frac{\ell}{r} = \cos (\theta - \theta_0) + 1. \tag{10}$$

The parabola is the locus of the points which are equidistant from the focus O and a straight line D called the *directrix* (figure 118). This is a special case of the more general relationship for the three curves considered in that they are the locus of points for which the ratio (distance of point from focus/distance of point from directrix) $= e$. The distance between the focus and the directrix is ℓ and it is easy to verify geometrically from the figure that the equation of a parabola is given by (10).

Of the three orbits the ellipse is the only closed orbit. In the case of the parabola and hyperbola the orbiting body escapes from the influence of the sun. In the solar system the planets all move in approximately elliptic orbits. However the orbits are not strictly closed paths because of the perturbative effects of other planets. Certain comets appear to be moving in parabolic or hyperbolic orbits although this is often difficult to ascertain from a small section of the orbit plotted in the neighbourhood of the sun. Furthermore the orbit of any comet can be changed substantially by the influence of planets which lie close to its orbit.

The total energy $\mathscr{E}$ of an orbiting particle is given by

$$\mathscr{E} = \tfrac{1}{2}mv^2 - \frac{\gamma m_{\mathrm{s}}m}{r}, \tag{11}$$

where v is the speed of the particle, and the second term is the gravitational potential energy. Whether the orbit is an ellipse, hyperbola or parabola,

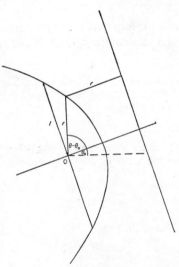

FIGURE 118   The parabolic orbit

it must have an apse at $\theta = \theta_0$ with an apsidal distance of $\ell/(1 + e)$. Let V be the speed at this apse. Since the energy is conserved,

$$\mathscr{E} = \tfrac{1}{2}mV^2 - \gamma m_{\mathrm{s}}m(1 + e)/\ell, \tag{12}$$

the value of the energy at the apse. The angular momentum per unit mass

$$h = \ell V/(1 + e) = \sqrt{(\ell \gamma m_{\mathrm{s}})}$$

by definition. Substituting for V from this equation into (12), we find that

$$\mathscr{E} = \gamma m_{\mathrm{s}}m(e^2 - 1)/2\ell. \tag{13}$$

We conclude that the orbit is an ellipse, hyperbola or parabola according as the energy is negative, positive or zero. Put another way, a body will escape from the sun's influence if $\mathscr{E} \geqslant 0$, that is, if $V^2 \geqslant 2\gamma m_{\mathrm{s}}(1 + e)/\ell$.

The energy equation provides a simple formula relating speed and distance. From (11) and (13),

$$\tfrac{1}{2}v^2 - \frac{\gamma m_{\mathrm{s}}}{r} = \frac{\gamma m_{\mathrm{s}}(e^2 - 1)}{2\ell},$$

or

$$\frac{v^2}{\gamma m_s} = \frac{2}{r} + \frac{e^2 - 1}{\ell}.$$

If the orbit is elliptic, the semi-major axis $a = \ell/(1 - e^2)$ and

$$\frac{v^2}{\gamma m_s} = \frac{2}{r} - \frac{1}{a}. \tag{14}$$

It follows from this relationship that the maximum and minimum speeds of a body circling the sun occur at the perihelion and aphelion respectively.

Example 2   What is the minimum period of an earth satellite if it is assumed that the earth has no atmosphere? The gravitational mass of the earth is about $4.0 \times 10^{14}\ m^3/s^2$ and the earth's radius is about 6,400 km.

The minimum period occurs when the satellite is moving in a circular orbit slightly larger than the earth's radius. The required period T is therefore given by equation (8):

$$T = \frac{2\pi a^{\frac{3}{2}}}{\sqrt{(\gamma m_e)}},$$

where m_e is the mass of the earth. Thus

$$T = \frac{2\pi (6.4 \times 10^8)^{\frac{3}{2}}}{2 \times 10^{10}}\ \text{s}$$

$$\approx 5,100\ \text{s} = 85\ \text{min}.$$

The presence of the atmosphere makes the actual minimum orbit have a slightly larger radius which, in any case, is no longer a circle but becomes distorted into a spiral by the continuous drag of the atmosphere on the satellite.

Example 3   A two-stage rocket is fired with speed V in a direction at an angle α to the vertical from a launching site on the earth. When at the apogee of its initial orbit the second stage is ignited to put the payload into orbit. Obtain the additional speed required at the apogee to make this orbit circular.

We shall ignore the rotational effect of the earth and atmospheric resistance. The fuel burning times are assumed to be of short duration so that the rocket can effectively change speed instantaneously. Let μ_e be the gravitational mass of the earth and c its radius.

Equation (14) immediately gives the semi-major axis a:

$$\frac{1}{a} = \frac{2}{c} - \frac{V^2}{\mu_e}. \tag{15}$$

The angular momentum per unit mass,

$$h = r^2\dot\theta = Vc \sin\alpha = \sqrt{(\mu_e\ell)}, \tag{16}$$

where ℓ is the semi-latus rectum. This, in turn, is related to the semi-major axis through

$$\ell = a(1 - e^2). \tag{17}$$

If we take the equation of the initial orbit to be

$$\frac{\ell}{r} = e\cos(\theta - \theta_0) + 1,$$

we must have

$$\frac{\ell}{c} = e\cos\theta_0 + 1, \tag{18}$$

since this orbit must pass through the launching site. The four equations (15), (16), (17) and (18) enable us to determine the four parameters a, ℓ, e and θ_0 for the orbit in terms of μ_e, V, c and α.

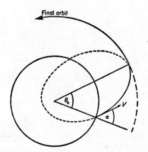

FIGURE 119   Two-stage rocket path for satellite placed in a circular orbit

At the apogee $r = a(1 + e)$ and by equation (14) again the apogee speed v_a is given by

$$v_a^2 = \mu_e\left[\frac{2}{a(1 + e)} - \frac{1}{a}\right] = \frac{\mu_e(1 - e)}{a(1 + e)}.$$

To put the satellite into a circular orbit we need to increase its speed to v_c, say, where

$$v_c^2 = \mu_e/a(1 + e),$$

the radius of the circular orbit being $a(1 + e)$ (see figure 119). Consequently the speed at the apogee must be increased by

$$v_c - v_a = [\mu_e/a(1 + e)]^{\frac{1}{2}} \cdot [1 - \sqrt{(1 - e)}].$$

For the earth, $\mu_e = 4 \cdot 0 \times 10^{14}$ m³/s² and $c = 6{,}400$ km. A few quick calculations yield the additional boost the rocket needs if it is fired initially with speed 6 km/s at an angle $\alpha = 30°$. From the equations listed above,

$$a = 4 \cdot 5 \times 10^6 \text{ m}, \qquad\qquad \ell = 9 \cdot 2 \times 10^5 \text{ m},$$

$$e = 0 \cdot 89, \qquad\qquad v_a = 2 \cdot 3 \times 10^3 \text{ m/s},$$

$$v_c = 6 \cdot 8 \times 10^3 \text{ m/s}.$$

Thus the satellite requires an additional speed of 4·5 km/s at its apogee.

9.3 Orbital period: Kepler's laws

Kepler's first law of planetary motion asserts that the planets move in elliptic orbits with the sun at one focus of the ellipse. We have already seen that gravitational central orbits must be *conics* (ellipse, hyperbola or parabola); for the planets the eccentricities of their orbits are considerably less than unity (see the table on p. 243).

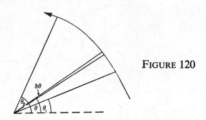

FIGURE 120

The conservation of angular momentum embodied in the equation $r^2\dot\theta = h$ for central-force orbits can be used to find the time taken by a particle to cover a part of its orbit. Suppose the position vector sweeps through the angle between $\theta = \theta_1$ and $\theta = \theta_2$ in a time t_1. The time-integral of $r^2\dot\theta = h$ over this angle gives

$$\int_{\theta=\theta_1}^{\theta=\theta_2} r^2 \, d\theta = h \int_0^{t_1} dt = ht_1.$$

By the usual techniques of elementary integration in polar coordinates, the left-hand side of this equation represents twice the area enclosed by the orbit and the extreme position vectors (see figure 120). The implication of this result is that the position vector sweeps out equal areas in equal times. This is *Kepler's second law* of planetary motion. It should be noted that it holds for any central orbit and is not restricted to gravitational orbits.

For a particle moving in an elliptic orbit, the period T of the orbit will be

$$T = \frac{2}{h}(\text{area of the ellipse})$$

$$= \frac{2\pi ab}{h},$$

where a and b are the semi-axes of the ellipse. The semi-latus rectum $\ell = h^2/\gamma m_s = a(1 - e^2)$ and $b^2 = a^2(1 - e^2)$ so that

$$T^2 = 4\pi^2 a^3/\gamma m_s,$$

which is equivalent to the statement of *Kepler's third law:* the ratio of the square of the orbital period to the cube of the semi-major axis is the same constant for all planets.

Kepler's laws pre-date Newton's laws of motion and gravitation and were obtained empirically on the basis of data collected for planets adjacent to the earth.

Some data concerning the planets is given in the following table.

Name	Mass (mass of Earth = 1 unit)	Period of revolution about sun (period of Earth = 1 unit)	Semi-major axis of orbit (Distance of Earth = 1 unit)	Eccentricity of orbit	Mean diameter (Earth diam. = 1 unit)	Sidereal period of rotation (period of rotation of Earth = 1 unit)
Sun	331,950·0	—	—	—	109·187	24·65
Moon	0·012	—	—	—	0·273	27·32
Mercury	0·05	0·241	0·387	0·206	0·366	0·59*
Venus	0·81	0·615	0·723	0·007	0·960	30·0 (?)
Earth	$5\cdot976 \times 10^{24}$ kg	365·256 days	$149\cdot5 \times 10^6$ km	0·017	12,735 km	23 hr 56 min
Mars	0·11	1·88	1·524	0·093	0·531	1·029
Jupiter	318·4	11·862	5·203	0·048	10·969	0·411
Saturn	95·3	29·458	9·539	0·056	9·036	0·419
Uranus	14·5	84·015	19·182	0·047	3·715	0·449
Neptune	17·2	164·788	30·058	0·009	3·538	0·66
Pluto	?	247·697	39·518	0·249	?	?

For reference, units are used in the table opposite the entry for Earth.

N.B. Gravitational constant $\gamma = 6\cdot67 \times 10^{-11}$ m^3/kg s^2.

* Until 1965 thought to be equal to its orbital period (88 days). Cf. *Nature*, **206**, 1240 (1965).

Example 4   By using the table above find the acceleration due to gravity at the surface of Jupiter. By how much is this reduced at the equator of Jupiter by its rotation?

The acceleration due to gravity at the surface of the earth,

$$g_e = \frac{\gamma m_e}{r_e^2} = \frac{4\gamma m_e}{d_e^2},$$

where m_e is the mass of the earth and d_e is its diameter.

Similarly the acceleration due to gravity at the surface of Jupiter

$$g_j = \frac{4\gamma m_j}{d_j^2} = \frac{m_j d_e^2}{m_e d_j^2} g_e$$

$$= \frac{318\cdot4}{(10\cdot969)^2} g_e$$

$$= 2\cdot645 g_e$$

$$= 25\cdot94 \text{ m/s}^2.$$

Due to the rotation the acceleration at the equator of Jupiter is reduced by an amount

$$r_j \Omega_j^2 = \left[\frac{2\pi}{0\cdot411 \times (86,400 - 240)} \right]^2 \times \frac{10\cdot969 \times 12,735 \times 10^3}{2}$$

$$= 2\cdot20 \text{ m/s}^2 \text{ or } 8\cdot5\%.$$

9.4 Orbital transfer

A straightforward application of the results of the previous two sections is provided by the problem of finding an optimal path for a rocket to be transferred from one circular orbit to another circular orbit. Figure 121 shows the orbits of earth and Mars as coplanar circles with centres at the sun (this is a first approximation since we shall ignore the small eccentricities of the orbits and their mutual inclination). We shall suppose that the rocket is fired some distance from the earth and neglect the gravitational forces on the rocket due to the earth and Mars. After the initial firing the rocket moves in a free orbit about the sun.

Since the earth is moving around the sun, any rocket fired from the earth will itself have this velocity in addition to its projected speed. In order to take maximum advantage of this fact we shall fire the rocket in a direction tangential to the earth's orbit as shown in figure 121. Let the rocket start from the point A of the earth's orbit with absolute speed V. The point A must be an apse of the orbit whose equation can be written

$$\frac{\ell}{r} = e \cos \theta + 1.$$

When $\theta = 0$, $r = r_e$ so that

$$\ell = r_e(e + 1). \tag{19}$$

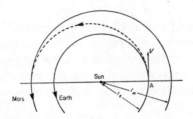

FIGURE 121   Orbital transfer path

The angular momentum per unit mass

$$h = \sqrt{(\ell \mu_s)} = V r_e,$$

where μ_s is the gravitational mass of the sun. Thus $V = \sqrt{(\ell \mu_s)}/r_e$. We shall consider the optimum orbit which makes V as small as possible which, in turn, means that the initial kinetic energy required to fire the rocket is a minimum. It is easy to see that we must make ℓ as small as possible consistent with the rocket reaching the orbit of Mars, which by (19) implies that e must be minimized.

Suppose the rocket reaches the orbit of Mars where $\theta = \alpha$ so that

$$\frac{\ell}{r_m} = e \cos \alpha + 1. \tag{20}$$

Eliminating ℓ between (19) and (20), we find that the eccentricity

$$e = (r_m - r_e)/(r_e - r_m \cos \alpha),$$

which is clearly a minimum when $\cos \alpha = -1$ or $\alpha = 180°$. This means that the aphelion of the orbit must lie on the orbit of Mars as shown in figure 121. It is easy to verify that the minimum firing speed is then

$$V_{\min} = [2 r_m \mu_s / r_e (r_e + r_m)]^{\frac{1}{2}}.$$

By Kepler's third law, the time τ taken by the rocket is equal to half the period of the orbit:

$$\tau = \pi [\tfrac{1}{2}(r_e + r_m)]^{\frac{3}{2}} / \mu_s^{\frac{1}{2}}.$$

In order to compute the firing velocity and flight time we require the following data:

$$\mu_s = 1\cdot3 \times 10^{20}\,\mathrm{m^3/s^2}, \qquad r_e = 1\cdot5 \times 10^{11}\,\mathrm{m}, \qquad r_m = 1\cdot5 r_e.$$

A straightforward calculation gives $V_{min} = 3\cdot4 \times 10^4\,\mathrm{m/s}$ and $\tau = 250$ days. A more realistic value for the firing speed is really the difference between V_{min} and the orbital speed of the earth which is $3\cdot0 \times 10^4\,\mathrm{m/s}$. The relative speed of firing is therefore about $3\cdot7 \times 10^3\,\mathrm{m/s}$.

9.5 Mutual orbits

When the masses of two bodies are comparable, each influences the other and both bodies describe orbits. In the two-body system the centre of mass moves as a fictitious particle with the total external force acting on it. Let G be the mass-centre of the system with $\mathbf{r}_1$ and $\mathbf{r}_2$ the position vectors relative to G of the two bodies idealized as particles (figure 122).

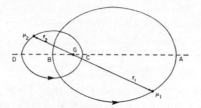

FIGURE 122   Mutual orbits

If μ_1 and μ_2 are the gravitational masses of the two bodies, then, by definition,

$$\mu_1\mathbf{r}_1 + \mu_2\mathbf{r}_2 = 0, \tag{21}$$

the two particles being disposed on either side of the mass-centre in a straight line through the mass-centre. Under the influence of no other forces, the equations of motion for the system are

$$\ddot{\mathbf{r}}_1 = \mu_2(\mathbf{r}_2 - \mathbf{r}_1)/|\mathbf{r}_2 - \mathbf{r}_1|^3, \qquad \ddot{\mathbf{r}}_2 = \mu_1(\mathbf{r}_1 - \mathbf{r}_2)/|\mathbf{r}_1 - \mathbf{r}_2|^3. \tag{22}$$

Eliminating in turn $\mathbf{r}_2$ and $\mathbf{r}_1$ between (21) and 22), we obtain the separate equations for $\mathbf{r}_1$ and $\mathbf{r}_2$,

$$(\mu_1 + \mu_2)^2\ddot{\mathbf{r}}_1 = -\frac{\mu_2{}^3\mathbf{r}_1}{r_1{}^3}, \qquad (\mu_1 + \mu_2)^2\ddot{\mathbf{r}}_2 = -\frac{\mu_1{}^3\mathbf{r}_2}{r_2{}^3}.$$

These equations when compared with the central orbit given by $\ddot{\mathbf{r}} = \mu\mathbf{r}/r^3$ indicate that both particles describe conics with respect to the centre of mass G. In, say, the first of these equations the orbit can be thought of as that due to a central force of magnitude $\mu_2{}^3/(\mu_1 + \mu_2)^2 r_1{}^2$ per unit mass.

Both orbits lie in the same fixed plane and, if they are ellipses as shown in figure 122 with semi-major axes a_1 and a_2 respectively, then AB $= 2a_1$ and CD $= 2a_2$ in the figure. Since the magnitudes of the position vectors are in the same proportion, the two ellipses are similar and have the same eccentricity; thus $a_1/a_2 = \mu_2/\mu_1$.

The periods of both particles must be the same since they always remain in line with the mass-centre. By analogy with the central force problem, the period T is given by

$$T^2 = \frac{4\pi^2 a_1{}^3(\mu_1 + \mu_2)^2}{\mu_2{}^3} = \frac{4\pi^2 a_2{}^3(\mu_1 + \mu_2)^2}{\mu_1^3}.$$

The orbit of μ_1 relative to μ_2 can be determined easily by letting $\mathbf{r} = \mathbf{r}_1 - \mathbf{r}_2$ and taking the difference between equations (22) so that

$$\ddot{\mathbf{r}} = -(\mu_1 + \mu_2)\mathbf{r}/r^3.$$

This equation can again be interpreted as an equivalent central force problem, the force being $(\mu_1 + \mu_2)/r^2$ this time. The orbit of μ_2 relative to μ_1 satisfies the same equation; this can be verified by writing $-\mathbf{r}$ for $\mathbf{r}$. Both relative orbits are conics. In the case of mutual elliptic orbits the semi-major axis of the relative orbit is, in figure 122,

$$\tfrac{1}{2}(\text{AD} + \text{BC}) = a_1 + a_2.$$

Kepler's third law (section 9.3) now becomes

$$T^2 = 4\pi^2 a^3/(\mu_1 + \mu_2),$$

which means that for the planets the ratio T^2/a^3 is not quite constant. If μ_1 is the mass of the sun and μ_2 that of a planet there is a slight variation of T^2/a^3 between the planets.

Mutual orbits usually take place under the influence of a distant force centre as, for example, in the case of the earth-moon system in the sun's gravitational field. Let $\bar{\mathbf{r}}$ be the position vector of the mass-centre of the earth and moon in a sidereal frame, and let $\mathbf{r}_e$ and $\mathbf{r}_m$ be the position vectors of the earth and the moon relative to this mass-centre. Let the gravitational force on the earth and moon due to the sun be $m_e\mathbf{F}_e$ and $m_m\mathbf{F}_m$ respectively where m_e and m_m are their masses. The separate equations of motion for the two bodies are:

$$\ddot{\mathbf{r}}_e + \ddot{\bar{\mathbf{r}}} = \mu_m\frac{(\mathbf{r}_m - \mathbf{r}_e)}{|\mathbf{r}_m - \mathbf{r}_e|^3} + \mathbf{F}_e,$$

$$\ddot{\mathbf{r}}_m + \ddot{\bar{\mathbf{r}}} = \mu_e\frac{(\mathbf{r}_e - \mathbf{r}_m)}{|\mathbf{r}_m - \mathbf{r}_e|^3} + \mathbf{F}_m.$$

The position vector of the moon relative to the earth, $\mathbf{r} = \mathbf{r}_m - \mathbf{r}_e$, satisfies the equation obtained by taking the difference between the equations above:

$$\ddot{\mathbf{r}} = -(\mu_e + \mu_m)\frac{\mathbf{r}}{r^3} + \mathbf{F}_m - \mathbf{F}_e.$$

Since the sun is remote from both the earth and the moon, the difference $\mathbf{F}_m - \mathbf{F}_e$ is small and the relative orbit satisfies, to a first approximation, the relative equation for the isolated two-body problem.

9.6 A simple example of drag on a satellite

We consider the case of a satellite orbit whose apogee is at a much greater height than its perigee. This implies that the eccentricity e differs appreciably from zero. If the perigee is within the earth's upper atmosphere, the satellite then experiences a drag on a small part of its orbit which we can replace in our mathematical model by a small impulse at the perigee which causes its velocity there to be reduced on each orbit by a factor ε (see figure 123).

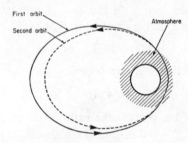

First orbit

Second orbit

Atmosphere

FIGURE 123

If μ is the gravitational mass of the earth, ℓ_0 is the semi-latus rectum of the first orbit and h_0 is the angular momentum of the first orbit, we have, from definitions in section 9.2, that

$$a(1 - e_0^2) = \ell_0 = h_0^2/\mu,$$

where e_0 is the eccentricity of the first orbit.

Therefore, since the distance to the perigee $r_p = a(1 - e_0)$, then

$$h_0^2 = \mu r_p(1 + e_0),$$

which rearranged gives

$$e_0 = \frac{h_0^2}{\mu r_p} - 1. \tag{23}$$

Now $0 < e_0 < 1$ for an ellipse and therefore

$$2 > \frac{h_0^2}{\mu r_p} > 1. \tag{24}$$

If subscript n applies to the nth orbit we also have

$$e_n = \frac{h_n^2}{\mu r_p} - 1. \tag{25}$$

Now, as indicated above, the model assumes that the satellite returns to the same perigee on each orbit but that its velocity there is reduced due to drag. That is, we assume r_p = constant, and $v_n = v_0(1 - n\varepsilon)$ using the binomial expansion and the assumption that $n\varepsilon$ is a small quantity whose higher powers may be neglected. Thus we have $h_n = r_p v_0(1 - n\varepsilon)$ and from equation (25),

$$e_n = \frac{r_p v_0^2(1 - 2n\varepsilon)}{\mu} - 1 = e_0 - \frac{2n r_p v_0^2}{\mu}\varepsilon,$$

indicating that e_n is becoming smaller and that the orbit is tending to a circle.

The period for each successive orbit decreases however, as we shall now show, and the speed at the apogee is increased. We have

$$\text{period for } n\text{th orbit} = \frac{\text{Area}}{\text{Areal velocity}} = \frac{\pi a_n b_n}{h_n/2} = \frac{2\pi a_n^2(1 - e_n^2)^{\frac{1}{2}}}{h_n}$$

$$= \frac{2\pi r_p^2}{h_n(1 - e_n^2)^{\frac{3}{2}}}, \tag{26}$$

where a_n and b_n are the semi-major and semi-minor axes respectively and where relationships derived in section 9.2 have been used.

Now,

$$h_n(1 - e_n^2)^{\frac{3}{2}} = h_0(1 - n\varepsilon)\left\{1 - \left[\frac{h_0^2(1 - 2n\varepsilon)}{\mu r_p} - 1\right]^2\right\}^{\frac{3}{2}}$$

from equation (25), and by rearrangement as a series in ε, becomes

$$h_n(1 - e_n^2)^{\frac{3}{2}} = \frac{h_0^4}{(\mu r_p)^{\frac{3}{2}}}\left[2 - \frac{h_0^2}{\mu r_p} + n\varepsilon\left(\frac{7h_0^2}{\mu r_p} - 8\right)\right]$$

to the first order. Therefore provided $h_0^2/\mu r_p > 8/7$, the implication of which we will examine shortly, the denominator of the right-hand side of (26) increases with each orbit and the period therefore decreases. From (23), $e_0 < 1/7$ if $h_0^2/\mu r_p < 8/7$. Such an eccentricity makes the orbit

virtually a circle for with $e_0 = 1/7$, and the ratio of the minor to major axes
$[= \sqrt{(1 - e^2)}]$ is approximately 0·99. By the time this orbit has been
attained the model will no longer be of value since drag would occur over
a considerable portion of the orbit.

Since the angular momentum is constant throughout each orbit,

$$\text{(speed at apogee)} \times a_n(1 + e_n) = v_n \times a_n(1 - e_n).$$

Therefore

$$\text{speed at apogee} = v_n\left(\frac{1 - e_n}{1 + e_n}\right)$$

$$= v_0(1 - n\varepsilon)\left(\frac{2 - h_n^2/\mu r_p}{h_n^2/\mu r_p}\right)$$

$$= \frac{\mu}{v_0 r_p}\left[2 - \frac{h_0^2}{r_p \mu} + n\varepsilon\left(2 + \frac{h_0^2}{r_p \mu}\right)\right].$$

Thus the speed of the satellite at the apogee increases with each successive
orbit.

The two results we have just found are, in a sense, paradoxical, for we
have found a dynamical system in which the introduction of drag caused
a speeding up of the processes. Closer examination, however, indicates that
both the path-length and the total energy are decreasing with each successive orbit.

Exercises

[Any additional data required should be taken from the table on p. 243]

1. Show that, if variations of gravity are taken into account, the time in which
a particle falls to the earth's surface from a height h is

$$\sqrt{\left(\frac{2h}{g}\right)\left(1 + \frac{5h}{6a}\right)},$$

approximately, h being much smaller than the earth's radius a.

2. A particle moves under an attractive central force k/r^α per unit mass. Show
that the orbit of the particle satisfies the differential equation

$$\frac{d^2u}{d\theta^2} + u = \frac{k}{h^2}u^{\alpha-2},$$

where h is the angular momentum per unit mass of the particle. Verify that this
equation has a solution $r = a$, where $a = (h^2/k)^{1/(3-\alpha)}$. Substitute $u = a^{-1} + x$

into the differential equation and show that approximately

$$\frac{d^2x}{d\theta^2} + (3 - \alpha)x = 0,$$

for small x.

What do you infer about the stability of the circular orbit?

3. At the end of the launching process a satellite is travelling with velocity 29,600 km/h parallel to the earth's surface at a height of 225 km. Find the subsequent greatest height achieved, the eccentricity and period of the orbit.

4. A particle is describing an ellipse of eccentricity e and latus rectum 2ℓ under a gravitational central force. When at the nearer apse, it is given a small radial velocity v. Show that the apse line is turned through an angle $\ell v/eh$ where h is the angular momentum.

5. The orbit of the earth about the sun is assumed to be a circle of radius R. The coplanar orbit of a comet about the sun is parabolic and the distance between them when they are closest is $kR(k < 1)$. Prove that the comet is within the earth's orbit for

$$(\sqrt{2/3\pi})(1 + 2k)\sqrt{(1 - k)}$$

years.

6. A satellite is describing an ellipse of eccentricity e about the earth as focus. At its greatest height above the surface, when its speed is v, it collides with a meteorite. As a result of the collision the satellite acquires an extra velocity v/n at an angle β to v and in such a sense as to increase its distance from the earth. If n is very large show that the eccentricity is reduced by $(2/n)(1 - e)\cos\beta$ approximately.

7. Halley's comet moves in a very eccentric orbit with $e = 0.97$ in a period of about 76 years. Find its semi-major axis and the distance of its perihelion from the sun.

8. A particle moves in a parabolic orbit under the influence of a gravitational central force. Show that its speed at a distance r from the centre is $\sqrt{2}$ times its speed in a circular orbit of radius r.

9. A satellite moves in an elliptic orbit of major axis $2a$ and eccentricity e about the earth. When at its apogee a small retrorocket on the satellite is ignited which reduces its speed from v to $(1 - \varepsilon)v$ where $\varepsilon \ll 1$. Ignoring any changes of mass in the rocket, show that the major axis of the orbit is reduced by

$$4\varepsilon a(1 - e)/(1 + e).$$

10. A communications satellite is placed in a circular orbit in the earth's equatorial plane in such a way that the satellite appears stationary relative to the rotating earth. Find the height of the satellite. What is the minimum number of communications satellites required for every point on the equator to be in view of at least one satellite?

11. A ballistic missile is fired with initial speed V from a point on the earth's surface at an angle β to the vertical. Show that the angle α between the radius to the launching site and the apogee of the missile's orbit is given by

$$\tan \alpha = \kappa \sin \beta \cos \beta / (1 - \kappa \sin^2 \beta),$$

where $\kappa = RV^2/\mu_e$, R is the earth's radius and μ_e the gravitational mass of the earth, provided $\kappa < 1$. Show that the range of the missile is a maximum when

$$\cos 2\beta = \kappa/(\kappa - 2).$$

12. A rocket is fired from the vicinity of the earth in the direction in which the earth is moving in its orbit round the sun. Find the minimum speed with which the rocket must be fired if it is to reach the orbit of Venus. Calculate the time of flight. Assume that the earth and Venus move in coplanar circular orbits centred at the sun and that the rocket is influenced only by the gravitational attraction of the sun.

13. Two particles with gravitational masses μ_1 and μ_2 move in elliptic orbits under the influence of their mutual gravitational forces. Show that their orbits intersect if their eccentricity is greater than $|\mu_1 - \mu_2|/(\mu_1 + \mu_2)$.

14. A satellite is circling the earth at a height b above its surface. A rocket is fired from a launching site in the plane of the satellite's orbit with speed V at an inclination β to the vertical. If the rocket and satellite rendezvous at the apogee of the rocket's path show that

$$R^3 V^2 \sin^2 \beta = (R + b)[R(R + b)V^2 - 2b\mu_e],$$

where R is the radius of the earth and μ_e the earth's gravitational mass, provided

$$\frac{2(R + b)\mu_e}{R(2R + b)} > V^2 > \frac{2b\mu_e}{R(R + b)}.$$

15. A satellite is moving in a circular orbit with speed V at a height b above the earth's surface. Retrorockets are fired which reduce the satellite's speed to kV $(0 < k < 1)$. Show that the satellite will collide with the earth if

$$k^2 \leqslant 2R/(2R + b),$$

where R is the radius of the earth. Show also that the impact velocity V_c is then given by

$$V_c^2 = \mu_e(2b + Rk^2)/(R + b)R,$$

where μ_e is the earth's gravitational mass.

16. What is the minimum orbiting time for a moon satellite?

17. A particle has an equation of motion

$$\ddot{\mathbf{r}} + n^2\mathbf{r} = 0,$$

where $\mathbf{r} = x\mathbf{i} + y\mathbf{j}$ (the motion is simple harmonic in two-dimensions). Show that the orbit of the particle is an ellipse with its centre as the centre of force.

18. The earth passes through a cloud of meteorites with relative speed V. By assuming a model in which the earth is stationary and the cloud of particles approach from infinity, show that the earth's gravitational field causes a cylinder of particles of radius

$$R(V^2 + 2gR)^{\frac{1}{2}}/V$$

to be deposited on the earth's surface where g is the acceleration due to gravity at the earth's surface and R is the radius of the earth. Evaluate this radius when the relative velocity is 3,050 m/s.

19. A satellite is describing a circular orbit about the earth with speed V. The satellite is separated into two pieces by explosive bolts which give them an equal but opposite velocity v relative to and tangential to the orbit of the original satellite. Find the two new orbits.

20. Two particles A and B have masses m and $2m$. Initially A is at rest and B is given a speed V perpendicular to AB. If AB $= d$, find the eccentricity and period of the mutual orbits for this two-body problem.

21. Show that part of the orbit of Pluto lies inside the orbit of Neptune.

22. Find the acceleration due to gravity at the surface of Uranus and its percentage reduction at the equator of Uranus due to the rotation of the planet.

Answers and comments

Chapter 1

2. (i) $10 \cdot 46\mathbf{i} + 12\mathbf{j}$.
   (ii) $15 \cdot 9$ km.
3. (i) 0; (ii) $2\mathbf{i} - 2\mathbf{j} + 2\mathbf{k}$; (iii) 2; (iv) $- 4\mathbf{i} + 4\mathbf{k}$.
4. $(- 2\mathbf{i} + \mathbf{j} + \mathbf{k})/\sqrt{6}$; an alternative unit vector could be formed by changing the sign of all the components.
5. $\mathbf{A}$ is the position vector of any point on the plane. $\mathbf{B}$ is any vector perpendicular to the plane.
8. $\mathbf{v} = - a\omega \sin \omega t\mathbf{i} + a\omega \cos \omega t\mathbf{j} + b\mathbf{k}$,
   $\mathbf{f} = - a\omega^2 \cos \omega t\mathbf{i} - a\omega^2 \sin \omega t\mathbf{j}$.
10. (iii) represents twice the area swept out by the radius vector in time t_1.
12. (i) $(2t + 1)\mathbf{i} + \mathbf{j} + \mathbf{k}$; (ii) $3t^2 - 6t$; (iii) $2(1 + t)\mathbf{i} - \mathbf{j} + (1 - 4t - 3t^2)\mathbf{k}$.
13. The radial and transverse components of velocity and acceleration are respectively (e^t, e^t) and $(0, 2e^t)$.
14. (i) $\frac{3}{2}$; (ii) $- \frac{1}{2}\mathbf{i} - \frac{1}{5}\mathbf{j} + \frac{1}{3}\mathbf{k}$; (iii) $\frac{62}{15}$; (iv) 0.
15. (i) $\frac{11}{10}$; (ii) $- \frac{1}{12}\mathbf{i} - \frac{3}{10}\mathbf{j} + \frac{5}{12}\mathbf{k}$.
16. $(yz\mathbf{i} + zx\mathbf{j} + xy\mathbf{k}) e^{xyz}$.
17. (i) and (iii) conservative, (ii) and (iv) not conservative.

Chapter 2

1. $12 \cdot 32$ hours; 8 km.
2. 16° west of north; 47 km out from port.
3. 8° 8′ west of north; 2 hr 21 min.
5. 117 km/h; 59° south of east.
7. $R(v^2 - n^2)^{\frac{1}{2}}/v$; east or west.
8. 54.
9. $3 \cdot 3$ s.
10. $\mathbf{v} = v\mathbf{e}_r + r\omega\mathbf{e}_\theta$; $r = v\theta/\omega$.
11. 8,170 km/h; 35,220 km.
12. (a) $50/27$ m/s^2; (b) $208 \cdot 3$ m; (c) $66 \cdot 7$ km/h.
13. 45 m.
15. 41 cm/s^2.
17. First-second gear, 30 km/h; second-third gear, 80 km/h; $9 \cdot 95$ s.
20. 166 s—the curved sections are taken at the maximum speed of 180 km/h, acceleration and braking take place on the straight.

21. $V\left\{\mathbf{i}\left[1 - \cos\left(\dfrac{Vt}{a} + \alpha\right)\right] + \mathbf{j} \sin\left(\dfrac{Vt}{a} + \alpha\right)\right\}$, where α is a constant denoting an initial position on the circumference. To prove perpendicularity show that the scalar product of the appropriate vectors is zero.

254

22. (i) 11·3 km/h; (ii) 17·0 km/h; (iii) 22·6 km/h; (iv) 45·2 km/h.
24. $a + b \cos \omega t$.
25. 19° 52′—it is assumed that the front wheels of a car point in the same direction. The minimizing direction is thus taken to be the mean of the two directions in which the individual front wheels would point for zero slip; 24·76 s^{-1}, 19·68 s^{-1}, 26·00 s^{-1}, 21·22 s^{-1}.
26. (i) 25 m/s; (ii) 2,100 m; (iii) 41 m; (iv) after 49 s.

Chapter 3

1. 2,000 N.
2. $\mathbf{r} = (t - a)\mathbf{i} - b\mathbf{j} - t^2\mathbf{k}$.
3. 1·23 m/s^2.
4. 11° 18′.
5. 23·9 m/s.
6. $M(f_1 + f_2)/(g + f_2)$.
7. Distance $3a/20$ along the axis of the cylinder from the circular face of the hemisphere.
8. 30 m.
9. 233·9 m.
10. 2·00 × 10^{30} kg.
11. (i) 127·5 s; (ii) 14·7 N.
12. 18·2 N.
13. 10^3 km/h.
14. Upper hinge: bMg/l; lower hinge: $Mg(l^2 + b^2)^{\frac{1}{2}}/l$.
15. Rear axle: 4,989 N; front axle: 4,821 N.
16. (i) 35·3 m; (ii) 5·1 m.
18. 22·1 m/s.
22. 5·05 s. For $V = 30$ m/s the maximum and minimum times of flight are 6·03 s and 0·98 s respectively. The reader should also show that for initial speeds of less than 30 m/s the time of flight lies between 0·98 s and 6·03 s *either* by showing that the roots of

$$g^2t^4 - 4V^2t^2 + 4R^2 = 0 \qquad (R \text{ is the range})$$

(derived by eliminating the angle of projection from the basic equations), lie between the two times given above by using appropriate inequalities *or* by plotting a graph of V^2 against t^2.
23. 3·57 m.
24. Your method of solution may lead to two roots for V^2. One of the roots is discarded since it implies either an imaginary angle of projection or an imaginary initial velocity.
25. 19·2 km/h.
26. $2m_A\sqrt{(2gh)}/(M - m)g$.
27. 1·8 s.
28. $s(r + 1)[2^n - (1 + e)^n]/rV(1 - e)(1 + e)^n$.
30. Velocity of D has magnitude $U(1 + \sin^2 2\alpha)^{\frac{1}{2}}/(1 + 2\sin^2 \alpha)$ in a direction making an angle $\tan^{-1}(\sin 2\alpha)$ with CA. Velocity of B may be found from the velocity of D by symmetry. Velocity of C has magnitude $U \cos 2\alpha/(1 + 2\sin^2 \alpha)$ in the direction CA.

31. (i) $U(1 - e^n)/2$, $U(1 + e^n)/2$; (ii) $2\pi a(1 - e^n)/Ue^{n-1}(1 - e)$.
32. (i) $1 \cdot 1$ m kg/s; (ii) $219 \cdot 5$ N.
33. (i) $\frac{1}{3}$; (ii) $1 \cdot 19$ m above ground level; (iii) $2 \cdot 69$ m above ground level; (iv) $2 \cdot 25$ m.
34. (i) $\frac{2}{3}$ m; (ii) No. His jump would be equivalent to a standing jump of 6 m; (iii) 145 m kg/s.

Chapter 4

1. (i) $x = 4/(C - t^4)$; (ii) $x = \ln(C - \cos t)$, $C > 1$; (iii) $x - t = C(x + t)^3$; (iv) $x + (x^2 + t^2)^{\frac{1}{2}} = Bt^2$; (v) $x = \frac{1}{2}t^5 + Ct^3$; (vi) $x = Ce^{\frac{1}{2}t^2} - 1$.
2. $104 \cdot 7$ min.
3. $(1 - e^{-t})\mathbf{i} + (1 - \cos t)\mathbf{j} + \sin t\mathbf{k}$.
4. Distance $4aV_0/3V$ downstream from where he started.
5. (i) $x = C_1 \cos 2t + C_2 \sin 2t$; (ii) $x = C_1 e^{-3t} + C_2 e^{-4t}$; (iii) $x = (C_1 + C_2 t) e^{-3t}$.
6. (i) $x = t^3 - 3t^2 + 6t - 6 + C e^{-t}$;
   (ii) $x = C_1 e^{-t} + C_2 e^{2t} + 24t^2 + 14t - 5$;
   (iii) $x = e^{-3t}(C_1 \cos 4t + C_2 \sin 4t) + 2 e^{3t}$;
   (iv) $x = C_1 \sinh kt + (C_2 + t/2k) \cosh kt$;
   (v) $x = e^{-4t}(C_1 \cos 3t + C_2 \sin 3t) + 2 \cos t$.
7. $x = e^t - e^{-2t} + 2e^{-t}$, $y = 3 e^t - 2 e^{-2t} + 3 e^{-t}$.
8. $x = Vm[1 - \cos(Het/m)]/H^2e$, $y = V[Het - m \sin(Het/m)]/H^2e$.
9. $y^3 + 15x = 0$.
10. Hint: one method of showing that the acceleration eventually approaches $g/7$ is to solve the differential equation for v^2 and obtain

$$v^2 = \frac{2gs}{7} + \frac{C}{s^6}.$$

12. $(0, 2/\pi)$.
14. Approximately 140 m.
15. $111 \cdot 5$ m.
17. $y + (x^2 + y^2)^{\frac{1}{2}} = d^k x^{1-k}$.
18. (i) $58 \cdot 6$ m. The transcendental equation can be solved with sufficient accuracy by expanding the exponential to its fourth term; (ii) 104 m/s.
19. $\frac{1}{2}V$.
21. $4 \cdot 0$ s.

Chapter 5

1. $8 \cdot 48 \times 10^6$ J.
2. 2,070 J.
3. Approximately $2 \cdot 5 \times 10^8$ W.
4. 87%.
5. (i) $0 \cdot 022$ m/s^2; (ii) 61 km/h.
6. 716 kW.
7. $m(v_1 - v_2)^2(1 - e^2)/4$.
8. $9 \cdot 6$ s.
11. $22 \cdot 5$ cm above the point from which it was released. Note that it traverses the final part of its path as a projectile.

12. Stiffness $k = 4.9 \times 10^4$ N/m.
13. $(w + W)/5$.
14. Equilibrium position given by $\cos \theta = (b/a)^{\frac{1}{3}}$; stable.
15. Equilibrium position given by $\tan \theta = m \sin \phi/(m \cos \phi + M)$; unstable.
17. Other position of equilibrium given by $\cos \theta = a/c$ where θ is the angle between the rod and the vertical.
18. Radius to R makes with the vertical (i) 15°, stable; (ii) 75°, unstable.
19. (i) $\lambda = 12mg$; $\theta = \frac{1}{2}\pi$, unstable, $\theta = \sin^{-1}(6/7)$, stable (spring subtends an angle of 2θ at the centre).
    (ii) $\lambda = mg$; $\theta = \frac{1}{2}\pi$, stable; no other position of equilibrium.
20. $M = 5,300(25 - 24 \cos \theta)^{\frac{1}{2}}/3$.
21. $2kd^2 > mgl$.
22. If there are three positions of equilibrium, the symmetrical position is unstable: if there is one such position it is stable.
23. (i) $a < l$; (ii) Show graphically that the straight line $y = a\theta/l$ will cut $y = \sin \theta$ an odd number of times if $a < l$ excluding the point $\theta = 0$. Examination of the derivative of the potential energy reveals that the positions of equilibrium are alternately unstable and stable.
24. $-h\sqrt{3} \leqslant x \leqslant h\sqrt{3}$.
25. (i) $m\ddot{x} + k\dot{x} + \lambda x/a = \lambda + kV$;
    (ii) $x = a(\lambda + kV)/\lambda$;
    (iii) displacement is $\frac{1}{2}w(e^{-t/2} - e^{-5t/2})$;
    (iv) velocity is $\frac{1}{4}w(5 e^{-5t/2} - e^{-t/2})$.

Chapter 6

1. The variables v and m separate giving a final velocity $-c \ln (1 - \varepsilon)$.
4. Height attained whilst the fuel is burning is about 56·8 km and in free flight about 75·8 km giving a total distance of 132·3 km.
5. (i) 12·3 m/s; (ii) 10·5 m/s. The rate at which momentum is removed by the rope falling on the ground exactly balances the force due to air resistance. Initially, therefore, since the weight exceeds the buoyancy force, the balloon accelerates until the buoyancy force is the larger. The balloon is then retarded.
7. The parametric equations of the path are:

$$x = t(V + c) + \frac{c}{k}(M - kt) \ln [(M-kt)/M]; \qquad z = -\tfrac{1}{2}gt^2.$$

9. The equilibrium point is 3.5×10^5 km from the earth. This large distance has two implications:
   (i) the velocity required is virtually the escape velocity,
   (ii) the height attained during burning is a negligible proportion of the total distance.
   By using the formula for speed at burn-out we find that ε would be 0·997, a figure far in excess of anything presently attainable.
10. (i) The second stage would have mass 900 kg; (ii) The final speed of the satellite would be 5,480 m/s (compared with 3,500 m/s for a single-stage rocket).

Chapter 7

1. (i) 1·4 s ; (ii) 0·71 oscillations/s, (iii) 4·46 rad/s.
2. (i) Distance a vertically below the beam ; (ii) $4\pi\sqrt{(a/5g)}$.
3. Arrangement in series gives the longer period.
4. 0·0493 N/m.
5. $4\pi\sqrt{(m/k)}$.
7. Note that, if $x_0 \leqslant 3F/k$, the mass comes to rest after $t = \pi\sqrt{(m/k)}$.
8. $\left[\dfrac{1}{m}\left(\dfrac{\lambda_1}{a_1} + \dfrac{\lambda_2}{a_2}\right)\right]^{\frac{1}{2}}$.
10. $F_0 t \sin \Omega t/2\Omega$.
13. Stiffness should be less than $4·57 \times 10^7$ N/m.
14. The length should be decreased by 0·2 mm.
15. $2(\pi + 4)\sqrt{(am/\lambda)}$.
16. $<7·95$ rad/sec.
17. If x_1 is the distance of m_1 from its original position and x_2 is the distance of m_2 from the original position of m_1, then
$$x_1 = -m_2a(1 - \cos \omega t)/4(m_1 + m_2),$$
$$x_2 = a(4m_1 + 3m_2 - m_1 \cos \omega t)/4(m_1 + m_2),$$
where $\omega^2 = \lambda(m_1 + m_2)/m_1m_2a$. Note that the centre of mass of m_1 and m_2 remains fixed.
18. $I/\sqrt{(mk)}$.
19. $2\pi\sqrt{(h\rho_1/g\rho_2)}$.
20. (i) Strongly damped; (ii) weakly damped; (iii) weakly damped; (iv) strongly damped.
21. If x is measured from the equilibrium position,
   (i) $m\ddot{x} + c\dot{x} + 2kx = 0$;
   (ii) $m\ddot{x} + (c_1 + c_2)\dot{x} + kx = 0$;
   (iii) $m\ddot{x} + c\dot{x} + (k_1 + k_2)x = 0$.
22. 0·867 N/m.
24. 12.
25. (i) $2 \times$ (velocity) N; (ii) 308·7 N/m.
27. (i) 4·1 rad/s, (ii) 73°.
28. Note that the mass of water hitting the ball per second when it is moving with speed $\dot{x}$ is $kM(v - \dot{x})/v$.
30. Speed of rotation > 273 r.p.m.
31. $v \exp(-ct/2m) \sin \beta t/\beta$.

32. (i) $F(t) = F_0 + \dfrac{2F_0}{\pi}(-\cos \omega t + \frac{1}{3}\cos 3\omega t - \ldots)$;

   (ii) $x = \dfrac{F_0}{k} + \dfrac{2F_0}{\pi}\left\{\dfrac{-\cos(\omega t - \alpha_1)}{[(k - m\omega^2)^2 + c^2\omega^2]^{\frac{1}{2}}} + \dfrac{\cos(3\omega t - \alpha_3)}{3[(k - 9m\omega^2)^2 + 9c^2\omega^2]^{\frac{1}{2}}} - \ldots\right\}$,

   where $\tan \alpha_n = cn\omega/(k - mn^2\omega^2)$.
33. $2\pi P^2 r\omega/\{m[(5r^2 - \omega^2)^2 + 4r^2\omega^2]\}$.

Chapter 8

1. 4·48 cm.
3. (i) In the rotating frame, $\mathbf{v} = -V \sin(Vt/a)\mathbf{i} + V\cos(Vt/a)\mathbf{j}$, and
$$\mathbf{f} = -V^2[\cos(Vt/a)\mathbf{i} + \sin(Vt/a)\mathbf{j}]/a;$$
   (ii) In the fixed frame,
   $\mathbf{v} = -(V + a\omega)\sin\{(v + a\omega)t/a\}\mathbf{I} + (V + a\omega)\cos\{(V + a\omega)t/a\}\mathbf{J}$,
   and $\mathbf{f} = -[(V + a\omega)^2]\{\cos[(V + a\omega)t/a]\mathbf{I} + \sin[(V + a\omega)t/a]\mathbf{J}\}/a$.
9. $m\omega^2 a$.
10. $m\omega^2 a(1 + e^{\omega t} - e^{-\omega t})$.
11. (i) $2Ma^2/3$; (ii) $\frac{1}{4}Ma^2$; (iii) $\pi a^4 \rho(h/2 + 8a/15)$; (iv) $3Ma^2/5$;
   (v) $M(a^2/4 + h^2/12)$; (vi) $Ma^2/12$.
13. (i) $\frac{3}{4}mV^2$; (ii) $(4gx \sin\alpha/3a^2)^{\frac{1}{2}}$.
14. (i) 8×10^4 J; (ii) 7×10^3 kg.
15. $2\pi\sqrt{(7a/5g)}$.
16. (i) Point of contact of cylinder with plane.
   (ii) With the perpendicular wires as axes and with $(\bar{x}, \bar{y})$ the coordinates of the centre of mass, the instantaneous centre has coordinates $(2\bar{x}, 2\bar{y})$.
17. The reaction has components $5\,mg \cos\theta/2$ along the rod and $mg \sin\theta/4$ perpendicular to the rod.
19. $(Ma^2(3\omega_1^2 + 4\omega_1\omega_2 + 12\omega_2^2)/16)$.
23. 6·2 cm east.
25. 126 sec. Note that the variation of mass of the spacecraft due to the loss of approximately 1 kg of air may be ignored.

Chapter 9

2. Since the differential equation for x is oscillatory for $\alpha < 3$, the circular orbit is stable for $\alpha < 3$.
3. (i) 2030 km; (ii) 0·12; (iii) 1 h 48 min.
7. (i) $a = 2·7 \times 10^9$ km; (ii) 8×10^7 km. Note that the orbit of Halley's comet does not extend beyond the orbit of Pluto.
10. 42,100 km; 3.
12. $2·71 \times 10^4$ m/s (that is, 2,700 m/s less than the orbital speed of the earth); (ii) 145 days.
14. Inequalities for V^2 imply that if V is too small the rocket will not reach the satellite orbit, and if V is too large the rocket trajectory cannot have an apogee at such a small height.
16. 110 min.
18. $2·45 \times 10^4$ km.
19. The two orbits each have semi-latus rectum and eccentricity given respectively by $\mu(V + v)^2/V^4$, $v(2V + v)/V^2$ and $\mu(V - v)^2/V^4$, $v|2V - v|/V^2$.
20. (i) $|V^2 d - 3\gamma m|/3\gamma m$; (ii) $6\pi(d^3/\gamma m|V^2 d/\gamma m - 6|^3)^{\frac{1}{2}}$ if $V^2 < 6\gamma m/d$. Otherwise no period since orbit not closed.
22. (i) 10·3 m/s^2; (ii) 6% reduction.

Index